INTRODUCTION

Running is a very simple and effective activity. It requires no pitch or court, no special skills and a bare minimum of equipment. You can do it whenever and wherever you like and for as long or short a time period as you have available.

Yet, despite this apparent simplicity, running is still thought of as a difficult activity. How far, how fast, how often? That's just the start. What shoes do I need? Should I stretch before my run or afterwards? What's the best food to eat to lose weight and run stronger? Can I run when I'm pregnant?

These are all good questions and you'll find answers to all of them as well as thousands of others in the pages that follow. But don't let them confuse you. Running is a simple activity. It requires nothing more than putting one foot in front of the other. We all know how to do that, we just need a little guidance and motivation to take that first step.

Even though I've been running for more than 30 years, I appreciate that taking that first step is difficult. It was a subject at the forefront of my mind when we started working on this project, but I also know that new runners quickly become experienced runners and their goals and aspirations change. So this is far more than just a book for beginners. It's a complete running book that covers a wide range of subjects from the latest equipment to the best cross-training activities. Whether you are running for competition, recreation, stress relief, weight control, or any of countless other reasons, you'll find useful tips and advice in this book to help you achieve your goal.

I am certain of that because I have already road-tested much of this advice myself and so have thousands of other runners just like me. The material that appears over the next 300-odd pages represents the best of RUNNER'S WORLD magazine from the past decade. It's the pick of the advice from literally hundreds of articles and thousands of pages. It's been a struggle to hone it down into a package that we confidently believe is the only running book you'll ever need.

Of course reading about running is all very well and good but this is a participatory sport. This book will only be a success if it helps you fulfil whatever running goal you have set yourself. So what are you waiting for: lace up those shoes and off you go.

—Steven Seaton, Editor

CONTENTS

CONTENTS

RUNNER'S WORLD GUIDE TO RUNNING

Published by NatMag Rodale Ltd
72 Broadwick Street, London, W1F 9EP
Tel 020 7339 4400
Fax 020 7339 4420

Editor Steven Seaton
Deputy Editor Rob Spedding
Art Editor Russell Fairbrother
Sub Editor Edward Gibbes
Senior Writer Alison Hamlett
Editorial Assistant Elizabeth Hufton
Design Assistant Rupert Elkington-Cole

Publisher Nick Troop
Advertising Director Pauline Carter
Sales Executive Heidi Wilson
Sales Executive Neil Tillott

Production Manager Andy Parslow
Assistant Production Manager Nicky Rouse

Runner's World is published in the UK by NatMag Rodale Limited – a joint venture by the National Magazine Company, a wholly owned subsidiary of The Hearst Corporation and Rodale International, a division of Rodale Inc. RUNNER'S WORLD is a trademark of, and is used under license from, Rodale International.

ISBN 09545 30896 Printed and bound by Ancient House, 8 Whittle Road, Hadleigh Industrial Estate, Ipswich, Suffolk, IP2 0HA
Repro by Wyndham Graphics Kent, 2-4 Powerscroft Road, Sidcup, Kent, DA14 5DT

Helping all children to be born healthy and stay healthy!

SPARKS is a children's medical research charity, dedicated to helping all children to be born healthy and stay healthy. Since 1991 we have committed £11 million to help fund over 140 medical projects into curing conditions such as spina bifida, premature birth, cerebral palsy and childhood cancers.

Every year supporters join SPARKS for a variety of events including the Flora London Marathon, London Triathlon, Hydro Active Challenge and our overseas events to raise vital funds for children's medical research throughout the UK.

If you would like to join the SPARKS team, contact us on 020 7799 2111 or run@sparks.org.uk

www.sparks.org.uk

CHAPTER 1

Getting Started

Welcome to running! You're about to embark on a journey that is guaranteed to change your life: in just a few weeks you'll be fitter, slimmer and happier than ever. But before you pull on your shoes and head out of the door, take some time to read this no-nonsense guide to your first running steps. Here you'll find the best beginner's strategy, meet a trio of new runners to inspire you and discover a few reasons to run that you might not have thought of.

BEGINNING RUNNING: THE FIRST OF MANY MILES

Your first few steps as a runner are among the most important... and the most rewarding you'll take

All running programmes for beginners are the same: they move you from walking, which anyone can do, to running, which anyone can do if they have the determination. The difference between walking and running isn't speed or biomechanics. It's determination.

If you have the determination to stick with a simple programme, you'll soon be a runner. Trust us. It won't be long before you learn that we're right. The beginning of your life as a runner might just be the most exciting time in your entire running career. Of course, you won't necessarily realise that at the time. It may take months or years before you can look back and see what you've achieved. But rest assured – you will.

GETTING STARTED: FIRST STEPS... THE BEGINNING OF A GREAT ADVENTURE

In many ways, beginning to run is a declaration of personal independence and physical intent. A statement that says, "In a world that confronts me with mechanical convenience and idle luxury at virtually every turn, I have decided, nonetheless, to improve my physical fitness."

Later, of course, you realise running offers so much more than more muscle tone and a longer, more energetic life. For most of us, body and soul both tune in to this stimulating activity we call running. Running strengthens the body while it soothes the soul.

So what are you waiting for? The sooner you get started, the better.

WALK BEFORE YOU RUN

More than a few training programmes – especially the New Year's-resolution variety – are doomed almost before they start. Why? Because the schedules are overly ambitious and complex. Or, in direct contrast, they are completely lacking in a goal. The first step for an exercise programme (after a medical check-up) is to ask yourself: what's realistic for me?

THE IMPORTANCE OF SETTING REALISTIC GOALS

Unless you are coming from a strong (and recent) background in another physically demanding sport, don't jump right into a running programme. Instead, begin with a run/walk programme. An excellent goal for a run/walk programme is four workouts per week, with each one lasting 20 to 30 minutes.

THE BEST PLACES TO RUN

One of the first questions beginners ask is, where should I begin my running? It's probably not best to start on the street right outside your door, though certainly many runners do, if for no other reason than convenience.

Running on a smooth, soft surface is the key. Avoid roads with a steep camber; these can throw off your foot-plant, leading to sore muscles and injuries. Whenever possible, choose Tarmac roads over concrete (concrete is harder), and if there isn't a pavement, always run against oncoming traffic. This makes you more visible to the driver (especially if you're wearing light or reflective clothing) and allows you to spot threatening situations before they develop.

RUNNING HILLS

Eventually, you will encounter hills. You won't

consider them a friend at first, but they can really help you improve your fitness. Physically, running hills builds muscular and cardiovascular strength. Mentally, hills add a challenging touch to an advanced workout and therefore can be a good weapon against boredom. But both uphills and downhills add entirely new and taxing elements to your running programme.

Olympic marathon gold medallist Frank Shorter once referred to hills as speedwork in disguise. Treat hills as such; you'll probably be ready to run a hilly course at about the same time you might be ready to attempt an introductory pace/speed session on the track. Therefore, avoid hills in the very early stages of your training programme and introduce them in very small doses (and sizes) after you have logged more than a month of flat running at a comfortable pace.

If you do eventually add hills to a programme as you advance beyond the beginner stage, start

with some slight inclines; save the mountains for the future. Be particularly careful to avoid pounding on the descents. As with flat running, hills that feature grass and soft paths are preferable to hard surfaces. Regardless of where you decide to walk and run, do some light stretching before you begin the workout. Stretching reduces muscle tightness and allows for a more comfortable stride action.

THE NEXT LEVEL: RACING

The late running philosopher Dr George Sheehan once noted that the only difference between a jogger and a runner was an entry form. There's much truth to that statement. Most local races contain a number of runners who are lined up primarily to finish the course, even if just slightly faster than they might run the same route during a typical training jaunt.

The point is, if you're curious about racing – and you sense improved fitness in your training runs – try it. It's natural to feel anxiety over where you might finish or how fast you will (or won't) run, but recognise such thoughts as the self-imposed barriers they are.

In your first race, be careful, above all else, not to start too fast. The excitement and adrenaline you feel will tend to make you run faster than your accustomed pace, but you won't notice it. At least, not at first. Then, after a half-mile or so, you might realise you're gasping for breath and your legs are beginning to feel like anchors. To avoid this, concentrate on total relaxation at the start and during the early going. Breathe comfortably, settle into a moderate pace and enjoy yourself.

There's an old running maxim that holds for everyone from beginners to Olympic champions: if you start too slow, you can always pick it up later; but if you start too fast, your goose is cooked. It takes most runners several races to find their perfect pace – a pace that spreads out their reserves equally over the full distance.

BEWARE THE BUG

With the possible exception of the very beginning of your running programme, the most dangerous time for a novice runner is just after completing that first race – especially if the initial racing experience has been both a successful and enjoyable debut.

The danger, of course, comes from being bitten by the racing bug. The temptation for some runners is suddenly to race every weekend, but this multiplies the possibility of injury or burnout.

Along the same lines, beware of "marathon fever". Some novice racers run a couple of local 5K events and, flush with excitement, jump right into training for a mega-marathon, such as London, Paris or New York City. Resist the temptation. The marathon has been around since the ancient Greeks. It will still be there when your running has progressed to the point that your first marathon experience can be an enjoyable run. It doesn't do you any good to enter a marathon that reduces you to a survival crawl punctuated by self-doubt and tagged with the postscript "I'm never running one of these things again!"

THE LONG RUN

Instead, prepare yourself for the transition to marathon running with a gradual introduction of weekly or bi-weekly long runs. A long run, by definition, is what's long for you in relation to your present level of training. For runners training for their first marathon, the long run might start in the 10- or 12-mile range and gradually progress over several months to distances approaching 20 miles.

Also, some race experience at the 10-mile and half-marathon distances can serve as dress rehearsals for the big one. Both the long runs and the race distances between 10K and 26.2 miles will prepare you mentally and physically for the marathon challenge.

You don't have to finish a marathon, however, to be a runner. There are lots of great runners who never run 26.2 miles. A runner is someone who runs; it's that simple – and that grand. Be that someone. Be yourself. Be your own runner, whether the challenge is four times around the school running track or running the London Marathon. ■

THEY DID IT... SO CAN YOU

Running a marathon is one of the biggest physical challenges you can undertake, but don't be daunted; these three people went from non-runners to marathoners in just six months, and you can too

Have you ever watched the London Marathon and sighed to yourself: "I could never do that"? That's just what Kerry Neale, Phil Wilson and Philippa Braidwood thought, but with six months of training with coaches Keith Anderson and Phil Magner, they all achieved what they thought would be impossible: they went from being non-runners to marathoners. And with thousands of readers of RUNNER'S WORLD following their progress both online and in the pages of the magazine, they had the additional pressure of publicity that most runners don't feel. Here's how they achieved the impossible.

Kerry Neale, 32, from Hatfield, Hertfordshire – computer software analyst

When Neale took up the marathon challenge, she knew she wouldn't be able to think about running the 26.2 miles unless she lost weight. Initially she didn't even run in training; she did non-weight bearing exercise, such as swimming, and transformed her diet, then, once she was in better shape, started a run/walk programme.

"After watching the race I was so inspired, I decided I'd try running. Logging on to the

RUNNER'S WORLD forum and seeing lots of other beginners in the same boat as me gave me a real boost," she says.

Neale became the toast of the www.runnersworld.co.uk Beginners' Forum, initially shedding two stone, mainly by changing her eating patterns and doing one to two hours a day of cardiovascular exercise. She swam, biked, walked and jogged, and after two months, her resting heart rate had dropped to 48 beats per minute, her motivation was sky high, and she was able to fit in the demands of her training around a busy work and social life. "I'd been going away a lot on the weekends and that was when Keith schedules the long sessions. Sometimes it was a real pain having to fit more than two hours of training in – especially if I was travelling with a non-sporty friend," she says.

As she needed to lose weight before she could start running, Anderson set an uncompromising diet for Neale. He set strict rules about her food intake, and demanded that she follow them to the letter. There were no cakes, no biscuits, no sweets, cheese, crisps, fast food, and no alcohol allowed. Surprisingly, the diet wasn't the hardest thing for Neale. Anderson wouldn't allow her to jog during the first six weeks of her schedule – getting her to swim and cycle instead – and she found it incredibly frustrating. Once she was allowed to run, it was hard to hold back. She also admits that simply having to do things like staying hydrated throughout the day was tough. "I actually found having to drink so much water one of the hardest things," she says. "The only time I used to drink water was when I was exercising."

Understandably Anderson was delighted with Neale's progress. "She was absolutely fantastic," he beams, "I can't praise her enough." Throughout the programme he stayed in close contact with her by email and phone, and kept her spirits up when she hit a rare low patch. "She was totally committed. It was an amazing turnaround," he says. He firmly believes that their relationship had to be absolutely honest if Neale was to reach her goal, but that doesn't mean he was a complete ogre: on Christmas Day he allowed a slight relaxing of the rules. He knew that all three runners were attending a marathon training camp soon after the holidays, which meant that any major seasonal lapses would be found out. "That was the carrot," he says, "the promise of a day off!"

Four months into her training, Neale showed no sign of flagging. With plenty of advice and support from Anderson, she made incredible progress – the figures spoke for themselves. She had lost four stone (56lb) and was running for up to two-and-three-quarter hours. The marathon training camp in the Forest of Dean was a big boost. "It was just fantastic. I'm going on another one, I liked it so much," she says. "We did an easy 5K, a threshold session and a long run, and there were lots of informative talks." But one of the best aspects of the camp for Neale was having people to run with. "I usually run alone, so it was nice to have other people to train with. Everyone was so encouraging."

It also made a welcome change from the tough regime Neale followed during the working week. She got up at 5am to fit in her run before going to the office. "I liked to know it was out of the way," she says. "And at that hour, I'm not awake enough to know how stupid it is!" Running four or five times a week, plus some cycling and swimming, filled a lot of Neale's leisure time, but she enjoyed it.

In fact, she enjoyed it so much that a two-week business trip to Singapore left her frustrated at the limits it put on her time to run. "We were working 12-hour days, but I was getting back at 8pm and still hitting the gym," she says. Anxious that the trip should have a minimum of impact on her training, Anderson scheduled Neale's rest days for when she flew, with the days immediately following for recovery runs, to allow for jet lag.

As far as she had come, Neale knew there was a long way to go if she was to reach her marathon goal, but she planned ahead. She held off from shopping for new clothes, determined to wait until she had lost even more weight. Most of all, though, Neale realised that running had become a

permanent part of her life. She ran every weekend, and had pacing events or races mapped out as she built towards the marathon itself. Then there was a second weekend training camp, and a week's spring training camp in the Algarve.

Having cut down her training in the build-up to the big day – "I think I took the tapering to an extreme!" – Neale found the marathon tough from around 16 miles. "I ran a bit and walked a bit. I could probably have kept running but I wanted to enjoy it; there was so much going on – the bands, the RW forumites at mile 18 – and I wanted to soak up the atmosphere."

She came home in 5:27:12, to the relief of Anderson. "If I'd run under five hours, Keith was going to have to let me take him to aerobics. I even had a pink leotard lined up for him," said Neale, who instead had to make do with running the Auckland Marathon in her native New Zealand with her coach.

Phil Wilson, 36, from Nottingham – sheet-metal worker

Wilson was "volunteered" for the challenge by his friend Tom Butcher. "At the beginning of the year, I decided it was time to get fit and joined Tom for a couple of runs," Wilson says. His biggest challenge was to quit smoking. "I'd been a smoker for eight years, but I thought that if I was going to take this seriously I'd have to give up. It was hard, especially on nights out, and I used nicotine patches and gum," he says. His aim for the marathon itself was to get all the way round without walking. For Wilson, it was the training, rather than the event, that was the most daunting.

"I was more worried that I wouldn't keep up the training. My problem is I'm not very good at sticking to things, and find it quite difficult to keep up the motivation to see things through to the end. I was concerned that I'd give it a go, but then fail halfway through, but the fact that thousands of people were reading about me was all the motivation I needed."

Phil's efforts to give up the cigarettes showed a good level of determination and was a sign that he was serious. From a physical point of view, Phil naturally had a reasonably athletic build, so was quite well suited to running. "The challenge for us with Phil, and with all three of the team, in fact, was to get them to enjoy running for the sake of running, rather than just because there's a marathon to train for," says Phil Magner.

In the first month, the running went well for Wilson – he was doing 12-15 miles a week – but kicking his smoking habit proved to be a bigger challenge. "I had a stressful couple of weeks," he says. "My mum went into hospital, so I was smoking one or two cigarettes." He realised that he would have to quit completely if he was to achieve anywhere near his potential at the marathon.

He enjoyed his running from the start, though. "It was such good stress relief, and really good fun," he says, "especially after a day's work. I used to just get home and sit down in front of the TV with a cup of tea and a fag." In fact, most of Wilson's weekday miles were done on the way home from work – he did the two-and-a-half mile route home each day, with a longer session over the weekend.

Like Neale and Braidwood, Wilson also noticed the weight-loss benefits of his new regime. He shed five pounds over the first month, and felt much fitter. "I cut down on fat and rubbish. I cut down my drinking, too," he says. His only problems – apart from the cigarettes – were a couple of blisters. He remained very motivated, even though he did all his training by himself, and could not keep in such close contact with Anderson as the other two runners. "Sometimes, when it was cold, I just didn't want to go out, but once I was out there it was great," he says.

Anderson was impressed with Wilson's inner determination, but was mindful of keeping in contact with him in case things got difficult. "If Phil was not communicating with me, it could mean one of two things: either he was not doing it, or he was happy to get on with it. Thankfully, he was quietly getting on with it".

Running a marathon is an enormous challenge, and takes up a huge part of a runner's life. But there are some things that make it shrink to insignificance. Wilson's mother lost her battle with leukaemia in January, and his running simply wasn't a priority. "I've had a lot on my plate," he says, "but what I decided to do was run the marathon for charity, Leukaemia Research and the City Hospital in Nottingham [where his mother was cared for]. It gave me a bit more of an incentive."

After such a tough time, Wilson found that getting back into training helped him regain a semblance of normal life. He had managed more than two months without a cigarette, and although understandably – he had a lapse, he was sure he could now quit for good. "I'd pretty much given up – I went 10 weeks without, so I knew I can do it for good," he says.

A 10K race after Christmas was Wilson's first competitive outing, where he posted an impressive 44:05. Shortly afterwards, he started getting pains in his knee, but a short break from running let it heal. He started building up his distances, and roped in a friend or two. "Tom Butcher, the guy who put me up for this, was also doing the marathon, so he came over from Derby for some long runs at weekends," he says.

Agreeing to the challenge had also unexpectedly rekindled an old friendship for Wilson. Through his forum thread on the RW website, got back in touch with a friend he had lost contact with. "It was a bit weird, but a nice surprise," he says. It was the support from friends that got him through the toughest times, whether they were running-related or not.

On the day, Wilson crossed the line first of the three in a superb 4:36:31. "I wanted to get under five hours so I was delighted with my time," he says "and I beat Jeffrey Archer! It was great overtaking him."

Philippa Braidwood, 48, from Kingston-upon-Thames – writer

"I'd put on about two stone in the last couple of years," says Braidwood of her pre-running fitness. "In fact, my weight just seemed to be going up and up, and I wanted to reverse that trend. I did join a gym, because I wanted to get fit, but to be honest I hardly went at all, I was too busy." Being challenged to run the marathon was the target she needed to get into shape. "I thought it would be a great incentive to achieve both my goals. I didn't think it would be easy, but having to report to RW readers proved a big motivation."

"When I was slim and fit I would run around Clapham Common every morning. Over the years, though, as I got busier with my children – I have five aged from 18 down to seven – and stressful jobs, I found that I had little time for keeping fit. I was rather daunted by the challenge, as April seemed very close and I'd never run more than 10K, and that was a long time ago. Six months seemed a short time, and I was not convinced that it would be enough to get to the level of fitness required for a marathon. I wasn't 100 per cent confident that I would achieve it, but I was committed to trying."

Phil Magner was optimistic about Braidwood's chances of meeting the challenge. "Although Philippa was nervous about the time she had to prepare, I had a good feeling about her and I was sure that she'd last the course," he says. "By getting the ball rolling early – we got her on an easy walking regime to get her used to regular exercise – she actually had plenty of time. Many beginners don't even start training until January and as she had been a runner, albeit a few years ago, she did at least have an understanding of what training for a race involves. She was a few rungs further up the ladder than she realised."

Unfortunately, Braidwood didn't get off to the best of starts. A few weeks into training, she tore a muscle in her right calf. After a couple of days off, she resumed the walk/jog sessions set by Anderson, but the pain soon flared up again, and she was forced to stop running. "I went swimming – aiming for 75 minutes a day – and cycling," she says, "and visited a local physiotherapist for some ultrasound treatment and deep-tissue massage." Braidwood found, as most runners do, that there was no instant cure. In fact, she was forced to avoid running for eight weeks. "I couldn't believe it took so long to heal," she says. "I found it very frustrating, and the lay-off meant that I was increasingly nervous about the idea of the marathon."

Like Neale, Braidwood was set a strict diet by Anderson, and she admitted to him that she had slipped. "She had a bad couple of days, and she had a couple of glasses of wine," says Anderson, "but after that hiccup, Philippa became a lot more positive and got back into the swing." In fact, the determination Braidwood showed to maintain her fitness while unable to run delighted Anderson. "Seventy-five minutes of swimming is mind-numbingly boring, so well done to her," he says.

With the support of her children, Braidwood followed a detailed plan throughout the school holidays, lost a stone, and started to feel fit. She and Neale emailed each other regularly, and Braidwood says that the support of her fellow beginners, on the forums on www.runnersworld.co.uk, and from Anderson, inspired her when she needed it most. "I think we were lucky to have such a superb coach on tap," she says. "Keith patiently responds to endless questions and really inspired us to carry on when we felt like giving up."

» TOP TIPS

- If you haven't participated in sport recently, start your programme with swimming, walking or cycling, before moving on to a walk/run programme
- If you are injured, don't be disheartened. Find an alternative exercise, such as swimming, so you can maintain your fitness without exacerbating the problem
- Get to know other beginners, either at your local running club, or on the **www.runnersworld.co.uk** Beginners' forum
- Raise money for a charity that's important to you and you'll never lack motivation
- If you're struggling with your diet, keep a food diary for a week

After two frustrating months of being unable to run because of her injury, Braidwood turned a corner in her marathon training. "I ran for an hour non-stop – I couldn't believe it," she says. "Admittedly, it was a slow jog, but I'd never in my life been able to do that before."

Braidwood's gym became a haven from the stresses of combining working and family life, and after sticking rigidly to her programme, when her calf healed, she was not as behind schedule as she feared. "All the time, I kept exercising," she says. "It never felt like it was making a difference, but it obviously worked." For Braidwood, the easiest way to deal with the problems she has faced was to take one week at a time. Anderson sent her a weekly programme, and did not allow her to slack. "He was tough, but it was helpful to have someone to push you," she says. For example, Anderson made Braidwood email him details of what she ate every day for a fortnight. "It made me think twice before I put anything in my mouth," she says. Having over-indulged at Christmas, she got her weight back down again, and in January was 17lb lighter than before she began training.

Anderson has great respect for Braidwood keeping training having recently fostered a premature baby with pneumonia and bronchiolitis, who needed feeding and medication every two hours. "It's a superb effort," he says. Braidwood comments that her husband, Steve, was mystified as to why anyone would want to run 26.2 miles, but he still helped out when she was training.

On the big day, Braidwood said she'd be happy as long as she didn't come last. She didn't, of course, and finished in 5:49:21, well inside her target of six hours. "When I came up The Mall I could hear the commentator saying, '31,500 have already finished', and I thought 'shut up!'" She soon started planning for another race. "I enjoyed every minute of it and would love to do it again in a faster time." she says.

It wasn't just the intrepid trio who benefited from their six-month programme. "Coaching Kerry, Philippa and Phil was one of the best experiences of my life," says Anderson, who also ran the race. "To see all three go from being non-runners to marathon runners was immensely rewarding." ■

YOUR **RUN** TRUE LOVE

Worthy sporting pursuits abound but, in our book, none of them touches running. Don't believe us? Here's 40 reasons why

Running is the oldest, purest and simplest sport. Adam and Eve chased each other around the garden. More than a million years ago, early African hunter-gatherers logged 10 miles a day on the high East African plains. The ancient Greeks staged running events in their original Olympic Games, and the marathon stole the show at the first modern Olympics of 1896 in Athens.

Running is the biggest fitness activity worldwide, and the best. We're absolutely confident that once you've discovered the simple pleasures and rewards it can offer, you'll stick with it. But just in case you need further convincing, we've laid out a few arguments in its defence.

1 It makes you feel better every day This doesn't mean beating depression, heart disease, diabetes or any of the other illnesses that running can help stave off. We're talking about the fact you always feel better after a run – and that's a powerful medicine.

2 Running offers endless competitive opportunities We human beings love to challenge ourselves; it's coded somewhere deep in our DNA. It undoubtedly explains why we're always trying to shrink the size of the silicon chip, build solar-powered vehicles, populate Mars and develop protein-packed strains of rice. Oh, and run new marathon PBs.

3 You can go at your own pace You don't have to run fast to have a rewarding run, and you don't have to set a PB to enjoy a race. You can receive almost as many mental and physical benefits from a slow mile as you do from a fast mile. We have a friend who likes to say, "I've never had a bad run. Every run is its own reward." It's an attitude we'd recommend.

4 You don't need an instruction manual If you can walk; you can run. If you run a little bit more, you can enter a 5K. A little more, and you're on the way to a half-marathon. It's as easy as that.

5 It's the world's best weight-loss exercise Every single weight-loss expert advises two things: exercise and sound nutrition. Running is the king of calorie-burning exercises, and it's easy to do – any time, any place, any season. The added bonus is that, when you begin to exercise regularly, you eat fewer harmful fats and more of the recommended nutrients (that was the conclusion of a seven-year, 10,000-person study published last spring).

6 You can run errands (and exercise the dog, too) We know someone who returns videos to Blockbuster and books to the library on an every-other-day jaunt that also takes her to the post office to pick up packages and deliveries – and every dog owner we know has an eager four-legged training partner.

7 Running boosts your energy levels This is one of our favourites, and one of the more difficult to explain. Running is something of an energy paradox, because most people assume running tires you out, which seems a logical assumption, but it's wrong. In fact, runners report having more energy than non-exercisers.

8 Running gives you time to be with yourself For every proponent of social running, there's someone else who savours it as private time to be alone with his or her thoughts. There's no reason to pick sides. We think both solo running and group running are great activities.

9 It helps you reach creative breakthroughs Writers, musicians, artists, managing directors, software engineers and many others use running to solve mental blocks and make must-do-it-today decisions. As prolific author Joyce Carol Oates wrote: "Running! If there's any activity happier, more exhilarating, more nourishing to the imagination, I can't think what it might be."

10 It's a positive addiction This expression was first made popular by Dr William Glasser, who theorised that you can replace a harmful addiction – such as smoking, alcoholism, overeating – with a positive one such as running. The result being that you will become a happier, healthier person.

11 Running gives you an excuse to soak in the bath First you ice any sore leg muscles for about 10 minutes, then you slide into the steaming, frothy waters. It's the perfect therapy. Just be sure to have a bottle of your favourite carbohydrate or recovery drink nearby.

12 Running is a family affair Many races have events for everyone in the family, ranging from a children's 1K to a walking event, and it's easy to plan an exercise activity for the whole family. The smallest can clamber into their baby stroller, parents can take turns pushing while running, and the four-year-old can follow on their new two-wheeler.

13 Running is like a best friend It's always there and always dependable. We all go through phases in our lives. Sometimes we run more; sometimes we run less. That's fine. Running adapts itself easily to your ebbs and flows.

14 Running improves your time management Whether loosely lodged in your mental schedule or time-tabled in your diary, your daily run is a focal point of your day. It can help you organise everything else you need to do in the day.

15 Running is honest The distance and the stopwatch don't lie. The winner isn't determined by a group of judges assigning point scores for form, clothing, and hairstyle. You get back what you put into it.

16 You can use running to help others Running and charity fundraising are now seemingly inseparable activities. No other sport or activity comes close to running's record of raising money for good causes. Every year, thousands of runners collectively raise millions of pounds for charities throughout the UK. Top of that list is the Flora London Marathon, which now raises more than £20m for charity every year.

17 Running increases your appreciation of the environment You crave fresh, clean air when you run. You long for forest trails, towering trees, pure water, bird song. You have plenty of time to ponder the big questions. You resolve to save the Earth. It's a lovely place.

18 Running lets you set and reach new goals Last month you could only run a mile at a time. Now it's two miles. That's real progress. Well done! It's a cause of immeasurable satisfaction, and the desire to set and reach another goal. Some runners set distance goals. Some aim for faster times. Some want to run in every European country. Others want to lose 50lbs or live long enough to see their grandchildren graduate from university. Pick any goal, no matter how small, as long as it has meaning for you. Then try to achieve it.

19 It's a great way to explore new places We know lots of runners who go out for a run as soon as they arrive at a new location. It energises you after a long drive or flight, helps reset your biological clock to the new time zone and gives you a great way to become oriented to the city's basic layout. If you're visiting as a tourist, there's no better way to explore a new place than to see it on foot.

20 Running makes you look younger We can't prove this, as the Government refuses to fund vanity research, but go to any road race and look around at the vigorous, well-toned runners. You might be surprised how many are in their 40s, 50s or even 60s.

21 Running gives you a legal high And a healthy one, too. After all these years, the "runner's high" remains a fairly uncertain subject, at least to scientists. No one is quite sure what causes it or why, and most runners would admit they don't feel a high on every run – just often enough to make it very rewarding.

22 Running teaches discipline And that's a good thing. It'll serve you well in almost everything you do. In field after field, research has shown the most successful people are those with a modest amount of talent and a mountain of discipline. Practise makes perfect, in running and in life.

23 Women rule, genetically speaking Running philosopher George Sheehan counselled runners interested in fast performances to "choose your parents carefully". As it turns out, he was half right. The mitochondria in your muscle cells are their powerhouses – they control energy production, and all your mitochondrial DNA came from your mother. Your father doesn't contribute. So, if you want to run fast, choose your mother carefully.

24 Running will build your daughter's confidence and self-esteem So she'll be less likely to have sex or fall pregnant at an early age. The US-based Women's Sports Foundation announced these findings in 1998. They apply to girls in all sports, but especially lifetime sports such as running.

25 Running improves your regularity This is why the portable toilet industry loves runners, but it's a good thing for you, too, as it may be one of the primary reasons why runners have a low risk of colon cancer.

26 The last-place finisher receives the biggest cheer And they deserve it. After all, he or she has been running longer than anyone else in the race. We like the way spectators and other runners applaud the back of the pack.

27 Size doesn't matter In fact, small men and women may have an advantage – just look at the elite runners in a marathon. Nevertheless, there are enough larger people in the mass fields of any major race to realise that not only is running sexless and ageless, it's sizeless too.

28 You can do it with a partner Running is a great activity to share. Even if your paces aren't perfectly matched, you can make time for those runs when one of you slows down, and both of you simply enjoy each other's company.

29 Running is efficient In a world so crowded with activities and responsibilities that it can be difficult to make time for all necessities, running is able to deliver a terrific workout in just 20-30 minutes. If company CEOs and other high-fliers can make time to run, the rest of us can, too.

30 Running requires minimal equipment Shoes, shorts, T-shirt. Everyone's got them, and that pretty much completes the equipment list. Toss on another layer when it gets chilly. Strip down somewhat when it gets warmer. It's that simple.

31 Running is child's play Every child runs. Then stops. Then runs again. It's not a training session. It's play. And when you run, you can return to this kind of play. Very beneficial.

32 It's okay to walk Just like the child, run for a while, then walk for a while. Smell the roses. Look for the robin's nest. Feel the soft earth compress beneath each footfall. Run some more. Keep at it for 30 minutes. Maybe an hour. Call it a training session. Bravo!

33 Running helps you sleep better Recent national health statistics have shown an alarming trend in the average amount of sleep we're all NOT getting. Alarming, because this can only lead to lower productivity, more accidents and more disease – but running can help. A 1998 study published in the *Archives of Internal Medicine* concluded exercise could be of benefit to people with sleep disorders. Hit the road regularly, and try to hit your pillow for eight hours a night.

34 Running makes you smarter We first started to report this research more than a decade ago. That first study has produced a steady stream of follow-ups, all concluding that running is good for the brain. The most recent update came in December when Japanese researchers found that a 12-week running programme significantly improved the reaction times and memory skills of their subjects.

35 Running makes your baby smarter It sounds amazing, but this was the conclusion of a study conducted a few years ago at Case Western Reserve University in Cleveland, Ohio. Head researcher Dr James Clapp found that the five-year-old children of women who had exercised during pregnancy scored significantly higher on an IQ test than the children of women who had remained predominantly sedentary through their pregnancy.

36 Running gives you several recycling outlets You can donate your old T-shirts and shoes to an organisation that collects them (a number of charities will collect). We've even heard from an organisation that uses old foil "space blankets" to help stimulate severely disabled children.

37 Running shoes make your feet happy Running shoes are about the most comfortable and healthy footwear you can buy. Your feet are the foundation to your body, so be kind to them. Wear running shoes on and off the roads, although beware of using them for other sports as their performance can diminish.

38 Running is the core fitness activity for most other sports Whether you want to climb Mount Everest (like blind marathoner Eric Weihenmayer) or score the goal that secures England's World Cup qualification (like David Beckham, who was once a county-standard runner, did in 2001), running is the place to begin. Running makes you better at other sports.

39 Running is full of great quotes From the Bible, the great poets and thinkers, to the modern-day rockers and plenty of others. The all-time greatest running quote, according to Mark Will-Weber, author of *The Quotable Runner*, is "Bid me run, and I will strive with things impossible." (Shakespeare, *Julius Caesar*)

40 Every run is a journey You never know what you'll find. You don't know who or what you'll see, or – even more interesting – what thoughts might flash into your mind. Today's run could change your life in a way that you could never have imagined when you were lacing up your shoes – and that's powerful stuff. ■

FITTING IT IN

Once you've found the time to step out of the door and fit in your run, you're halfway there already

With so much to do in our action packed days, from the shopping to putting the children to bed, it's not surprising that running often gets squeezed out. Survey after survey reveals that lack of time – whether actual or perceived – is the biggest barrier to getting in a run or running as much as we would like. Well, we feel your pain. And we're here to help.

The way we see it, time problems fall into three categories: making time (questions of when, where and how); saving time (little dos and don'ts that add up to serious savings); and re-thinking time (new ways to examine the relationship between your running and the time you need to do it). Here are 35 can't-fail time-management tips from all three of these categories. So stop making excuses and go running.

1 Make time in your schedule for a run every other day with your most important client – yourself. Do this first thing, at the start of the week, before the blank spaces start filling up with other priorities.

2 Take the most out of what you have. Several times a week, think quality, not quantity. Finding time for a 20-minute run – outside, or on a treadmill, wherever – can be pretty easy. Just make every minute count. Alternate one minute a little faster than 5K pace with one-minute recoveries. Or, one of our favourites, run four times two minutes at around 5K pace with 90-second recoveries. Do a two- to four-minute warm-up first and a similar cool-down afterwards.

3 Give yourself an unexpected bonus: you don't just become stronger, but leaner, too. Alternating fast and slow running not only helps to build running strength and speed, it also burns more fat. What's more, according

to a 2001 study in *Medicine and Science in Sports and Exercise*, alternating fast and slow running helps you lose weight faster than a steady-pace effort.

4 Run before anyone else is even out of their bed, because there are no appointments that can get in the way of an early morning run. If rolling out of bed at 5.30am still doesn't serve up the minutes necessary for the run you want, then...

5 Drag yourself up and out of your bed even earlier, advises running coach Jeff Galloway, "and have a stronger cup of coffee to wake yourself up." Once outside, you'll soon shake off any lingering sleepiness.

6 Get yourself a dog, because there's no way to ignore a wet snout in your face saying "now, now, NOW!" Having to exercise the dog will push you out of the door in the mornings.

7 Swap your responsibilities. One morning, afternoon or evening, let your other half look after the children while you run. The next day, reverse the roles.

8 Take the children. Many gyms now offer in-house nurseries. In one gym we know of, staff link the children together with a piece of rope and lead them from one activity to another like a band of tiny chain-gang convicts. The children think it's hilarious. In 90 minutes, you can get in an hour on the treadmill and a 20-minute circuit-training session on the weight machines – an excellent all-round work-out.

9 Give them the run-around. While the children are playing football (or whatever), run loops around the outside of the field. "I do this twice a week," says mother-of-two Judie Simpson. "Once as a steady one-hour run. The second time I'll pick it up on the long side of the field and jog the short side for 45 minutes or so."

10 Forget the rush hour. Take your kit to work, and do your run from the office after work, while everyone else is spending a miserable hour in fingernail-gnawing gridlock. By the time you've finished your run – sweating, pleasantly tired, totally de-stressed after work's rigours – the whole smoggy mess should have cleared out, and you can cruise home comfortably (feeling very, very smug).

11 Don't go home before your run if you can help it. Even if your commute is clean and fast, park a mile or so away from your house and start your run from there. Afterwards, you can either finish at your car and drive home, or just run the rest of the way to your door. TV, food, cleaning, children, newspapers, phone calls: there are too many things to do other than running once you step through the front door.

12 Fast-forward your run. Many people who claim to have no time to run find plenty of time to develop blisters on their remote-control thumbs. The average Brit watches 25 hours a week, but, hidden away inside programmes, are little blocks of running: the adverts. Instead of watching Coronation Street live, watch it on tape – fast-forward through the ads, and free up enough time for a decent little run.

13 Goal for it. Too many runners think too far ahead – a six-month or year-long plan – when laying out their training. "That vision can be lost pretty quickly when you're feeling bad," warns Dave Scott, six-time Ironman Hawaii winner. "Instead, set a fortnightly goal, and make it specific: run three times a week for the next two weeks." Then set another, and so on.

14 Bet on it. A study at Michigan State University in the USA found that people who bet £25 that they could stick with their training program for six months had a 97 per cent success rate. Less than 20 per cent of those who didn't place a bet stuck it out. Bet against a friend, and the first to give up pays up. Times to do your running will suddenly, almost magically, start popping up.

15 Run little and often. If you're new to running, aim for frequency, not duration, to make running a regular part of your life. Instead of trying to find time for a 45-minute run two or three times a week, shoot for shorter sessions of 15-20 minutes, but run most days.

16 Veteran runners looking to get stronger should focus on two "key" runs every week, sessions where they really push. Try a one-hour interval, fartlek or hill run during the week and then a weekend long run. Fill in around them with short, easy runs, cross-training and rest days. Two very tough runs will make you faster and stronger than five or six so-so weekly runs with little rest between them.

17 Recruit a regular training partner and agree on time, place and distance. If someone is expecting you to show up, you're more likely to – and less likely to claw around for excuses not to.

18 Evolution, not revolution. The prospect of getting up to run every morning or in every lunch hour can be daunting. So commit to running just one morning and/or one lunch hour per week for just a month, and stick to your usual schedule the rest of the time. See how it goes. Two small steps rather than a giant leap is best.

Saving time

Fifteen seconds here, a minute there. It doesn't seem like much, but watch how fast it all adds up.

19 Prepare your kit the night before. Even loosen your laces so your feet slide straight into your shoes. That way, you sit down and dress for battle quickly. No back-and-forth from bedroom to laundry and back to bedroom, tracking down clean T-shirt, shorts, socks, shoes. They're all there. Waiting for you to take them out for some sweaty fun.

20 Plop your smoothie ingredients in a blender the night before an early run, and put it in the fridge. After your run, hit the switch, and eight seconds later... breakfast. (I tried this one. Assembling from scratch in the morning: 1:53. Time saved: 1:45.)

21 Don't spend time stretching cold muscles before you train. Instead, walk briskly for a few minutes, then jog slowly to start your run.

22 Run before you talk. You meet your running partners and start talking while doing some lame trunk twists as a warm-up. Don't do it. Say hello, and start jogging slowly into your run. Talk then, before the pace picks up.

23 Order up all four items (numbers 19-22), and you save from seven to 10 minutes – enough time to turn your usual five-mile run into a six-miler. Over the course of a working week, you net at least 35 minutes of extra running time.

24 "Wear running shorts as underwear," says American running guru Galloway, thus rendering yourself run-ready the instant your antennae pick up a 10-minute block of free time. "Accumulate enough short runs," he says, "and they add up." A Stanford University study found that multiple bouts of moderate-intensity exercise produce significant training effects; leading us to...

25 Divide and conquer. On the off chance that solution 24 seems too unconventional for you, don't ignore the underlying message: on busy days, beat the clock by breaking up your run into two shorter sessions. Instead of a single 40-minute run, maybe do 20 in the morning and the same at lunchtime, or whatever fits your schedule.

26 The 10-minute miracle. "Run faster-than-normal training pace (but don't sprint) for 10 footfalls of your right foot. When you reach 10, do 10 more steps of easy jogging," says exercise physiologist Jack Daniels. Then do 20-20 and so on up to 60-60. Then work back to 10-10.

27 Turn down the volume. Research at the University of Northern Iowa in the USA found those running 50 miles a week had marathon times no faster than those who logged just 40 at a similar intensity. Moreover, the 50-mile runners were no fitter than the 40-milers. More isn't always better, so don't scramble to find time for miles whose only purpose is to pad your weekly total.

Re-thinking time

Some time barriers to running are external – work, picking up the children, root canals. But equally restrictive are internal roadblocks – attitudes toward running and/or ourselves that stop us working out.

28 Be realistic. Cut back on your running if you need to. But don't throw in the towel because of facts of life – deadlines, sick kids, holidays etc. Ride these periods out, and fit in a run of some kind – 15 minutes, 10 minutes – every second or third day. Then resume your routine when you can. When your impeccably laid-out schedule implodes, think short-term change, not major catastrophe, and don't fret your way into sofa sloth. Don't get caught in that "all-or-nothing" snare.

29 When you're busy run for maintenance. When your schedule lightens, pick up the intensity.

30 A little is better than nothing. If all you have is 17 minutes, run for 17 minutes.

31 Be selfish. By giving your run a high priority, you're boosting your physical

» TOP TIPS

- Make time in your schedule to run every other day. Try to do this at the start of each week – and don't double book
- Greet the dawn. Not only will it energise you for the day ahead but appointment clashes are pretty uncommon at 6am
- Take the kids to the gym. Many have excellent crèche facilities and some even organise "junior" work-outs while you do your grown ups' thing
- Get a training partner. There are few better motivational tools than a running accomplice
- Set your kit out the night before. It'll save you precious morning minutes
- Have fun. New routes, new surfaces. New you

and emotional health, and living up to your obligation to your family to be healthy and happy.

32 Be flexible. If circumstances change don't simply not run. If a surprise meeting cancels the lunchtime run, do your miles after work while the traffic clears (see tip 10). If you miss the alarm, bring your kit to work and run at lunch.

33 Burn the alternatives. Take a torch to "I don't feel like it," or "I should wash the car/water the plants/sort out my loose change."

34 "If you really want to run, you'll find the time," says former 2:09 marathoner Ron Hill. "It's really no different than finding time to shave, eat or read the paper," he adds.

35 Have fun. Enjoying a run greatly increases the likelihood that you'll want to – and will – find time for the next one. Run a new route; run an old one backwards. If you usually run on roads, head for the park and run through the trees.

So here's the plan: pick any three of the strategies – one from each section – and try them for a month. If any work, great; if not, pick three more. If, by the end of the year, you've used them all and you still can't find time to run, you probably don't really want to, which would be a shame. Chances are, however, you'll find two or three strategies that work like a charm every time. ■

IT'S GOOD TO **WALK**

There's no shame in adding a little walking to your running. It may even help you run faster

Shhhh. I, Amby Burfoot, have got a little secret to share with you. You see, I used to be a fairly fast runner. In fact, 30 years ago, I won the Boston Marathon. And there's a certain amount of honour among Boston winners – a sort of "pain is my friend" ethic – that we're sworn to uphold. Now, about that secret. I wouldn't want anyone to think I've gone soft or anything but... um, this is hard to get out... I often take walking breaks during my daily runs.

There, that feels much better. Though I don't know why it was hard to say in the first place. After all, it makes perfect sense to mix running and walking. Think about it: when new runners begin a running programme, they often start by following a run-walk routine; they run for maybe 30 seconds, walk until they feel recovered, then repeat the process for 20-30 minutes. This system has proved successful a thousand times over.

When world-class runners peak for the Olympics, they concentrate on "interval" training – the still-unsurpassed method for achieving maximum results. They run hard for one to five minutes, then walk or jog very slowly until they're ready to run hard again.

When ultra-distance runners participate in those seemingly crazy races of 100 miles or more, they inevitably alternate running and walking. It's hard to imagine any other way to cover the mega-mile distances. You, on the other hand, probably view walking as the enemy. The thinking is that you run, and this is good. You are proving and improving yourself; you are determined; you are a moral person. Whereas when you walk, it is bad. You are lazy; you are a loser; you don't deserve to be loved (not even by your mother).

Mental-health therapists have many words for this sort of inflexible, perfectionist thinking, and I have one, too. I call it "stupid". (None too

elegant, but it has the benefit of clarity.) The goal of a session is not to avoid walking. The goals are to feel better, get in better shape, reduce tension, lose weight, train for an upcoming race and so on. Take your pick. They're all worthwhile goals.

Run/walk training, which I like to call "R/W training" is a simple, common-sense approach to conditioning. It can help you to train more (for better marathon preparation and calorie-burning); it can help you to train healthier (who needs injuries and burnout?); and it can even help you to get faster (through interval training).

Enough talk. Let's be more specific.

The Galloway Marathon

In recent years former Olympian marathon runner Jeff Galloway has pioneered the idea of walking breaks during marathons. Jeff advocates this programme not only for many first-time marathoners, but also for those who have previously hit the wall and experienced the crushing fatigue and depression of those last few miles. By walking early and often, Jeff has found, most runners survive the final miles in much better shape. They feel better, and they often run faster.

You can run/walk a marathon any way you want, but the simplest is to run the first mile, then walk for 60 seconds. Run the second mile, then walk for 60 seconds (and have a sports drink). Repeat 24 more times, then hold your head high and sprint like a hare.

The Galloway run/walk marathon has been used successfully by thousands of marathoners. Jeff says it's possible to run under 3:30 this way, and several runners did so at the last Chicago Marathon. But fast times aren't the point. The point is that you can finish the marathon, feel good, run strong to the end, and admire that gleaming finisher's medal for the rest of your life.

The Next Step

The Galloway programme has made many converts, and I'm one of them. I've now run four marathons with walking breaks, in times ranging from 3:45 to 4:30. Walking breaks have added confidence to my marathoning. Since I'm a modest trainer these days, averaging 20-30 miles a week, the marathon can easily intimidate me. A few years ago, I was beginning to dread the thought of running 26.2-milers. Now I don't even think of the marathon that way. I think of it as a one-mile run that I just happen to repeat 26 times. Piece of cake.

R/W training has also made my daily training easier. It used to be that, much as I love running, I sometimes felt too tired to get through the door. I talked myself out of many sessions: when you're already tired, why drag yourself out on the roads for 40 minutes?

I don't have this problem any more, because I don't run for 40 minutes. I run for four minutes, then walk for a minute, then repeat the process until I've completed 40 minutes. All I care about is getting into the session and feeling wonderfully energised afterwards, which I always do.

A Step Backwards

Let's pause for a moment to consider some of the differences between running and walking. Some are small, others more significant. Running and walking have much in common, with one significant difference. Runners "jump" from foot to foot, walkers don't. When you run, the knee flexes more than in walking, the quadriceps muscles contract, and you "toe-off" in more or less the same way as the long jumper who explodes off the jump board.

Because you toe-off and jump, you come down forcefully on the other foot. This is the infamous "impact shock" of running – said to be two to three times your body weight – that can lead to over-use injuries of the foot, knees, tendons and so on. Walkers don't jump, so they are less likely to get injured.

Because you jump when running, you can cover ground much faster than a walker and burn many more calories per minute (because moving faster requires you to consume more oxygen). In other words, you get a superior session in less time, which is one of the major benefits of running.

Unfortunately, many potential runners never

get into the rhythm of running. They set out to run around the block a few times, but find themselves breathless and bedraggled at the first corner, which is not a pretty sight. So they repair to the sofa and never leave it again. Or maybe they do try another time, but on this next effort they decide to skip the running. They walk. It's hard to fail at walking, but a leisurely stroll, while better than nothing at all, probably doesn't produce as many benefits.

These are the people who need to learn about R/W training. They're already motivated to exercise; they just have to step up the pace a little, which is what a programme of running and walking does. You won't get exhausted and frustrated (thanks to the walking breaks), and you'll get all the benefits that vigorous exercise brings (thanks to the running). There are many varieties of R/W training. Some are physical, some mental, but all are guaranteed to change (and probably improve) your running. Here are a few:

Running further, easier All runners, from beginners to veteran marathoners, would like to run longer and easier. The R/W system gives you a new tool to help achieve this. Does it come at a cost? Sure. Your overall session is slower, so you get slightly less training effect, but most of the time you do long runs to build overall endurance and increase your body's ability to burn fat and calories in general. A long R/W run does this just fine.

Increased variety Far too many runners do the same session at the same pace every time they run. It's boring, and it's not a smart way to train. An R/W session naturally has many small segments, which encourages you to experiment.

Better speedwork An R/W session is an offshoot of the classic interval session, so it's easy to make it a real gut-buster. Here's one of my favourites, built on the four-to-one pattern. During each four-minute running segment, jog for one minute, run hard for two minutes and jog for one minute. Then do the one-minute walk. Repeat this eight times, and you've come reasonably close to the 8 x 400m interval torture that my college coach loved to inflict on us.

On the topic of intervals, exercise physiologist Jack Daniels recently had two groups of women run three times a week, either continuously or with walking breaks. After 12 weeks, the run/walk group was more fit. Why? "In effect, the walking breaks turned the sessions into one big interval session," says Daniels. "It allowed the women to go faster overall."

Fewer injuries Walking doesn't cause as many injuries as running, and R/W training shouldn't cause as many either. No, I can't prove this, but it makes intuitive sense. Since walking uses the leg muscles and connective tissues in a slightly different manner than running, it should reduce over-use injuries. During R/W sessions, I walk with a deliberately slow, elongated stride. This is a change from my normally short, choppy running stride, and I can feel other muscles coming into play.

More sightseeing What's the point of running in some gorgeous environment if all you see are the rocks and gnarly roots on the trail right in front of you? Yet that's all many trail runners see, because they're concentrating so hard on avoiding falls and twisted ankles. With your new R/W philosophy you can drink in those scenic views during your walking breaks.

More effective recovery days This one's easy and obvious. Some days you need to run slow. Maybe you ran long or fast the previous day. Maybe you've been having a tough time in the office or at home. You want to run, but you're not exactly bursting with mental or physical energy. Try an R/W session. You won't regret it.

Faster comebacks You've had a sore knee, a bad Achilles or a nasty cold. You're ready to get back into your training routine but want to make sure you don't overdo it and suffer a setback. A series of progressive R/W sessions may do the trick. Try a couple of two-to-one sessions, then a couple of three-to-one runs, and keep building. Listen to your body, and don't run further or faster than what feels right.

More quality time My wife runs, but my teenage kids don't. They do all the other things kids do – football, computers, tae kwon do – but probably wouldn't make it through a steady 30-minute run. They will, however, do an R/W session with us. We pick something easy, keep it relatively short and enjoy the time together.

» TOP TIPS

- If you want to call yourself a runner, walking's out, isn't it? Not really. Running is good, but so is walking. It's a valid form of interval training employed even by elite runners
- R/W training can allow you to run longer, healthier and, yes, faster – even on marathon day
- Try this marathon day plan – run a mile, walk 60 seconds. Repeat 26 times until complete in good time and with no walls hit
- Incorporating walking into your schedule reduces your chances of injury and assists injury recovery
- Ease the pain of those long runs with an R/W strategy that'll deliver near-full endurance benefits
- R/W sessions are a great way to involve your family in your running efforts

Final Thoughts

The aspect of R/W training that I find most appealing – the mental breaks provided by the brief walking periods – won't prove equally compelling to all runners. Many will staunchly resist. "I didn't start running to become a walker," they'll snort derisively. We runners succeeded as runners because we're an extremely determined, motivated breed, and we don't take easily to anything that smacks of laziness or backsliding.

Okay. I understand that. Old habits die hard, and R/W training isn't for everyone. Or for every session. I do it a couple of times a week, usually when I run by myself and often as a long run.

However – and this is the most surprising thing about it – I've found that it has motivated me to do more speedwork and tempo training. That's because R/W training is so close to classic interval training that it seems to nudge me in that direction. In fact, you could simply say that,. in a sense, R/W training is classic interval training that's been liberated from the track and allowed to roam wherever you want to take it.

Free at last. You just might discover an entirely new, enjoyable (and effective) way to run. It's worth a try, isn't it? ■

CHAPTER 2

Equipment

Running is a simple sport: all you need to start is a good pair of shoes – and we'll tell you how to make sure that your trainers really are the ones for you – but of course, when you pop into the shop to buy your shoes you'll notice lots more great kit on the shelves. To help you choose the apparel that will keep you running year-round and the tools to boost your training, here's the low-down on all the essential gear for runners.

HOW TO CHOOSE THE **RIGHT SHOE**

There's no such thing as the "best shoe" – everyone has different needs. Biomechanics, bodyweight, the surfaces you run on, and the shape of your feet mean one person's ideal is someone else's nightmare

» JARGON-BUSTER – SHOES

Making your first trip to your local running specialist to choose a pair of shoes can be a daunting prospect. A reputable shop will always try and make sure they sell you the best shoes for you, rather than the most expensive ones, but in order to understand your needs, you have to be able to communicate them. Check out our jargon-busting guide to the technical talk before you make your purchase.

Biomechanically efficient A runner with a foot which follows the natural gait cycle, with no excessive inward or outward rolling. A foot like this does not need added stability features in a shoe. Also called "neutral" or "efficient".

Blown rubber The lightest, most-cushioned and least-durable form of rubber used on a shoe's outsole. It is made by injecting air into the rubber compound.

Carbon rubber A harder, more durable outsole, made from solid rubber with carbon additives.

Cushioned shoe Our term for a shoe without added stability features, for biomechanically neutral runners.

Cushioning The ability of a shoe to absorb the extreme forces of footstrike. Softness varies between shoes. Except at

Shoes can be divided into three main categories: cushioned, stability and motion-control; and three minor ones: performance training, racing and off-road. The first three are everyday options and are categorised essentially by your biomechanical needs; the second three are more specialised categories and you'd usually only consider them as second shoes.

The first step in finding your shoe needs is to try our "Wet Test", or, preferably, to visit a biomechanics expert or experienced shoe retailer. The Wet Test works on the basis that the shape of your wet footprint roughly correlates with the amount of stability you might need in your shoe. "Roughly" is the key word here, though: it's a handy starting point, but no more.

The Normal Foot

A normal-sized arch will leave a wet footprint that has a flare, but shows the forefoot and heel connected by a broad band. A normal foot lands on the outside of the heel and rolls inwards slightly to absorb shock. It's the foot of a runner who is biomechanically efficient and therefore doesn't need a motion-control shoe.

Best shoes Stability shoes with moderate control features.

The Flat Foot

This has a low arch and leaves a print which looks like the whole sole of the foot. It usually indicates an over-pronated foot – one that strikes on the outside of the heel and rolls inwards (pronates) excessively. Over time, this can cause many different types of overuse injuries.

Best shoes Motion-control shoes, or high-stability shoes with firm midsoles and control features that reduce the degree of pronation. Stay away from highly cushioned, highly curved shoes, which lack stability features.

The High-Arched Foot

This leaves a print showing a very narrow band or no band at all between the forefoot and the heel. A curved, high-arched foot is generally supinated or underpronated. Because it doesn't pronate enough, it's not usually an effective shock absorber.

Best shoes Cushioned (or "neutral") shoes with plenty of flexibility to encourage foot motion. Stay away from motion-control or stability shoes, which reduce foot mobility.

---

the extremes, there's no right or wrong, though heavier runners tend to do best with firmer shoes.

Efficient See biomechanically efficient.

Flex grooves Indentations moulded into the midsole and outsole to make a shoe more flexible, usually under the ball of the foot.

Flexibility The ability of a shoe's forefoot to bend under the ball of the foot. If the shoe does not flex easily under your weight, your foot and leg muscles have to work harder, which saps energy and can cause injuries such as shin splints.

Forefoot The broad, front section of the shoe or foot. This is the point from which you propel yourself forward, so the shoe should be protective yet responsive. Some runners land on the fronts of their feet, and need maximum cushioning in the forefoot of their shoes. They're called, appropriately, forefoot strikers.

Gait cycle The natural movement of the foot against the ground when you walk or run. The rear, outer part of the heel hits the ground first: the foot then rolls forwards and inwards (pronates) as the arch collapses to absorb shock; then it moves

The best shoes for difficult runners

Most runners find it relatively easy to find at least a nearly ideal shoe, assuming they have access to a specialist running shop. What we call "cushioned" shoes are normally for runners with neutral, efficient biomechanics; "stability" shoes are mostly for runners whose feet roll inwards slightly too much when they run (mild overpronators); and "motion-control" shoes are for severe overpronators. Once you've determined which category you fall into, you have a wide range of shoes to choose from. All you have to do is decide which shoe within your category provides the best comfort, fit and performance for your needs.

A minority of runners have very specific needs, which can make shoe buying an altogether more frustrating business. Sometimes there are very few shoes that meet the runner's particular needs; in other situations, shop assistants simply don't know what to recommend.

If you face any of these problems, this article should give you a headstart. It's a guide to shoes for runners with the four most common "minority" biomechanical problems (forefoot striking, heel striking, underpronation and orthoses-wearing), as well as runners with very wide or narrow feet.

Most of the categories are self-explanatory, but in case you're not sure whether they apply to you, there is an introduction to each below. Either way, you should go to an experienced specialist retailer or biomechanics expert who can analyse your running style, and if your current shoes aren't causing you any problems, keep replacing them with the same model or its nearest equivalent.

If you have feet bigger than size 13.5 or smaller than 4.5, we don't recommend specific shoes here, but for big shoes you could look to Asics, Brooks, Etonic and New Balance, which all offer some models at size 15. At the other end of the spectrum, Puma and Brooks start at size 3; Nike and Saucony from 4. If you have very tiny feet, beware of junior models: a few, such as the Asics 1100 (stability) and New Balance 764 (stability) are made to full specification, but most are non-technical lookalikes.

As well as using our own expertise, we asked Bryon Newbery, the owner of Alexandra Sports in Portsmouth, and Brad McGregor of Runner's Need in London, how they go about fitting the right shoes to their most problematic customers. Because, as they'd agree, there's more to shoe categories than just cushioned, stability and motion-control.

›› JARGON-BUSTER – SHOES

on to the inner and front part of the forefoot as the foot stiffens and pushes away from the ground (toe-off).

Heel counter A firm, usually plastic cup that is encased in the upper and surrounds the heel. It helps to provide a good fit and control excessive rearfoot motion.

Heel tab The back of the heel collar, which provides a secure fit and nearly always has a notch cut in the top to prevent irritating the Achilles tendon.

Insole The foot-shaped insert, usually removable, which sits between your foot and the shoe. Sometimes called a sockliner.

Last The foot-shaped mould on which the shoe is constructed, the shape of which strongly influences the function of the shoe. The straighter the last, the more stable the shoe. The more curved it is, the faster but more unstable the shoe.

Lateral The outside (little-toe) edge of the shoe.

Lugs Deep, rubber tread on the underside of the shoe to provide grip in off-road conditions.

Medial The inside (big-toe and arch) edge of the shoe.

Medial post A firmer density

The life of a pair of running shoes is dictated by you, the type or running you do and where you run. An average pair of road shoes should last at least 500 miles, perhaps longer. How you care for your shoes will affect how long they last, so here's a four-step plan to ensure you maximise the effective life of your shoes.

FORGET ABOUT BEING DAVID BECKHAM

Running shoes are designed specifically for running. They aren't designed for other sports. There's no quicker way of shortening the life of your shoes than trying to bend it like Beckham in a Sunday morning kickabout. Any sport that involves kicking or a high degree of lateral movement will age the upper and the stability and cushioning of the midsole.

SCRUB 'EM, DRY 'EM

Mud and water are shoes' biggest enemies. Mud adds unnecessary weight, clogging the upper and outsole, while water penetrates the midsole foam and, if you run in wet shoes, destroys the integrity of the upper. Clean off the mud with a stiff brush and a bowl of warm

water; then remove the insoles, stuff your shoes with newspaper and leave them to dry naturally.

ROTATE YOUR SHOES

If you are running every day or even on consecutive days it's worth investing in a second pair of shoes and alternating between them. After a heavy pounding on the run, it's believed that this extra day of rest helps to restore the integrity of the midsole foam's cushioning and stability. At the very least, it'll give the shoes time to dry out fully.

HANDS ARE BETTER THAN MACHINES

It's very tempting to toss your filthy, sodden shoes into the washing machine. Resist the temptation: the shoes may come out as bright and clean as new, but they may also be fatally damaged. Detergents can attack the glue that holds the shoes together and penetrate the foam in the midsole. Even the action of the machine can undermine the shoes' construction.

---

of foam, sometimes with an additional plastic device, inserted into the rear, arch-side section of the midsole to add support to the foot or to control excessive rearfoot motion.

Midfoot The section of the shoe around the arch. Plastic shanks are often built into the midfoot of the shoe under the foot to provide added stability.

Midsole The foam cushioning layer of the shoe between the upper and the outsole. It's the technical heart of the shoe and contains its primary cushioning and stability features.

Motion-control shoe Our term for a shoe with added heavy-duty stability features, for big runners or runners with severe stability problems.

Neutral See biomechanically efficient.

Outsole The outer rubber section of the shoe which comes into contact with the ground.

Overpronation Excessive inward rolling of the foot, which prevents normal toe-off and exposes you to a host of injury problems, particularly in the knee.

Over-supination An extremely rare condition in which the foot fails to roll inwards as

If You're A Forefoot Striker...

You... land and push off from your toes when you run, rather than following the normal pattern of landing on the outside edge of your heel and rolling through to push off from your toes. The normal pattern absorbs shock much better.

You need shoes that... have excellent forefoot cushioning, flexibility and stability. However, you need to have an expert assess why you're a forefoot striker. If it's because you have a high arch and a rigid ankle, you need a neutral, relatively curved shoe to encourage foot motion, with a flexible forefoot and a high arch support. If you're a forefoot striker simply because you have tight calves, you should address this problem with stretching and/or physiotherapy rather than shoes. Finally, some runners favour the forefoot simply because they run quickly; they need light, responsive shoes, with an emphasis on forefoot cushioning and stability.

If You're A Heel Striker...

You... prematurely destroy the outsole rubber (and probably the cushioning) on the outside heel of your shoes. This is usually because you land in an exaggerated way, though if you're heavy, that could also contribute.

You need shoes that... have thick, durable outsoles and resilient midsole foam. Because the composition of the outsole compound is at least as important as its thickness, you need to know about a shoe's reputation before you buy.

If You Underpronate...

Your... feet and ankles don't roll inwards enough when you run – a rare condition. This movement would normally help to absorb shock every time your feet strike the ground.

You need shoes that... encourage the inward movement of the foot (pronation). Look for a soft midsole, and a curved last (the shape around which the shoe is built). Avoid shoes with added stability features, such as medial posts (these are firm sections on the arch side of the midsole, designed to limit pronation).

If You Wear Orthoses...

You... have custom-made insoles designed to correct biomechanical imbalances. They are usually – but not always – built to provide additional stability.

You need shoes that... fit your orthoses, and work with them in the way that your podiatrist

» JARGON-BUSTER – SHOES

you run. Instead, it strikes on the outer edge of the foot and continues to roll outwards.

Performance trainer Our term for a light shoe with enough cushioning and stability for some everyday training.

Pronation The inward rolling of the foot, which is a natural part of the gait cycle.

Rearfoot The back section of the foot immediately behind the arch which takes the primary force of footstrike.

Responsiveness The ability of your forefoot to feel the ground as you push away from it.

Ride The overall feel of the shoe through the complete gait cycle. In a smooth-riding shoe, the gait feels like one continuous movement rather than impact, then forward rolling, then push-off.

Stability The ability of a shoe to reduce excessive foot and ankle movement, which can lead to injury throughout the body. Overpronation is the key danger. Simple design elements such as a straight shape, firmer cushioning or a thinner midsole help stability, as do added features such as a medial post and midfoot shank. A runner's stability needs depend on how unstable their natural running style is.

» TOP TIP

LOOP-LACING LOCK

This is a great way for anyone to create a secure, tight fit. Just put each lace end back into the same hole it just exited, leaving a small loop on the top side of the shoe; now thread each loose end through the loop on the opposite side; then pull to create a super-tight closure.

Problem Narrow foot
Solution Using the loop-lacing lock halfway up the shoe doubles the laces over your midfoot, ensuring a tight fit.

Problem Heel slipping in your shoe
Solution Lace the shoe using the normal criss-cross technique, then tie a loop-lacing lock on the last eyelet.

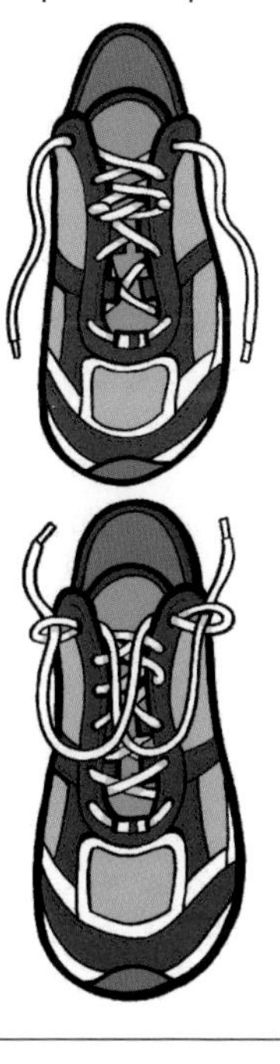

Problem High instep
Solution Start with normal criss-cross lacing, but over the midfoot feed the laces up each side of the shoe. Finish with the criss-cross technique at the top.

Problem Wide forefoot
Solution Over the width of your foot just feed the laces up each side of the shoe, again using the criss-cross technique at the top.

Stability shoe Our term for a shoe specifically designed to help runners with an unstable gait. Not as extreme as a motion-control shoe, though.

Supination A natural outward rolling of the foot, which is a small part of the gait cycle just before the foot starts to leave the ground.

Toe-box The front part of the fabric upper surrounding the toes.

Toe-off The final stage of the gait cycle, which propels you forward as your foot pushes off from the ground.

Upper The fabric section of the shoe that surrounds the top of the foot and holds the laces.

...AND THE TECHNOLOGIES

Abzorb SBS New Balance's rubber cushioning insert.

Adiprene Adidas's viscous EVA rearfoot cushioning insert. Adiprene+ is springier, foam-based forefoot cushioning.

Air Nike's pressurised cushioning units, in various sizes. Zoom Air is a thinner, more flexible version. Tuned Air contains pairs of plastic hemispheres for stability.

Cell Puma's honeycomb-shaped cushioning technology.

intended. Usually, if your orthoses provide all the correction you need, your podiatrist is likely to recommend using them in a neutral but supportive shoe. Extreme overpronators may be recommended a motion-control shoe, especially as, in the view of podiatrist Simon Costain, the chance of having too much stability is slim. In either case, look for shoes that are roomy enough to accommodate orthoses comfortably. Look particularly for a deep heel counter, as built-up orthoses can compromise stability and fit in shallow-fitting shoes.

If You Have Wide Feet...

You... are not alone. Asics says that over 15 per cent of its GT-2080 sales were in a wide fitting (the equivalent of a 2E) – and New Balance reports that a huge 51 per cent of its 855 sales were in 4E.

You need shoes that... keep pressure off the sides of your feet, and allow the usual thumb's width of space between your longest toe and the end of the shoe. In addition to New Balance's longstanding range, Asics and Nike now offer a width option in three of their most popular shoes, while Etonic also has a good range of widths. New Balance offers width options on almost all its shoes, the widest (4E) typically on big-guy shoes. Here's the tricky part: the right shoe for you depends on why your feet are wide relative to their length (it also has to meet your stability and cushioning needs). If you have short toes, you'll need a shoe that flexes further forward than normal, as, relatively speaking, that's what your feet do. Look for the position of the flex grooves on the underside of the shoe, and if you have wide and high feet, you need to pay special attention to the vertical space inside your shoe, as well as the width.

If You Have Narrow Feet...

You... need to do more than just lace up normal shoes tightly.

You need shoes that... don't allow your feet to slip inside. Not only will over-wide shoes feel less responsive, but you'll also be more at risk of blisters in the areas where your feet do touch the shoe. Only New Balance makes shoes in specifically designated narrow widths, but other makes and models have a reputation for slenderness – often in the faster shoes. Some brands, such as Asics, Mizuno and Reebok, are not known for narrow shoes. ■

» JARGON-BUSTER – SHOES

Duocell in the heel provides cushioning and stability.

DMX Foam Reebok's system of foam pillars within the midsole for cushioning.

Gel Asics' pads of silicone (or silicone-based) cushioning gel. They are available in various sizes, shapes and densities depending on the shoe.

GRID Saucony's cushioning and stability cassette. Hytrel strands are strung in a similar pattern to a tennis racquet. 3D GRID is more stable.

HRC Saucony's cushioning foam insert in the forefoot.

HydroFlow Brooks' cushioning pads, containing silicone oil. HydroFlow ST adds stability.

Shox Rearfoot polyurethane cushioning pillars used by Nike.

Stable Air Etonic's rearfoot cushioning insert.

Substance 257 Brooks's high-durability, cushioning foam insert.

Wave Mizuno's large, flexible fan-shaped midsole insert. Different configurations for stability and cushioning are availble. X-Wave has a flat, central "sweet spot".

VS1 Mizuno's forefoot cushioning pad.

KITTED **OUT**

Running is the ultimate no-fuss sport: all you need to run is a pair of decent trainers, right? Well, up to a point

Proper shoes may be all you absolutely need to start training, but investing in some technical clothing will mean you can run in comfort in all conditions. You don't need a whole new wardrobe – just a few well-chosen items to keep you cool in the summer, warm in the winter, and ready to run whatever the weather.

SUMMER KIT

No matter what outfit you select to run in this summer, you're going to sweat – and sweat a lot. By picking clothes made from the right materials, you can make running more manageable when the heat is on and the humidity is up. Today's fabrics breathe as much as you do. They won't get clammy and heavy with moisture like your cotton

T-shirts, and they'll help to make your summer miles more enjoyable.

Cool ideas

This doesn't mean you have to part with your favourite cotton T-shirt. Put it on after the run. For scorching sessions, consider a mesh top made with Coolmax polyester that wicks perspiration away from the skin to the outside of the fabric, where it evaporates quickly. And shorts made of Supplex nylon will drape comfortably rather than cling to your wet skin. They feel like cotton but are lighter and dry more quickly.

Try a few of the latest high-tech tops and shorts and after a couple of days of running in the heat of the day, you'll probably be convinced. You'll stay drier than before and feel cooler and more comfortable.

These materials hate moisture, too. The structure and design of their fibres are what make them work. The fibres on the outer surface of the fabric are finer than those on the inner surface, causing a one-way, capillary action. Moisture is absorbed by the inner surface and pulled and diffused over a wider area of the outer surface to speed evaporation. Cotton T-shirts just don't work like this – and you can test it yourself. Wear a cotton T-shirt for a 40-minute run on a hot, humid day. Afterwards, remove it and squeeze out as much moisture as you can. Then wear a high-tech top and do the same. You'll be amazed at the difference.

Room for manoeuvre

Protection from the sun, heat and humidity isn't all you have to decide on for a comfortable hot-weather run. A pleasant summer run also demands that your clothes fit well and feel right. Look for clothes that are cut to allow plenty of room for movement and that won't rub you raw. You'll want tops that don't slip off and shorts that don't ride up.

To achieve the maximum coolness and comfort, you'll have to spend from £15 to £30 for tops, and the same for shorts. The investment will pay off every time you run. Instead of thinking about how sweaty you feel, you'll be thinking about the extra miles you want to cover.

WINTER KIT

The secret of maximum comfort during your winter run is layering – rather than wearing one thick layer, you need two or three lightweight ones. Such a system allows perspiration to escape more readily while holding in more heat, so it will keep you warmer and drier. If you get over-heated during your run, you can remove a layer – and if you get too cold, slip it back on.

How to layer the upper body

A good layering system for a runner uses, at most, three layers on the upper body. Add another, and

it's too bulky and uncomfortable for running. First, put on a layer against the skin, add a second light top if it's really cold outside, and finally, wear an outer protective layer. The following is a brief explanation of each one:

First layer This innermost layer should wick moisture away from your skin and move it to the outside to protect you from chilling. The first layer should be lightweight and fit snugly against your skin. It's important to wear synthetic, wicking materials, rather than absorbent fabrics that get wet and stay wet, such as cotton.

Middle layer The primary function of this layer is to insulate the body by creating additional air-space. You need a middle layer only in very cold conditions. Although this second layer might be a bit heavier than the first, it must still wick moisture outwards. This piece should fit loosely over the first layer and should be easy to remove, so you can adjust for any weather conditions.

Outer layer This last layer should be a protective

shell or vest that shelters you against cold, wind, rain and snow while still allowing perspiration to evaporate. The garment should be large enough to fit loosely over the other layer(s). If the insulation layer is compressed by a tight outer layer, your system will lose efficiency. Ventilation is important, too, because this allows the other layers to perform better.

Layer the legs, too

Even though your legs perspire less than your

» RUNNING ADDITIONS

So, you have the perfect running wardrobe and you're braving the elements in style and comfort. But if you want to make your training more effective and more focused, there are some optional extras that can help you to stay out longer, a few push you to work harder, and others contribute to a faster recovery afterwards.

1 A Watch With A Lap Memory

Why? If you want to progress as well as you can, a good digital watch is a must. We're not suggesting you become time-obsessed (leave the watch at home for leisurely recovery runs and long, slow sessions), but once you've passed your beginner months, structured speedwork and controlled racing are the keys to helping you run faster, easier. The watch's memory will store your lap times or mile splits, helping you to learn from your session afterwards: did you set off too fast and then deteriorate, for instance? Watches come with anything from eight- to 250-lap memories.

2 High-Impact Sports Bra

Why? There's only one excuse for not wearing a sports bra when you run, and that's being male. Otherwise, no matter what size you are, you need to arm yourself against the irreversible effects of gravity as you run. Once the ligaments around the breasts stretch, there's nothing you can do to shorten them again. Normal bras reduce breast movement by around 35 per cent, but a good sports bra achieves closer to 60 per cent. Crop-top styles normally suit A- and B-cup sizes; larger sizes require moulded cups; and either way you should look for a bra which has been designed for high-impact activities. See page 228 for a look at women-specific kit.

3 Training Log

Why? Every run is an achievement, and a training log is a record of that. More importantly, it helps to show where you've gone right and where you may have gone wrong in your training. If you want to build on a successful 10K from last year, for instance, you can discover what the key ingredients were in your build-up by checking your log. If your marathon didn't go to plan, your log doubtless has the answer. Did you really do as many long runs as you thought? Or did you take enough rest days and cross-train enough? Some people record everything from the weather to what they thought as they ran, others just note the bare-bones, such as routes and times.

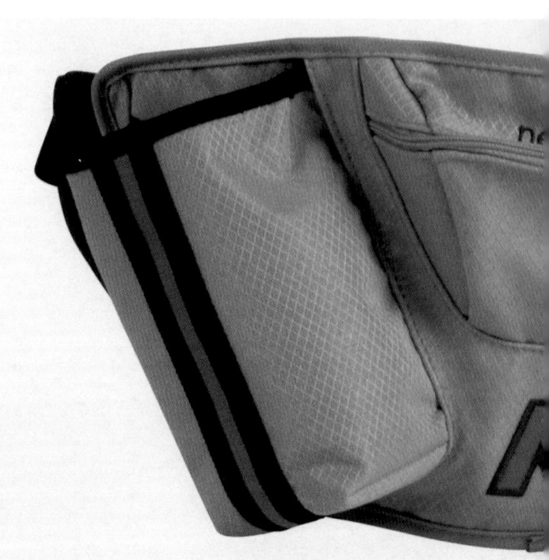

4 A Bag Of Frozen Peas

Why? Promptly icing an injury is the best way to minimise tissue damage, but ask any expert and they'll tell you it's one of the most underused treatments there is. If you'd rather go through months of physio and running at half-speed to clear up your injury, fine; but we'd advise you to use the quicker (and much cheaper) option of reducing the inflammation with a bag of frozen peas as soon as it happens. Here's the drill: wrap a bag of frozen peas in a damp tea towel and compress it firmly against the injury site for 12-15 minutes. Try to elevate the injured area. Repeat this hourly, or as often as you can for the next three days. You can use it again if you feel twinges as you gently stretch out the injury on subsequent days.

5 Heart-Rate Monitor

Why? Runners are notoriously bad at judging the effort they're putting into a run. A heart-rate monitor gives you an objective snapshot and helps you know whether you should be speeding up or slowing down. For a full rundown of how to use an HRM, turn to page 58.

6 A Comfortable Drinks Carrier

Why? Think of your body as a car engine. Carbohydrate is its petrol, but water is the oil that keeps all the internal processes moving smoothly. You can put your body on top form before a run by drinking regularly throughout the day, but if you're training for more than an hour, it's worth topping up your fluid levels as you run. You can lose more than a litre of water an hour through sweat, and this will start to affect your efficiency if you don't replace it. There are various ways of carrying water, but it's important that the method

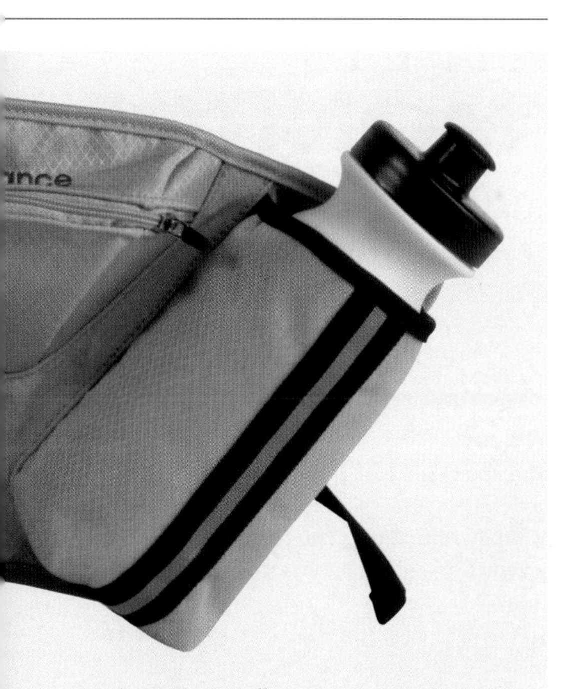

you choose doesn't affect your running style. A bottle belt can carry plenty of liquid, but make sure it doesn't bounce; a hand-held bottle is convenient but it carries less liquid, and the bigger ones may weigh you down.

7 A Complex-Carbohydrate Energy Drink or Gel

Why? A sports drink is the best way to take in large quantities of easily digestible energy, while gels are easy to carry, and work well if you are on a run that passes water fountains, or a race with water stations. You can use them before training (particularly useful for pre-breakfast runs); during sessions over 90 minutes; and in between speed reps to help you stay stronger for longer. Good sports drinks and gels are made with "complex" carbohydrates – usually maltodextrin – which pack more energy than "simple" carbohydrates such as sucrose and fructose. They may also contain minerals to speed water absorption and replace what you've sweated out, but the real key is simply to find a brand with a taste that you like. See page 116 for more on the benefits of on-the-run fuelling.

torso, you may still need to wear more than one layer on them, especially if the temperature drops below zero. On cool autumn days, wear thin, nylon tights. You'll need heavier tights (eg ones made with brushed fabric) on cold winter days.

Other body parts

Now that we've got your upper body and legs covered, let's consider your extremities.

Hold on to your hat Does a hat on your head in the winter really help keep the rest of your body warmer? You bet. The human body works hard to keep the brain warm, so when it's cold, the heat goes to your head, and the other extremities (such as fingers) suffer. When you wear a hat, you save so much heat that the circulatory system can send plenty around to the rest of the body, and if it's really cold outside, wear a headband with a hat over it.

Mittens or gloves? Mittens keep your hands warmer than gloves because of the shared warmth of your fingers. However, light, breathable gloves are great for mild days. Whatever mittens or gloves you choose, make sure they wick moisture.

Socks Your feet need socks that provide warmth but wick moisture away from the skin. It's not necessary to layer socks; one pair is plenty. ■

» TOP TIPS

■ Don't wear cotton T-shirts for running – they're great for normal use, but as soon as you start to sweat they'll get wet, heavy and uncomfortable

■ When it's cold, wear layers – two, or even three thin layers are more effective than one thick one

When you are choosing a waterproof, opt for one with plenty of vents, so you can keep rain from getting in but still let sweat out

■ Put a label on the bag of frozen peas you use to ice injuries – after they've been in and out of the freezer you don't want to mistake them for the ones you bought for Sunday lunch

■ Don't become a slave to your watch – run without it once in a while, so you can savour the experience of running just for the pleasure of it

TRAINING WITH A HEART-RATE MONITOR

Once the preserve of elite athletes, the performance insights heart-rate monitors deliver are increasingly valued by runners of all abilities

Runners from track speedfreaks, through 10K specialists, to veteran marathoners wear heart-rate monitors for the same reason: they provide an objective gauge of your exertion that is often more exact than your own perceptions. While it's important to be aware of your effort so you're in touch with your body's subtle clues, your personal feeling doesn't always provide accurate feedback. Heart-rate monitors, however, are far more precise. No matter what type of runner you are – beginner, intermediate or advanced – a heart-rate monitor will help you train more effectively.

GETTING TO KNOW YOUR MONITOR

When you unpack your heart-rate monitor (or HRM for short), whether it's your first model or an upgrade, take the time to read the instructions and familiarise yourself with the equipment. The more sophisticated the monitor, the more "prep" you'll need if you want to make use of all its features. More basic models that display your heart rate and little else will be practically ready for use.

So what can you expect to find inside the packaging, and what should you look for in the instruction leaflet?

THE INGREDIENTS

HRMs usually come in two or three parts. Long gone are the days of clips wired to the ear lobe and attachments to the fingertip; nowadays you have a chest strap (transmitter) and a receiver (watch). Thankfully there are no wires.

LOCATION, LOCATION, LOCATION

It's important to put the chest strap on in the correct position. For men, this is central and just below the chest muscles: for women, just below the bra, but as high a possible.

THE FIT

The strap can be adjusted for snugness around your chest and should be as tight as possible, without restricting your breathing. This is one parameter you should establish before your first run; otherwise you will feel great frustration when you have to keep stopping to make adjustments.

GET WET

To ensure good readings, it will help if you dampen the contact area for the electrodes. This will make it easier for the transmitter to pick up the electrical activity in your heart. You can use electrode gel, water or – assuming the monitor is your own – good old-fashioned saliva.

MODE SELECTION

If your strap is fitted correctly and you are wearing your receiver, you should be able to see your heart-rate on the receiver. On some models the display will start immediately, without you having to do anything; other models require that you select the correct mode on the watch – another good reason to read the instructions before you start.

ALTERNATE MOUNTINGS

You don't have to wear the watch on your wrist: if you ride a bike or use a rowing machine or other gym apparatus, you can fix the watch to the handle and still get a perfectly good trace. The telemetry range between transmitter and receiver varies between models, but will usually cover a distance of up to two metres. Though this might sound like

a good feature, it also has its down side: if you run in a group and others are also wearing HRMs, the receivers will pick up heart rates from all the transmitters in range. So if you run in company, keep your distance.

OUTSIDE INTERFERENCE

Group training isn't the only potential hazard. Overhead power cables will disrupt your heart rate readings, as will any machinery with strong electric currents – motorised treadmills affect many monitors, often to the point where just walking elicits readings of above 200. Similarly, runners who train on the flight path to an airport can experience strange readings when low-flying aircraft pass overhead.

In time you will get to know what sends your monitor haywire, but as long as you're aware of the culprit, there's no need to panic when the occasional blip occurs.

HRM BASICS: How To Find Your Maximum Heart Rate

A heart-rate monitor can help ensure you don't work too hard – or take it too easy – in training sessions. Depending on the session, your target heart rate will be anywhere between 60 and 95 per cent of your "working heart rate".

Your working heart rate is the range between your resting heart rate, and your maximum. So to find out what it is, you first need to calculate your maximum. If you're carrying a little weight or you're a complete beginner, it's best to use the very approximate formula of 214 – (0.8 x age) for men and 209 – (0.9 x age) for women to estimate your maximum.

Unfortunately, for five to 10 per cent of the population this figure can be wrong by up to 24 beats per minute. It's much better to find your maximum through running. Do this by warming up, then running as fast as you can evenly for three minutes (ideally on a treadmill), then resting with two or three minutes gentle running, then repeating your three minute maximal run.

During your second run you should have a higher maximum heart rate than with any other method – though be sure to use your HRM to take readings throughout, as your heart rate may peak before the end.

Calculating Your Working Heart Rate (WHR)

- Find your maximum heart rate (see above).
- Find your resting heart rate (lying still, soon after you wake up. Ideally take an average over a few days).
- Subtract the resting rate from the maximum. This figure is your working heart rate (eg 206 – 56 = 150).
- Take whatever percentage of your WHR you're aiming for (eg: 60 per cent for an easy run would be 150 x 0.60 = 90), and add it to your resting heart rate, eg 90 + 56 = 146. The final figure is your personal target heart rate.

RW'S BEST HRM SESSIONS

Beginners

Beginners should choose a target zone of between 60 and 70 per cent of their WHR and stay within it for most of their running. Runners who haven't yet developed a sense of their speed and effort can learn from their monitor. "I love being able to keep a consistent pace without having to look at my watch all the time," says Kerrie Hardman, 37, who started running two years ago. "Nothing has helped my training more than monitoring my heart rate."

Suggested session This one comes from running coach Roy Benson, a long-time advocate of heart-rate training. Take 70 per cent of your WHR as your upper limit, and 60 per cent as your lower limit. Plan to run 20 minutes in total (head out for 10 minutes, then turn around). Start running until you hit your upper limit, then walk until it's back down to your lower limit. Run again up to 70 per cent, and then walk until you hit 60 per cent. Continue this way for the entire 20 minutes. "As you progress, you'll spend more time running than walking, because you'll take longer to hit your upper limit," says Benson. Extend the length of the run as your fitness progresses.

Intermediates

If you've run regularly for a year or more, you'll find that a heart-rate monitor is a great help as your training becomes more challenging. One of the best ways to use a monitor is to pre-set a target heart rate for a tempo run. This will keep you from going too fast (a frequent mistake with tempo running). Another great way to use it is on long runs, which should be neither too fast nor too slow (aim for 60-70 per cent of WHR, depending on your fitness).

Intermediate and advanced runners are renowned for running too hard on their recovery days. A heart-rate monitor can help you keep a lid on your efforts and ensure you really do recover properly on these days.

Suggested session This ladder session progresses through a range of heart-rate zones. After 10 minutes of jogging, run four minutes at 70-80 per cent of your WHR, three minutes at 80-90 per cent, two minutes at 90-95 per cent, and finally one minute flat out. Finish with 10 minutes of easy jogging. For a less challenging run, decrease the amount of time spent in each zone by a minute. For a more challenging session, do the ladder two or even three times.

Advanced Runners

Even the best runners can benefit from heart-rate feedback. South African coach Bobby McGee, who oversees some of the fastest runners in the world, relies on HRMs to train his athletes.

When distance runner Colleen De Reuck joined his group, McGee suggested she start wearing a monitor. "She knew how to run easy and how to run hard, but nothing in between," he says. "Being at altitude, I knew she'd need something other than pace-per-mile to ber able to determine her efforts." De Reuck, who now wears a monitor for easy and intermediate sessions, was a quick convert. "I stopped burning myself out," she says.

Many advanced runners use the monitor to track recovery during speedwork. Instead of waiting a predetermined number of minutes or jogging a certain distance between repetitions, you can check for your heart rate to drop before beginning the next repetition. Your recovery target should be less than 80 per cent of your WHR.

Suggested session Jog for 10 minutes, then run three repetitions of one-and-a-half miles at about 85-90 per cent of WHR. Rest three minutes between each repetition. Note the time for each repetition in your log. "You'll see your times decrease as your season progresses," McGee says. "You're not working any harder, but you should be running much faster at the same heart rate."

A rise in resting heart rate often indicates you're overtraining. An HRM can help make this diagnosis. For this you'll need a monitor that stores information for later recall. "My elite runners sleep with their monitors on," McGee says. "The resulting information is an important indicator, telling me if they're overtraining." According to McGee, an erratic heart rate with lots of variation throughout the night is typical when an athlete is training hard.

When tapering and resting for a race, the heart rate should be steadier and more consistent. If yours is still erratic leading up to a big race, consider a longer taper, or cut your mileage and intensity during your taper.

» HEART RATE AND FAT-BURNING

The key to fat-burning is to realise there is not an instant "switch" from fat-burning "on" to fat-burning "off". Assuming the same terrain, you will burn a similar number of calories per mile of running regardless of your pace. It's just a case of whether carbohydrate is taking up a little (40 per cent) or a lot (80 per cent) of calories burned.

Ultimately, it's the overall number of calories you burn that determines how much weight you lose, but staying below the excessive carb-burning zone helps use more fat as immediate fuel. If you were to "go for the burn", you'd experience a build-up of lactic acid – the result of very high sugar-burning with the use of very little fat for fuel. Hard runs are also a big psychological effort.

So, although some faster running is good for our egos, economy and pace judgement, to lose the lard it's better to put your energy into more miles at a slower pace, rather than fewer at a faster tempo. A good rule of thumb devised in the US is to train up to a heart rate calculated by taking your age from 180. So at 40 you train up to a HR of 140.

If you have to walk occasionally to keep your heart rate down, then walk – your aerobic system is still being strengthened, and going too high will only result in lactic acid flooding your muscles. There is no short cut to weight loss: it's about consistency, a slight reduction in calorie intake and, ideally, some resistance training to complement your running. Fat is slow on and slow off – you can't run hard to lose it faster. You'll only end up overloading muscles and joints – and your brain.

HOW TO CHOOSE A **RUNNING WATCH**

A good running watch will be hardy yet lightweight, water resistant, comfy, easily readable, user-friendly, and, oh, accurately time your training and racing efforts

If you don't feel ready to shell out for a heart-rate monitor, a running watch is also a great training tool. The kind of watch you need depends on the kind of runner you are. If you never race, never do speed sessions and all your runs are leisurely lopes, you may not need a watch, but most of us – whether we run a mile in 12 minutes or five – like to check our progress at least once in a while.

The most basic thing to look for is a memory function to record mile times in races or lap times in speed sessions. Many running watches also have countdown timers. While not essential, they can help a great deal when you're doing repetitions.

Running watches come with a multitude of extra functions – some more useful than others. Dual-time clocks may do little for your running, while a pacing option you can set to beep 150 times a minute can be of great benefit. The good news is most models are surprisingly easy to use, with prompts on-screen telling you which mode you have entered and what happens if you hold down a particular key.

Don't be so dazzled by functions you forget the basics – is the screen readable at arm's length, and are the buttons easy to use on the run? Does it have a lap timer? A watch that tells you how far above sea level you are and the time in Vladivostok will lose its sheen if it doesn't do what you need it to do, on the run.

WHAT DOES IT ALL MEAN?

Chronograph/stopwatch The stopwatch mode (or "chronograph") times your runs in hours, minutes, seconds and fractions of a second. On most watches the screen is split in two: one half

shows your overall time and the other shows your current lap time. You could calculate lap times in your head, but even the slowest runner will find a built-in lap timer useful for racing and training.

Memory Good watches store lap times so you can look at them afterwards. Capacities vary from 10 laps to 120 laps, and most allow you to store as many sessions as you want within that limit (eg a 120-lap memory could store 10 x 12-lap sessions or 60 x 2-lap sessions).

When you enter the memory recall mode, each session has a header page showing the date of the session (and sometimes its overall time). You choose the session you want to view, then scroll through lap by lap. Some watches also highlight the session's best lap and calculate your average lap time. A 100-lap memory is more than most of us need, but you'd be surprised how much you can fill – see the chart of a good training week below. In practice, most runners probably store no more than three or four sessions at a time, using a maximum of about 50 laps in total.

You could get away with less memory by writing down the details of each session upon completion, freeing up storage space for next time. A 26-lap watch is a good example of the basic amount of memory you should look for – it's enough for all the full mile splits in a marathon as well as most runner's speed sessions.

Countdown timer If you do speed sessions based on effort over time rather than distance, a countdown timer function helps. They vary in sophistication, and, in truth, most aren't so great. The classic version lets you set a single time and specify whether you want the timer to beep and repeat the countdown at the end of the first cycle; beep and stop; or beep and count upwards.

Unless you plan to run a continuous session of equal-length efforts and recoveries, you'd have to do a lot of button-pushing to make this kind of timer useful because it's so inflexible. A timer that lets you programme different-length segments into the same cycle (eg catering for a repeated session of five minutes fast, two minutes slow) is better.

If you want a good session that even a basic timer can manage, you need a fixed distance to cover. Then you can run, for example, 12 x 400m setting off every two and a half minutes. You'd put the timer onto a continuous loop, and it would keep going in the background while you were using the stopwatch mode to time your laps. ■

Day	Session	Laps used
Monday	Jog out (1), 2 laps easy (2), jog back (1)	4
Tuesday	Jog out (1), 12 x 400m with 100m jog recoveries (24), jog back (1)	26
Wednesday	Jog out (1), 4 laps steady (4), jog back (1)	6
Thursday	Jog out (1), 10 x hill reps and recoveries (20), jog back (1)	22
Friday	Rest	0
Saturday	Jog out (1), 3 laps fartlek (3), jog back (1)	5
Sunday	Jog out (1), 8 laps slow (8), jog back (1)	10
Total		73 laps

CHAPTER 3
Training

After a while, simply putting one foot in front of the other isn't going to be enough for you. If you want to run further and faster, and avoid becoming stuck in a rut, you'll need to follow a structured training programme. Don't worry, this isn't as scary as it sounds, and in this chapter you'll find the best ways to boost your endurance, increase your speed, tame the treadmill, and recover effectively from all the hard work you've been putting in.

THE 15 BEGINNERS' ESSENTIALS

Running doesn't have to be complicated: arm yourself with some basic knowledge and you can start training with confidence. Think of these as crib sheets for your basic "running course". Learn them, and you can make it through your first running efforts with flying colours

1 WELCOME TO THE START LINE

This might be your first try at running, or a return visit, or an attempt to improve on what you already do. The less running you've done recently, the more you can expect to improve your distances and speeds in the first 10 weeks. On the other hand, the less you've run lately, the more likely you are to hurt yourself by doing too much, too soon. That's why it's so important to set two related goals as you start or restart your running programme – to maximise improvements, and to minimise injuries. You win by improving. You lose by getting hurt.

2 BUY THE RIGHT SHOES

Shoes are the biggest equipment expense for runners, so it's important to get this right. Spend wisely by buying well-made shoes from a serious brand. Remember pages 42 to 48, it can't be repeated too often, and search out a model that fits you properly, and is designed for the surface you'll run on most often – road, track, or trail. If you're not sure which shoe will work best for you, go to a specialist running shop where staff can advise you (there is a list of such shops in the runner's resource, at the back of this book). After you buy your shoes, remember that even the best have a limited lifespan. Plan to replace them after about 400-600 miles of wear.

3 MAKE A PLAN

The two basic raw materials for a running routine are time (see pages 30-35) and space. And the two main reasons given by those who don't run? "I don't have time for it", and, "I don't have anywhere to do it". Let's dissect those excuses. You can run well and get in great shape with as little as a 30-minute session every other day. Think of it as the time you won't waste by watching TV. As for finding places to run, anywhere that's safe for walking is also fine for running. Off-road routes (parks, bike paths, playing fields) are better than busy streets, and soft surfaces (grass and dirt) are better than paved ones, but any choice is better than staying at home. Map out the best courses in your immediate neighbourhood. That saves time, solves the "place" issue and makes it much more likely you'll execute your planned runs.

4 EAT AND DRINK THE RIGHT FOODS

Sports nutrition is a big topic, but, in general, the rules for good nutrition and fluid consumption are the same for runners as for everyone else. Three areas of special interest to runners: (1) control your weight, as extra pounds will slow you down; (2) eat lightly after training and racing; (3) drink 250-500ml of water or a carbohydrate drink an hour before running, as dehydration can be dangerous.

5 GET F.I.T.

Kenneth Cooper, a giant in the fitness field, long ago devised a simple formula for improving as a runner. Run two to three miles, three to five days a week at a comfortable pace. It's easier to remember as the F.I.T. formula: frequency (at least every other day); intensity (comfortable pace); and time (about 30 minutes). Even with some walking breaks, you can cover two miles in 30 minutes, and you might soon be running three miles in that time. It's important to run these efforts at an easy, comfortable pace. Think of yourself as the Tortoise, not the Hare. Make haste slowly.

6 FIND YOUR PACE

We've told you to make it comfortable, which sounds simple. The problem is that most novice runners don't know what a comfortable pace feels like, so they push too hard. As a result, they get overly fatigued and discouraged, or even injured. Here are some more guidelines. A comfortable pace is one to two minutes per mile slower than your trial mile time. Or you can use a heart-rate monitor and run at 65 per cent of your working heart rate. (To calculate effort based on your WHR, see the heart-rate training section, starting on page 58). Alternatively, listen to your breathing. If you aren't gasping for air, and you can talk while you're running, your pace is about right.

7 REMEMBER TO WARM UP AND COOL DOWN FIRST

Don't confuse a little stretching with a good warm-up. Stretching exercises generally don't make you sweat or raise your heart rate, which is what you really want from a warm-up. A proper warm-up begins with walking or running very slowly to ease your body into the session. Try walking briskly for five minutes (about a quarter of a mile), and then break into your comfortable running pace. (Don't count the warm-up as part of your run time or distance.) When you finish your run, resist the urge to stop. Instead, walk another five minutes to cool down more gradually. After this is the best time for stretching – when your muscles are warm and ready to be stretched a little.

8 DON'T HESITATE TO WALK

Walk is not a four-letter word for runners. Pausing to walk during a run is not a form of cheating, but a common practice among experienced runners (see pages 39 to 42). It is a form of interval training that breaks a big piece of work into smaller pieces, making it more manageable. Mix running and walking in these circumstances: when you're starting to run for the first time; to regain fitness after a long lay-off, injury or illness; to warm up before a run, and to cool down afterwards; to make your fast running faster (which is the basic principle of interval training); to make long runs longer; and to make easy runs easier. Walk breaks tend to work best when you walk for at least one minute but no longer than five minutes.

9 RUN SAFELY AT ALL TIMES

The biggest threat you'll face as a runner on the road, by far, is the car. Traffic zips past you. A moment's lapse in attention from either you or the driver can bring disaster, and you'll be the one to suffer – not them. The best way to lower this risk is to avoid running near roads, but for many of us, this is a near impossibility, or it's an approach that adds time and complexity to our routine (if we have to drive to a park, for example). So most of us adapt and learn to be extremely cautious on the roads. Try to find quiet roads with wide pavements; if there is no pavement, run on the right side of the road, facing the oncoming traffic; obey traffic signs and signals; and follow every road rule your parents taught you. Run as if every car is a lethal weapon.

10 USE PAIN AS YOUR GUIDE

Runners get hurt. We rarely hurt ourselves as seriously as skiers or rugby players, but injuries do happen. Most are musculoskeletal, meaning we recover rapidly when we take days off or other appropriate action (such as ice treatment), and most are self-inflicted – we bring them on by running too far, too fast, too soon or too often. Prevention is often as simple as a change of routine. If you can't run steadily without pain, mix walking and running. If you can't run-walk, simply walk. If you can't walk, cycle. If you can't cycle, swim. As you recover, climb back up this fitness ladder.

11 PAY ATTENTION TO YOUR FORM

Running form is as individual as a fingerprint and is too inborn to change very much. But, with practice, you can improve your efficiency. Run upright, not with a pronounced forward lean. Look toward the horizon, not at your feet. Run faster by increasing your stride turnover, not by overreaching with each stride. On uphills, shorten your stride and drive more with the arms. Try to maintain even effort, not pace. When running downhill, let gravity work for you by leaning forward slightly.

12 TAKE THE MILE TRIAL

Friends who hear that you've begun running will soon ask what your best mile time is – so you might as well get used to it. Before long, you'll be calculating your pace per mile on longer runs, but you should begin with a simple one-mile test run (four laps on a standard track) to determine your starting point. Think of this run as a pace test, not a race. Run at a pace a little beyond easy, but less than a struggle, and count on improving your mile time in later tests as your fitness improves.

13 STRETCHING AND STRENGTHENING

Running is a specialised activity, working mainly the legs. If you're seeking total-body fitness, you need to supplement your running with other exercises. These should aim to strengthen the muscles that running neglects, and stretch those that running tightens, which means strengthening

the upper body and stretching the legs. Add a few minutes of strengthening and stretching after your runs, because that's when these exercises tend to have the most benefit.

14 FOLLOW THE HARD DAY/EASY DAY TRAINING SYSTEM

Most runs need to be easy. This is true whether you're a beginner or an elite athlete. (Of course, the definition of easy varies hugely; an easy mile for an elite runner would be impossible for many beginners or even experienced runners.) As a new runner, make sure you limit yourself to one hard day a week. Run longer and slower than normal, or shorter and faster than normal, or enter a short (5K) race and maintain your best pace for the entire distance.

15 CONGRATULATE YOURSELF

One of the great beauties of running is that it gives everyone a chance to win. Winning isn't automatic; you still have to work for success and risk failure, but in running, unlike in other sports, there's no need to beat an opponent or an arbitrary standard (such as "par" in golf). Runners measure themselves against their own standards. When you improve a time or increase a distance, or set a personal best in a race, you win – no matter what anyone else has done on the same day. You can win even more simply by keeping at it for the long haul, for years and decades. You don't have to run very far or fast to outrun people who have dropped out. It's the *Tortoise and the Hare* all over again. Slow and steady always wins the most important race. ■

LONG MAY YOU RUN

If you manage them right, your long runs will help you run better from 10K to marathons and beyond

Compared with other training sessions, the long run is fairly simple: put one foot in front of the other and stop when you've done 20 miles, but its simplicity is deceptive. Like an onion, the long run has many layers; and, like an onion, a long run can make you cry. "The long run is the single most important work-out you can do," says Jeff Galloway, who ran the 10,000m for the USA in the 1972 Olympics, "but it's more complex than you would think, and most runners still don't do it right."

There are many questions about the long run, including the big four: Why? How long? How fast? How often? We'll answer those, and take a look at related issues such as eating and drinking, rest and recovery and fat-burning. So put your feet up and read on at a comfortable pace.

WHY?

Long runs give you endurance – the ability to run further. Yet they can help 10K runners as well as marathoners. Long runs do several things.

- They strengthen the heart.
- They open capillaries, speeding energy to working muscles and flushing away waste products from

tired ones. "Long runs build a better plumbing system," says Galloway.

- They strengthen leg muscles and ligaments.
- They recruit fast-twitch muscle fibres to assist slow-twitch tasks – such as marathon running.
- They help burn fat as fuel.
- They boost confidence. "If you know you can go that far in training, it gives you the confidence that with the adrenalin of the race, you can get around that too," says Danielle Sanderson, a former European 50-kilometre champion.
- They make you faster. "Increase your long run from six miles to 12 – change nothing else – and you will improve your 10K time," says Galloway.

HOW LONG?

"When I started running in 1989, I gradually built up to 12 miles for my first half-marathon," says Sanderson. "Now, if I'm training for a marathon, I do 24 miles at least eight times in the 14-week build-up. If I'm not training for anything, I do 12-14 miles every Sunday."

HOW LONG SHOULD A LONG RUN BE?

Fortunately, there are some general rules:

Time is a better gauge than distance "The duration of the long run will vary depending on the athlete's age, fitness, and the competitive distance they're training for," explains Norman Brook, Britain's former National Endurance Coach. "The run should usually be for at least 45

» FUEL FOR THE RUN

Early risers...

Early-morning long runs can make it hard to squeeze in breakfast beforehand. It's not that you really need that bowl of muesli and round of toast (most of us have enough stored energy to complete a long run in the morning), but blood-sugar levels are generally lower first thing, because you haven't eaten for 12 hours. This can cause light-headedness, and that's what you want to avoid, so eat light. Half a bagel, a banana, an energy bar or a carbohydrate drink an hour or so before your run will raise blood sugar levels and not upset your stomach. Or have a midnight feast. Well, a snack, anyway. Eat some toast, cereal or dried fruit before going to bed. "Anything that's high in carbohydrates," advises former RW Nutrition Editor Peta Bee. "That snack will carry over to the morning."

And during the run...

Make sure there's plenty of fluid available. Carry supplies in a bumbag or a Camelbak, plan routes that pass by water fountains, or double back to bottles at your house or car. If you're only drinking once every three miles, aim to down 225ml at a time. And yes, you can slow down, walk or even stop. The important thing is getting that fluid down.

"Water is the best choice on a long run, because it's less likely to cause stomach problems," says Galloway. But if you need a little extra energy, try a sports drink. A handy tip: mix the sports drink with plenty of water, especially early on in your long runs. Save the undiluted stuff for late fluid stops when you need it most, and if you're training for a marathon, practise drinking what you'll be offered on the course. (Contact the race organisers to find out, if you're not sure.)

Recovery routine

After your long run, remember this maxim: scoff, quaff and cool off.

Scoff We're not talking about a hearty Sunday roast once you've showered and changed. "It's important to eat as soon as you get back," says Sanderson. Whole foods can be rough on a stomach tender from 20 miles of running, so think liquid – fruit juices and carbohydrate drinks – when it comes to fuel. Those with cast-iron stomachs can go for bagels, bananas, cold pasta or anything high in carbohydrate.

Quaff No matter how slowly you go or how much you drink, your body will be dehydrated after a long run. So drink copiously, and far beyond your thirst. A good rule is to drink two pints of fluid for every half-hour you've run.

Cool off Try a cold shower directed at the legs, or an ice pack massage. Resist the temptation to jump into a hot bath or hot shower right away – it may feel good, but you're actually inhibiting recovery. Sanderson also recommends light stretching and keeping on the move. "If I stop for too long, I soon seize up," she says.

minutes and can extend up to three hours for elite athletes and those preparing for the marathon or ultra-distance events."

"You can use a heart-rate monitor to gauge your effort, or measure your course in your car or with a GPS watch," adds Sanderson, "but it's more about running for a length of time than anything else." Measure your long runs by all means, but for the most part, the goal of a long run is not covering a certain distance, but quality time spent on your feet.

Run for one-and-a-half to two hours That's the minimum – roughly 10-16 miles – needed to maintain a high endurance level. Increase your long runs by no more than 15 minutes at a time "Build up to the long run gradually," Brook advises. "If the longest you're running for in training is 30 minutes, gradually build up to an hour by adding five minutes to your run each week." Just a few minutes of extra running make a difference – but do too much and you're setting yourself up for injury or illness.

HOW FAST?

You want to run a marathon in 3:30, which is eight minute/mile pace, so you do your long runs at that pace. Sounds like a good strategy, right? Wrong. "It's a logical argument that you should do your long runs at marathon pace," says Benji Durden, a 2:09 marathoner who now coaches both elite and recreational runners, "but unfortunately,

» GOING LONGER

If you're training to run a marathon, whether it's your first or your 101st, your aim is to be fit enough to complete 26 miles and 385yards on a particular date. If you're just hoping to get round, then you should start off with a long "run" of about an hour – mostly walking if you're a complete beginner, with a little jogging mixed in. Build this up each month, to 90 minutes of walking and jogging (gradually increasing the proportion of running), then to two hours, and then two-and-a-half, with a single 18-mile effort at the end of the month before your marathon.

Faster and more experienced runners, spending about the same time on their long runs, will of course cover a greater distance. If you're hoping to run a sub-four-hour marathon, you should be doing weekly long runs of 10 miles in your first month of training, 12-13 in the second and 15 in the third, while the sub-3:30 crowd should be doing regular runs of 15 miles in the second and aiming to run 18-20 on their longest runs in the third month. As for the sub-three brigade, if you can make your five longest runs add up to 90-100 miles, you've done enough endurance training.

The easiest way to run, say, 16 miles on a Sunday is often to enter a half-marathon, do 10-15 minutes of warming up beforehand and 10 minutes of very slow jogging afterwards. If your schedule is calling for 20 miles, you could run seven miles before a half-marathon. In this case, you mustn't take the race too seriously – treat it as a training run with lots of company.

running isn't always logical." He's referring to the fat-burning issue: you should run long and slow to condition your body to burn fat, so you'll be able to run long and fast in the marathon. There are other reasons for going easy on your 20-milers:

- Long runs at race pace may be training sessions in your mind, but they're races to your body. That can lead to overtraining, injury or illness. "Running long runs fast causes more problems than any other mistake," says Galloway. Marian Sutton, winner of many marathons, agrees: "There's no point pushing too hard. Run at a pace that feels comfortable."
- Fast, long runs miss the point. "Long runs are for endurance," says Sanderson. "It's amazing how quickly they reduce your resting heart rate, making your heart more efficient."
- The ideal pace for long runs is at least one minute per mile slower than your marathon pace.

BURNING QUESTION

Do long, slow runs really help the body to burn fat, enabling you to run through the wall? There are two theories – but first, a quick physiology lesson. The body burns both fat and glycogen at all times for energy; fat stores are abundant; glycogen stores aren't, but they are the body's preferred fuel. Now here are the schools of thought:

Theory one

When you run slower than your aerobic threshold (roughly the pace at which you can carry on a conversation), you burn a higher percentage of fat, thus sparing glycogen. "The more often you do that, the more often you will burn more fat regularly and at a progressively faster pace," says Benji Durden. In other words, long, slow running teaches the body to burn more fat.

The wall – that feeling of light-headedness and fatigue that hits around the 20-mile mark – is the body's reaction to dwindling glycogen. But a body that has learned to burn fat "saves" glycogen, leaving more for those crucial miles from 20-26.

Theory two

The body doesn't learn anything. "The body doesn't get a degree in fat-burning," says physiologist David Martin. "Glycogen is always burned more readily than fat."

What happens during long runs is that the body runs low on glycogen. Afterwards, it stores an additional amount of glycogen to replenish what it has lost. "If you do this often enough, and rest before your big race, there's much more stored glycogen than before," says Martin. "Come race day, you can run through the wall."

"The intensity of effort is low, and you should ensure a steady state is maintained," says Brook. You should be able to conduct a conversation during the run without discomfort."

■ You might even walk at points during longer runs – it works for Sanderson. "It's good to just plod round, walk a bit if you need to, or even stop for a break," she says.

HOW OFTEN?

Don't run long more than once a week. It is, after all, a hard session, requiring rest or easy days before and after. The other end of the scale is debatable. Some runners have no problem going two or three weeks between long runs. Others will come back with a midweek long run if a shorter race precludes the weekend session.

Galloway recommends a simple formula: roughly one day's gap per mile of your long run. For example, if your long run is 12-17 miles, you can go two weeks between long runs without losing endurance; if it's 18-23 miles, three weeks. "That is, if you're running at least 30 minutes every other day in between," he adds. This rule can also be used to taper before a marathon. For instance, if your last long run is 22 miles, you'd run it three weeks before race day. If it's 16 miles, you get a two-week rest before the race.

WHICH DAY IS BEST?

Sunday is traditional, because that's when most people have most free-time. Also, most marathons are at weekends, so why not set your body clock in advance? There's no need to stick to a set day. "I'm not rigid about the day I do my long run," says world marathon record holder Paula Radcliffe, "because I never know when I'll be racing." Sanderson also plans her schedule around events. "I do my long run on a Sunday, unless I'm racing," she says.

DON'T GO SOLO.

Contrary to popular opinion, long runs aren't boring. You just have to know how to run them – that is, with friends. Find a Saturday or Sunday morning group, or arrange to meet a training partner regularly. "I do some of my runs with friends," says Sanderson, "and the time always goes so much faster." ■

SPEEDWORK FOR EVERY RUNNER

It may be a cliché, but that's because it's true: the only way to run faster is... to run faster

Most of us can come up with plenty of reasons to avoid speedwork: it hurts; it increases our chances of picking up an injury; it makes us too tired for our other runs; we don't need it for running marathons... the list is endless. The thing is, they're all unnecessary fears. What's more, whether you want to beat an ancient 800m best set on the grass track at school, or out-kick the runner who always sprints past you in the local 10K, adding speedwork to your regime will be immensely rewarding.

Speedwork doesn't just make you run faster. It makes you fitter, increases the range of movement in your joints, makes you more comfortable at all speeds, and it will ultimately help you to run harder for longer. If you've already added a speed session or two to your schedule then you'll know all of this already. If you haven't, then here are a few things to remember.

EASE INTO IT

When you started running, you ran for just a couple of miles every other day, and gradually built up to your current mileage. You didn't suddenly start running 35 miles a week, so adopt the same approach to speedwork. Put at least three months of steady running behind you, then start with just one session every 10 days or so. Then go on from there.

NOT TOO HARD

Speed sessions aren't about sprinting flat out until you're sick by the side of the track. They're about controlling hard efforts and spreading your energy evenly over a set distance or time, just like you would in a perfect race.

WARM UP AND WARM DOWN

Before each session, jog for at least 8-10 minutes to raise your blood temperature, increase blood-flow to the muscles and psyche yourself up for the fast running ahead. Follow that with some gentle stretching and then run a few fast strides before getting down to the tough stuff. Afterwards, jog for another 5-10 minutes, before stretching once again.

FIND A PARTNER

Speedwork takes more effort and willpower than going out for a gentle jog. It's much easier and more fun to train with someone else – and if you really want to improve, try running with someone just a bit quicker than you.

QUALITY NOT QUANTITY

Speed training should not account for more than 15 per cent of your total mileage. So slot in your speed sessions around the regular work you've been doing all along.

Speed Sessions That Will Guarantee Faster Running

Here are some sessions to help boost your speed. You don't have to try them all, but give some of them a go – and if you find one that you really like, just keep adapting it by adding repetitions (reps) or increasing the distances as you become fitter (and faster).

Beginners If you haven't tried speedwork before, here are some (relatively) gentle introductory sessions. Try one a week if you can. If that's too much, then try one every 10 days.

NIKE
INTERNATIONAL

1 You could start with a session of brisk efforts. Six minutes brisk, one-minute walk, six minutes brisk, one-minute walk, six minutes brisk and so on is a good place to start.

2 Hills are an excellent way to introduce yourself to speedwork. Try 6 x 1 minute uphill, then jog back down. Gradually add extra reps until you can complete 10.

3 Add some fartlek training to your schedule. To begin, add some quick bursts into your shorter runs. Each burst can be as little as 20 seconds or as much as a few minutes.

4 Interval session: 6 x 1 minute, with 3-minute jog/walk recoveries, or 5 x 2 minutes with 5-minute recoveries.

5 After two months or so of speedwork, you can try your first session of short repetitions: 5 x 300m, with 4-minute recoveries; 5 x 200m, with 3-minute rests; or how about 10 x 200m with 3-minute recoveries?

6 Glide downhill. On down slopes during long runs, go with the hill and allow it to pick up your pace to around 80-85 per cent of flat-out, allowing gravity to power you downhill. Don't go any further than 150m. The idea is to speed up without using any extra energy.

CORE SESSIONS

Once you've eased yourself into speedwork with two or three months worth of the above sessions, you may want to try something different. Here are a few ideas to get you started. If you're interested in improving your pure speed – you're trying a 1500m track race or want a killer kick – then concentrate on the shorter reps such as the 200s or 400s. Even flat-out 100s.

If it's speed-endurance you're after – you want to run longer distances quickly – then try the longer intervals – 800s and miles are ideal. You might balk at the idea of running five or six one-mile reps at 10K pace, but try to remember you have to do this, without any rest, in a race anyway. Try to fit in at least one session a week, and mix pure speed sessions with speed-endurance sessions for the best of both worlds.

7 Pyramid sessions. So called because you start with a short distance, gradually increase, and then come back down again. These, as well as the following two sessions – are ideal if you're planning a few track races. For example, start at 120m, add 20m to each rep until you reach 200m, and then come back down to 120m. Run these at 400m pace, with a walk-back recovery.

8 Fast reps of 200m or 300m: run 6-10 x 200m, with 3-minute recoveries, or 5-8 x 300m, with 5-minute recoveries. Start both at 800m pace, eventually running the last reps flat out. You can also combine the two, for example 3 x 200m, 2 x 300m, 3 x 200m.

9 Simulation session. In theory this should replicate an 800m race. Run two sets of either 500m + 300m, or 600m + 200m, at your target 800m pace, with 60 seconds or less to recover between each rep and 10 minutes between sets.

10 Run one set of 500m, 400m, 300m, 200m, 100m. Start at 1500m pace and get increasingly quicker on each rep. The recovery between each rep should be 60-90 seconds.

11 Find a large, open area such as a sports ground. Mark out a circuit of roughly 800-1,000m. Once you've warmed up, run a circuit at your 5K pace, jog for five minutes, then run a second circuit about three seconds faster than the last. Continue speeding up by three seconds until you've completed five circuits.

12 Now try 5 x 800m at a pace 10 seconds faster per 800m than your usual 5K pace. Recover between intervals for the same amount of time it takes you to run them. As you get fitter, increase the number of reps to seven and gradually cut recoveries to 30 seconds.

13 Begin with a two- to three-mile warm-up, then 4 x 1 mile at a pace faster than your 10K pace, with a 3-minute recovery jog between each rep. Finish with a 3-mile jog to warm down.

14 Pyramids work for long distances too. You could try 1,000m, 2,000m, 3,000m, 2,000m, 1,000m at your half-marathon race pace, with a 4-minute recovery jog between each effort.

15 Don't fancy a full pyramid? Then go for a half: 400m, 800m, 1,200m, 1,600m, 2,000m, each run faster than your 10K pace but not flat out. Jog 400m between each – but you can take three to four minutes for this.

16 Divide 2,000m into: 400m at 5K race pace, with a 400m jog; 300m at race pace, with a 300m jog; 200m slightly quicker than race pace, with a 200m jog; 100m slightly quicker, but still not flat out, with a 100m jog. Do all recoveries at marathon pace, and then repeat the session.

17 "Structured" fartlek: warm up, then run hard for five minutes at 5K pace, recovering with a five-minute jog. Alternate in this manner for a total of 30 minutes, then warm down. As the weeks pass, reduce the length of the recovery jogs to toughen the session, at first down to four minutes, and eventually to just one.

» PACING YOURSELF

When you start speedwork you might find monitoring your pace difficult. If you've run a 5K race and a session calls for that pace, you'll have an idea of what it feels like, but if you haven't raced the distance indicated for the session, don't worry, because you're most likely to find the right pace through trial and error.

While the point of speedwork is obviously to run quickly, you'll rarely be running flat out. Instead, the time for each rep should be pretty similar, unless indicated otherwise. Run too hard at the start of a session and your times will fall off; take it too easy to begin with and you will speed up, but the session won't benefit you as much as it should.

In fact, for your first sessions it's better to be cautious, because you don't want to immediately hate speedwork, and you'll know that next time you can push yourself harder.

18 4 x 400m (or 4 x 80-100 seconds) at slightly faster than 10K pace, with 1-minute recoveries, then a 3-minute rest, followed by 2-3 x 2-3K, with a 5-minute recovery between each rep. Finish with another 4 x 400m.

19 Simply try to run a negative split on an out-and-back run. That means run faster on the way back. Try three miles out at 70-80 per cent effort, returning at 80-90 per cent.

20 3-5 x 1,200m at 5K pace, with recovery jogs of about a minute less than the time it took you to do the rep.

21 Run five to six miles, alternating two- to three-minute bursts at 10K pace, with a 60- to 90-second jog recovery between each.

22 Run a mile at about 10 seconds per mile slower than your 10K pace; jog for two minutes, then run another mile, this time at 10K pace; jog for another two minutes, then do a last mile at about 10 seconds faster than 10K pace.

23 Run 800m at 10K pace, then jog for two minutes; run 400m at 5K pace, then jog for a minute; run 200m at your estimated one-mile race pace, then jog for 30 seconds; run a kilometre at 10K pace, then jog for four minutes. Repeat the session. Start with two sets, increasing to three.

24 Run eight reps of 200m two seconds faster per 200m than your 5K pace. Gradually increase the distance until you're running 600m reps at this speed. Then follow the same progression from 200-600m, this time at four seconds faster per 200m than 5K pace.

25 Find a flat stretch of trail or grass and jog for 10 minutes, then run at your mile pace for one minute and 40 seconds; slow down to a jog (don't walk), and recover for three minutes, then repeat another 100-second burst. Try four of these sessions to begin with, and gradually work up to 10. These 100s work on speed without the tedium of circling the track.

26 At a track, warm up, then run eight laps, alternating fast and slow 200s. The fast 200s should be hard, but not a full sprint – you'll soon learn just how fast you need to go. Each week add an extra lap until you run 12 fast/slow 200s.

27 Run 2 x 800m at 10K pace, with a two-minute recovery jog after each. Follow with 4 x 400m at 10K pace, with 60-second recovery jogs between reps. After the fourth 400m, jog for 60 seconds, then do 800m at slightly faster than 10K pace; jog for two minutes, then do another 800m at the same pace.

28 5 x 1,000m. Run the first 800m at your 10K race pace, then accelerate to 3K pace for the last 200m, with three-minute recoveries.

29 Long warm-up, followed by 4-5 x (2 x 1,000m). Eh? Well, once you've warmed up and run 1,000m at slightly faster than your 10-mile race pace, jog for two to three minutes, and then do another 1,000m fast. Recover for a mile at 60 per cent effort before repeating the 1,000m efforts. Finish with a long cool-down.

30 10 x 500m: run the first 400m at your 3K pace, then the last 100m flat-out, with 200m slow recovery jogs.

31 8 x 400m: run the first 200m of each rep at mile pace, and then accelerate for the final 200m. Your recovery jogs should be 400m.

32 Run at marathon pace for five minutes, then gradually increase your speed to 10K pace for one minute. Continue this five-minute/one-minute sequence until 30 minutes have elapsed. This session should improve your overall speed while breaking up the monotony of those long runs.

33 Here's a great session for 10K+ distances, particularly the marathon. If you want to complete a marathon in three hours 27 minutes, run 800m reps in three minutes and 27 seconds. If you aren't planning a marathon, run them at 10-mile race pace. Warm up for 10 minutes then run the 800s. After each, jog for the same amount of time that it took you to complete the 800s. Add one 800 a week until you can run eight reps. ■

» TYPES OF SPEEDWORK

Repetitions/intervals Periods of hard running at 5K pace or faster, between 200m and 1200m in length, or 30 seconds and five minutes. Recovery periods can be short (30-90 seconds), or of an equal time or distance to the reps. Running at harder than race pace for short periods not only improves speed, but also allows you to work on your running form. When you're pushing hard, it's important to concentrate on things such as arm and hand motion, posture and stride length. If you can keep these together during a hard session of reps, it will be easier to do so during a race. Don't attempt reps until you've tried other types of speedwork for a couple of months.

Tempo intervals These are longer than ordinary intervals in that they take between 90 seconds and 10 minutes (or between 400m and two miles) and are run a little slower than your 5K pace. These work a bit like threshold runs – they raise the point at which lactic acid builds up in the muscles.

Fartlek Fartlek is Swedish for "speed play" and is the fun side of speedwork. Best done on grass or trails, you simply mix surges of hard running with periods of easy running with no set structure. Run fast bursts between phone boxes, lampposts or trees when you feel like it, and as hard you like. Great for newcomers to speedwork.

Hills Simple: find a hill that takes between 30 seconds and five minutes to climb at 85-90 per cent effort, and run up it. Jog back down to recover. A great alternative to track intervals.

NOTHING BUT THE **BEST**

Presenting the greatest tips of all time – for beginners, veterans, racers, marathon runners and everyone in between

STARTING OUT

Accept the challenge (part I)

"Everyone is an athlete, but some of us are training, and some of us are not." ***—Dr George Sheehan, runner and writer***

Be a minuteman

"The biggest mistake new runners make is to think in mile increments – one mile, two miles, three miles. Beginners need to think in minutes, not miles." ***—Budd Coates, coach***

Learn from your mistakes

"You find out by trial and error what the optimum level of training is. If I found I was training too hard, I would ease back for a day or so. I didn't run for five days before the sub-four." ***—Sir Roger Bannister, the first man to break four minutes for the mile (in 1954)***

Come ready to play

"Fitness has to be fun. If it is not play, there will be no fitness. Play is the process. Fitness is merely the product." ***—George Sheehan***

BASIC TRAINING

Dare to be different

"Only by daring to go against tradition can new ways of training be learned. The trick is recognising quickly when a new approach isn't working." ***—Benji Durden, 1980 Olympic marathon runner***

Show some horse sense

"During long, slow distance training, you should think of yourself as a thoroughbred disguised as a Shire horse. No need to give yourself away by running fast." ***—Marty Liquori, former world number-one mile runner***

Build with care

"If you put down a good solid foundation, then you can build one room after another and pretty soon you have a house. After your base mileage,

then you add hills, pace work, speedwork and your ability to run races and think races out." *—Rod Dixon, Olympic 1500m medallist and former New York City Marathon winner*

Listen to your body (again)

"Your body is always trying to tell you where you are. Listen to it. Beware when you become tired and listless, when you lose interest in training sessions and approach them as a chore rather than a pleasure." *—George Sheehan*

Don't get stuffed

"Day-to-day consistency is more important than big mileage. Then you're never 'stuffed' the next day." *—John Campbell, former world veteran marathon recorld holder*

Keep it in proportion

"If you run 30 miles a week, about seven of those – or approximately one-quarter – should be quality miles. Quality miles will boost your aerobic capacity." *—Dr Owen Anderson, running researcher*

Don't force it

"Overly aggressive stretching can increase injury risk." *—Tim Noakes, author of Lore of Running*

ADVANCED TRAINING

Mind not grind

"Any idiot can train himself into the ground; the trick is doing the training that gets you gradually stronger." *—Keith Brantly, Olympic marathoner*

Pick fun hard runs

"Do sessions that you enjoy. I feel better about my running when I do the runs I enjoy and that I know I benefit from."*—Dan Cloeter, former winner of the Chicago Marathon*

Don't be a know-it-all

"When you try a new type of training, think like a beginner. Just because you can run 20 miles every Sunday, it doesn't mean you can survive 10 x 400m on the track at a fast pace." *—Jack Daniels, exercise physiologist and coach*

Don't always watch the watch

"I don't wear a watch during my long runs. That way I'm not tempted to compare my times from week to week." *—Lynn Jennings, three-time World Cross-Country champion*

Enough is enough

"Never run more than three hours straight when training for a marathon, whether you're aiming for 2:42 or 4:24."*—Ed Eyestone, coach*

Remain vigilant

"When training hard, never be afraid to take a day off. If your legs are feeling unduly stiff or sore, rest; if you're feeling sluggish, rest; whenever in doubt, rest." *—Bruce Fordyce, multiple Comrades Marathon in South Africa winner*

SPEED TRAINING AND RACING

Accept the challenge (part II)

"The difference between a jogger and a runner is an entry form." *—George Sheehan*

Join the "Q"

"Quality really counts, if you want to stay fast. Don't do all your training in the comfort zone." *—Dr Ken Sparks, former top veteran mile runner*

Stay in control

"Run your own race at an even pace. Consider the course, the temperature, the weather and, most importantly, your level of fitness." *—Marty Liquori*

Make a pass

"Passing competitors always gives you a lift. It probably has a physical effect, too, because you get a surge of adrenaline." *—Libby Johnson, world-class runner*

Be patient

"Expect to put in six to 10 successful speed sessions before you begin to see any effect in your races."*— Marc Bloom, writer*

Keep your finger on the pulse

"If your resting heart rate is 10 or more beats above average in the morning, you haven't recovered from the previous day's training. Take a day's rest or ease back until it returns to normal." *—George Sheehan*

Stay on pace

"It's better to run too slowly at the start than too fast and get into oxygen debt, which is what 99.9 per cent of runners do." *—Bill Bowerman, coach*

Don't dodge the draft

"Slip in behind someone running a similar pace and, yes, draft. It's not illegal. It's not even poor form. On the contrary, it's just common sense." ***—Priscilla Welch, former New York City Marathon winner***

Snap out of it

"Occasionally pick up speed – for two minutes at most – then settle back into your former pace. Sometimes this is all you need to snap out of a mental and physical rut." ***—Mark Plaatjes***

Step back a bit

"Build up your mileage in gradual increments, but every third or fourth week, drop back in mileage to recover. This will help you avoid your breaking point." ***—Lee Fidler, coach***

Taper on time

"The key step between a great training programme and a great race is a great taper. Your last long training run before a marathon should come three weeks before the race – not two." ***—Pete Pfitzinger, two-time Olympic marathon runner***

Home in on the range

"Rather than going into a marathon with just one goal – such as to finish in a specific time – have a range of goals so you increase your chance of success." ***—Jerry Lynch, author of The Total Runner***

HILL RUNNING

Join the resistance!

"Hills are the only beneficial type of resistance training for a runner." ***—Arthur Lydiard***

Adapt... or weaken

"Running hills breaks up your rhythm and forces your muscles to adapt to new stresses. The result? You become stronger." ***—Eamonn Coghlan, first Veteran to break four minutes for the mile***

Avoid the down side

"The advantage of running hills on a treadmill is that you can go 'up' without pounding 'down' the other side."***—Dr Ken Sparks***

Save something for the summit...

"Don't attack a hill from the very bottom – it's bigger than you are." ***—Harry Groves, coach***

...Then take off!

"I've always found it effective in a race to make a move just before the crest of a hill. You get away just a little and you're gone before they get over the top."***—John Treacy, two-time World Cross-Country champion***

FINISH LINES

Take baby steps

"You can't climb up to the second floor without a ladder. When you set your goal too high and don't fulfil it, enthusiasm turns to bitterness. Try for a goal that is reasonable, and then gradually raise it."***—Emil Zátopek, four-time Olympic gold medalist***

Muster your mental might

"Keep working on mental attitude. You have to fight that supposedly rational voice that says: 'I'm 50 years old, and I don't have to be doing this anymore.'" ***—Ken Sparks***

Train with someone... anyone

"Never underestimate the value of a good training partner, be it friend, spouse, or canine. Training allies will get you out the door on those days when exercise might otherwise be reduced to moving a finger on the remote control button." ***—RUNNER'S WORLD staff***

...But sometimes go solo

"The day after a hard session, I always train alone. If you run with someone else, there can be a tendency to push harder than you should." ***—Mark Allen, world-class triathlete***

...But do what you must do

"If one can stick to the training throughout the many long years, then willpower is no longer a problem. It's raining? That doesn't matter. I'm stressed? That's beside the point. It's simply that I have to." ***—Emil Zátopek*** ■

GOING NOWHERE FAST

Looking to broaden your running experience? Perhaps it's time you spent some quality time with "it indoors"

In 1980 Benji Durden had a secret. The soon-to-be US Olympic marathoner was sneaking over to the local univerity physiology lab to work out on (gasp!) a treadmill. "I didn't tell other runners I was using a treadmill," he recalls, reflecting the derisory attitude toward treadmills of the time. "They would have thought I was strange. Even the lab staff thought I was mad." They soon revised their thinking when Durden clocked 2hrs09mins and won many marathons.

Still, it took many years for the idea of treadmills to grab. At the time, they were considered tinny, cheap, noisy contraptions that cluttered the spare room and did little else (except deliver pangs of regret to their owners). It seemed, like the hula hoop, Rubik's cube and the mullet hairstyle, they were doomed to be nothing more than a fad. Few serious runners owned one and those that did kept it quiet. The distance running ethic was an outdoors one – no matter the conditions. To run indoors on a rattly machine was...well, a sell out really. Treacherous. Weak.

Fortunately that attitude has changed as have treadmills, which are vastly superior machines today. Just as cross-training doesn't diminish you as a runner, neither does engaging in the odd treadmill session. Once you've decided on treadmill running, you just need to work out how to incorporate it into your schedule to maximise its potential (and yours). The advantages of treadmills are numerous: from convenience to workout precision to injury prevention.

BEAT THE COLD

It's February and freezing outside, so you step on your treadmill for a six-mile run that beats scampering about on icy footpaths hands down.

This is the most obvious reason to use a treadmill. Severe winter weather can be tough to train in – as well as potentially dangerous. You may know someone who prided themself on running every winter day, no matter how miserable the weather was – that is, until they hit an ice patch and ended up in a cast for two months and out of running for four. "I don't mind the cold too much," says Bob Kempainen, a 1992 Olympic marathon runner. "But if it's icy, I'll do my 10-mile run on a treadmill. Why risk it?"

BEAT THE HEAT

Severe heat is another reason to head to the health club or wherever there's a treadmill . On a really hot day, an air-conditioned gym may be more attractive than a sticky road surface and punishng sun.

WORK V WORKOUTS

Sometimes a quick 30-minute run on the company treadmill at lunch is the only way to fit in a workout between job commitments. Durden, who coaches several runners by fax and phone, remembers a particularly busy month when he and his treadmill became very close. "I did 23 days in a row on a treadmill," he says. "I was afraid that if I went out on a long run I'd miss a lot of calls. It was either that or take a mobile phone with me. Mobile phones were pretty big back then so it wasn't really practical."

PRECISION

"Treadmills give you a much more evenly paced workout than running on a track," says world-class masters miler Dr Ken Sparks. "For instance, if you're doing 400-metre repeats on a track in 90 seconds, you might run the first 200 in 43 seconds and the second in 47. On a treadmill, you can't do that. Each 200 will be exactly 45 seconds."

PERFECT HILLS

Hill workouts are a special feature of treadmill running that win many over, even those, like Durden, who live in hilly areas. "You can duplicate your hill sessions from week to week almost perfectly," says Durden. "If you want to do a two per cent gradient and a one per cent recovery, you just punch some buttons. It's very precise and very easy to do."

RACE-COURSE WORKOUTS

Computerised treadmills come with built-in programmes that can take you up and down or increase and decrease the pace during your run. They also let you programme your own courses. Extreme marathoner Matt Carpenter is a regular treadmill trainer. Carpenter programmes in the exact ascent gradients in upcoming races and sets the pace at slightly faster than the course record. One year, Carpenter won a race but missed the record by 33 seconds on a day when rain made the footing slippery. "You can't put mud on a treadmill," he quips.

ESCAPE THE LONELY ROAD

Finally, treadmills come in handy for new runners and those who don't appreciate the loneliness of the long-distance runner, especially those concerned with the safety of solo jogging. ■

›› INJURY PREVENTION

Dr Ken Sparks, an exercise physiologist at Cleveland State University, recommends treadmill training to come back from injuries or avoid them altogether

"First of all, there's less pounding of the joints on a treadmill than on the roads," says Dr Sparks. "That's because the treadmill belt gives when you land on it, unlike concrete and asphalt."

"Second, there's no side-to-side slope on a treadmill as there is on roads. That slope forces you to overpronate (your feet rotate too far inwards on impact) and can lead to shinsplints, Achilles tendinitis and knee problems."

"And third, on a treadmill, there's no lateral pressure on your knees and ankles as there would be if you were running around a track, and this kind of lateral pressure can lead to injuries."

GETTING YOUR **TREADMILL LEGS**

Once adjusted to treadmill running you can begin to explore the myriad ways to employ it from speed training to hill sessions to recovery runs

Like a new pair of running shoes, a treadmill needs to be broken in – or, rather, you need to be broken in to the treadmill if you are to derive maximum benefits. "The first few times on a treadmill, start off slower than you think you should," says Benji Durden. "You need to become accustomed to it so you don't feel awkward or as though you're going to fall off."

Take Carol McLatchie and her husband, Jim, for example. They are both keen runners although Jim has had some treadmill "issues". "Jim has been periodically banned from the McLatchie treadmill," says Carol with a laugh. "He just can't get the hang of it. He keeps falling off it. Once he fell off and was lying half-stunned, pressed against the wall, while the belt was whipping around and thumping on his leg. Finally, he reached over and unplugged it."

Note: Jim is an extremely rare case. Most people have no problem on "the 'mill" once they adjust to the initial strangeness of running on a moving surface – it's like learning to ride a bike. Once you get the hang of it, it's easy.

"When I'm on the treadmill, I always have this feeling I'm going faster than on the roads," says

Carol McLatchie. "Without visual cues, like scenery going by, I get thrown a bit and my equilibrium can be slightly off when I step off. It's as if I was out at sea, and now I'm on land again. I have sea legs for a few minutes. But you get used to it pretty quickly."

THE TRICK IS NOT MINDING

The monotony of treadmill training is a big complaint among runners. And dedicated treadmill trainers won't argue with you on that point. Instead, they'll tell you how they've got around it. World-class marathon runner Ken Martin blasts music on his stereo system while on his treadmill. Durden watches videotapes from previous Olympics. McLatchie's treadmill is next to a window that looks out on her garden. Full-length mirrors are popular.

Another option is to schedule your treadmill sessions for peak hours at the health club — so you can socialise, or at least have something to look at. (But be aware that most health clubs have a time limit on treadmills, usually 20 to 30 minutes.) Avoid clock-watching. "If I look at my watch, time crawls by unbearably slowly on a treadmill," says Carpenter.

There's one perfect way of avoiding monotony on a treadmill. You simply take your cue from Peter O'Toole in *Lawrence of Arabia*, who, after extinguishing a match between his fingers, explained "the trick is not minding". And how do you not mind a treadmill workout? Throw in a little pain.

"I never get bored on my treadmill," says Dr Sparks, who treadmill trains alongside garden hoses, rakes and spades in his garage. "I know when I step on my treadmill, I'm going to be doing an intense speed workout." A positive attitude, as ever, is of crucial importance.

THE GREAT OUTDOORS, INDOORS

With few exceptions, anything you can do outside, you can do inside. Prior to his 2:09:38 second-place finish at the 1989 New York City Marathon, Ken Martin logged all his long runs on a treadmill. "I'd just get into a nice rhythm and stay controlled," he says. "I also thought it was good because I had my drinks right there beside me, so I didn't have to stop to drink, and I could practise drinking on the run."

But Martin's may be a special case. Many runners can't tolerate a two-hour easy run going nowhere, even if audio-visual enterntainment is on hand to ease the pain. Other workouts, such as tempo runs, hills, speedwork and specially designed race-course sessions, are more suited to the treadmill because the session is broken up into digestible segments.

MAKING SPEEDWORK COUNT

Dr Sparks has been running intensive speed sessions on a treadmill since the late 1960s, when he was a graduate student for Dr David L. Costill, director of the Human Performance Laboratory at Ball State University in Indianapolis. "I didn't have much time back then, and some of my workouts would actually be jumping on a treadmill and running a four-minute mile, then jumping off," he says.

Nowadays, on his homemade treadmill, Dr Sparks clicks off 63-second quarter miles with a 1-minute jog in between. But don't try this at home — or at the health club. Most treadmills won't go faster than a 75-seconds-per-quarter-mile pace. Therefore, you might want to limit your speed sessions on a treadmill to longer repeats of say, 800s or miles. ■

» TOP TIPS:

- Treadmill running is precise, convenient, safe and can reduce injuries
- Take the time to accustomise yourself to treadmill running to avoid accident and injury
- Treadmills are blissfully immune to extreme weather. Run all year round
- If your employer has a treadmill, employ it for extra lunchtime runs
- Make the most of your treadmill's interval and hill settings
- Input a race's exact gradient changes and distance to gain a training advantage over your competitors

LAY ME DOWN

Bolster your performance with sleep – the ultimate tool for dream running

Forget sex. When it comes to getting enough, sleep should be at the top of every runner's list – and we're in good company. Musicians, artists and poets become just as excited about their nightly fix. The Beatles refelected on their *Golden Slumber* after too many late nights in cosmopolitan clubs, and even Shakespeare mused about the joy of the pillow in *Hamlet*.

All of which should be remembered the next time you lace up your running shoes, because lack of sleep may be hampering your performance. Dr June Pilcher, of Bradley University in the USA, studied the effects of sleeplessness on 44 students. She found one sleepless night can diminish cognitive performance by between 25 and 40 per cent.

Dr Ken MacMahon from the Scottish Sleep Centre, who has also researched the link between sleep and performance, goes further: "With more sleep deprivation, you start to see effects on psychomotor performance."

In short poor sleep equals poor running. Which is where we come in. To make sure temporary insomnia doesn't derail your running plans, we've quizzed a team of experts and drawn up your 10 steps to the perfect 40 winks. So snuggle down and dare to dream of that new PB.

1 RHYTHM OF THE NIGHT

In the University of Sleep, routine is the guy at the front of the class wearing the mortarboard and cloak. "Routine is the master of good sleep," says Professor Kevin Morgan, from Loughborough University's sleep centre. Stay up late for a cable screening of Prisoner Cell Block H, and you're waving goodbye to a significant percentage of

adidas

» GOLDEN RULES OF REST

By listening to your body and adhering to the following three rules of rest, you'll have fresher legs, a lower risk of injury and the ability to run further and faster more easily.

Rest before you feel exhausted

If you don't take a little rest before you become tired, you'll need a lot more time to recover later. So be sure to schedule regular rest days, walk breaks and easy weeks into your training routine.

When in doubt, add more rest

A little extra rest is particularly important if you're doing long runs, speedwork or if you're just racing regularly.

Beware "junk" miles

A leisurely three-miler is not a rest day. Easy miles that you run just for the sake of bumping up your mileage prevent your legs from fully recovering. True rest days are non-running days. Remember: rest is training.

your performance. Morgan says altering your bedtime confuses your body's natural rhythms. "Sleep loves routine," he says. "Establish a pattern that suits you, and then stick to it."

What if pre-race nerves mean you're awake for most of the night before an event? MacMahon endorses advice that marathon runners should store up "sleep hours" in the week before an event. That way, it won't matter as much if they're too nervous to sleep well on the final night. "If your sleep patterns are well established, a poor night's sleep will simply mean that you sleep more soundly the next night to make up for it."

Sleep tip No late nights or lie-ins on training days or race days

2 IN YOUR OWN TIME

Margaret Thatcher famously balked at more than five hours sleep a night, but that doesn't mean you should. Dr Martin Moore-Ede, in *The Complete Idiot's Guide To Sleep*, says: "Sleep is a highly individual matter. Knowing your sleep needs, and doing your best to meet them, will help you avoid the perils of sleep deprivation."

Moore-Ede has defined sleep personalities. Larks are early risers, Owls come to life at night, and there are also Long and Short Sleepers, Flexible and Rigid types and those who do, or do not, like to nap. So it might be fine for one person to sleep for five hours, but another person might need 10.

Sleep tip Work out your needs and satisfy them

3 SWITCH OFF

The key to good sleep is not switching off the bedroom light, but switching off mentally. Brenda O'Hanlon, author of *Sleep: The Common Sense Approach*, says, "In 80 per cent of insomnia cases seen by GPs, the most common cause is a range of psychological problems such as anxiety and depression." Sleeplessness can be caused by increased workload or other stressful events. The key is finding a way to shut down for sleep even when life becomes hectic.

However, occasional bad nights are normal. O'Hanlon says you should de-stress before bed and adds, "Be philosophical. Accept an occasional bad night's sleep as part of living. It's a normal, healthy adjustment to changing circumstances or environmental conditions."

Sleep tip Determine to reduce your stress levels before going to bed

4 THE EARLY BIRD

When comedian and insomniac David Baddiel sat through the night writing his latest comedy, he could have done a lot worse than invest in a pair of running shoes. After all, exercise releases endorphins and other chemical by-products that help lull us to sleep. "You get a better 'quality' of sleep if you're fairly fit," explains MacMahon. He believes running first thing in the morning is the best option, adding, "Don't exercise just before bedtime, as your body will 'wake-up' because of the effort. Running first thing in the morning is best, but lunchtime or early evening are also fine."

Sleep tip Don't run after the watershed

5 LIE IN ALIGNMENT

Good posture is just as important beneath your duvet as when you run. Dr Paula Franklin, Bupa's assistant medical director, says, "Always try to sleep on your side, instead of your back." Franklin also advises keeping your body in alignment, which means there should be a straight line running through the centre of your body when you sleep. "Keeping the body in alignment, which could include raising the head of the bed, may also help reduce snoring. This should be done by raising the head of the bed itself, or by making sure your pillow is at the correct height," she says.

Sleep tip Sleep on your side

6 ON THE WAGON

Coffee and alcohol will both disrupt your sleep, and should be avoided after 7pm, but a Horlicks and a couple of biscuits aren't always the answer. According to Morgan, "The impact of routine is never more emphatic than in the relationship between food and sleep. Research shows that if you are accustomed to a particular type of bedtime drink, you respond to the metabolic signals it gives, and relax. Conversely, if you take that away, your sleep will be disturbed."

American sleep expert Dr James Mass says that some foods also have sleep-friendly qualities

– carbohydrates help induce slumber, while proteins do not. "Carbohydrates help speed the amino acid tryptophan to the brain where it is converted to serotonin. Serotonin helps induce sleep."

Sleep tip Embrace the routine of eating a bowl of cereal with warm milk before bed.

7. SOAK IT UP

Recreating hot-tub scenes from dubious Hollywood films may not prepare you for a good night's kip, but taking a relaxing bath will. Warm water sends blood away from the brain towards the skin surface, which makes you drowsy. "Make a warm bath part of your pre-bedtime ritual," advises O'Hanlon. "Add six to eight drops of a mix of essential oils including lavender, Roman camomile, sweet marjoram and sandalwood." Or try concocting your own aquatic tonic.

Sleep tip Take a hot bath with some scented oils before you go to bed

8 SLEEP LITE

Just as veterans slow down with age, so sleep patterns change as you age. People in their 40s, 50s and beyond will find their sleep becoming less regular. MacMahon says it's nothing to worry about. "During adulthood, you start to need less sleep and your sleep becomes 'lighter', so you wake more frequently during the night. That's normal. You should only worry if you find that you're becoming excessively tired during the day."

Sleep tip Don't worry if you sleep less as you age. It's normal

9 BEDROOM GYMNASTICS

First the good news. Running increases your sex drive. Now for the really good news. Sex makes you sleepy, and sleep makes you a better runner. According to the experts, runners are locked into an upward spiral of carnal pleasure and PBs. We run, therefore we want sex, so we fall asleep and

TAKING IT EASY

You're sleeping well and feeling energised, but hold on a minute: knowing when to rest is a lesson too many runners learn the hard way – by the scourge of injury. It needn't be like that

To run and race better, sometimes you have to run less or not at all. There are many ingredients in a successful running programme: long runs, speedwork and consistent weekly mileage, but the key ingredient doesn't even involve running – it involves resting.

When we run, our muscles are taxed, our tendons and ligaments are strained and our energy sources are drained, but thanks to the body's design, we recover from this stress and become even stronger, as long as we rest sufficiently. Without rest, the body can't rebuild. The result is fatigue, chronic injury and mediocre running.

REST MADE EASY

There are lots of ways to work rest into your running routine. For best results, experiment with the following forms of rest until you come up with a running/resting ratio that's right for you.

REST DISCOUNTS DURING A RUN

Just because you tell your friends you're going out for a run doesn't mean you have to run every step of the way. By taking walk breaks every mile or so, particularly on long runs, you beat fatigue as you build endurance. For example, a 10-

that makes us better runners who want more sex and more sleep. It's a viciously satisfying circle. Morgan adds we are genetically predisposed to feel sexy at bedtime. "Endocrinologically speaking, your body releases sleep hormones every time you have sex." he says.

Sleep tip Buy expensive (but comfortable) pyjamas

10 SOOTHING NOTES

Taking a leaf out of Bridget Jones's book may help you discover your sleep needs. Just as coaches tell runners to log their weekly mileage, so sleep doctors advise keeping a diary. "It's a good idea to keep a short sleep diary," says MacMahon.

"Record the time you went to bed, how long it took you to fall asleep, how long you were awake during the night, when you woke up and total sleep time." Do that for a couple of weeks, and you'll be able to see patterns emerge, which will help you alter your bedtimes and decide whether to stay up late or hit the sack early.

mile run done with walk breaks will leave most runners feeling as if they've run five to six miles, but their bodies will still have benefited from the 10-mile distance.

DAYS OFF FROM TRAINING

Taking an extra day off from running – before you need it – will allow your muscles to recover significantly faster from your challenging runs. You can still run the same number of miles per week simply by increasing the number of miles you cover when you do run, and at the first sign of lingering fatigue, switch to an every-other-day running routine until the fatigue subsides.

ONCE-A-MONTH BREAKS

Many runners get stuck in a mileage rut, averaging the same distance week after week. Once a month, reduce your mileage for one week by about a third. Think of this monthly rest break as an insurance policy for fresh legs.

ONCE-A-YEAR BREAKS

To stay rested and healthy during every running year, it helps to have a clear beginning and end to each 12-month period. So pick a month each year when you'll decrease your overall mileage by 50 per cent. Incorporate your favourite cross-training activities during this month. By the end of the month, your "holiday" from running will leave you refreshed and raring to go again.

CHANGING REST REQUIREMENTS

One of the best things about running is that it's an activity you can do for a lifetime. But as you get older, rest becomes more necessary. To allow for added recovery time and to decrease your injury risk, remember these general guidelines:

If you're:	Then rest:
Under 30	1 day per week
30-45	2 days per week
45-55	3 days per week
55 plus	every other day

RUNNING ROADMAPS

If you want to take the most out of your running, make some plans

Running goals can be tricky things. Set them too high, and they're bound to frustrate you. Set them too low, and they won't challenge you. Set them just right, and they'll be a powerful source of motivation, driving you to achievement. To set the perfect running goals, follow the five-step plan below. Don't forget, the paths you take to reach your running goals are just as important – and just as rewarding – as achieving the goals themselves.

1 MAKE A LIST

In order of importance, write down two to four running goals you'd like to achieve in the next six months. They can be as general as to run injury-free; to feel good on almost every run; or to balance your running with your family life and career, or they can be more specific, such as completing a particular race or achieving a certain time. You'll need to review this list every so often to make adjustments as needed. For example, as the date of a 5K goal race gets close, it will move higher on your list than when it was months away.

2 PENCIL IT IN

With your list of goals in hand, you can begin to sort out how you'll achieve each one by plotting the key sessions you'll need in a training log, notebook or on a calendar. If one of your goals is to enjoy your runs more, you'll need to schedule social runs, runs in scenic locations and runs with your favourite four-legged friend. Time-specific goals mean you'll need to chart a series of speedwork sessions, and if you're looking to complete a marathon or half-marathon, you'll need to map out your long-run strategy. Use a pencil to schedule these runs, just in case changes need to be made later.

3 MAKE IT STICK WITH INK

After you've pencilled in all the sessions, you need to make sure you have time to achieve those goals – so take an overall look at your calendar to assess things. Do you have the time and the resources to follow through with your plan as scheduled? Are you willing to make the sacrifices necessary to achieve your specific race and time goals? If so, take out a pen and make your schedule permanent. If not, scale down your goals, and set up a new programme based on your time and energy constraints. Then put it in ink.

4 BREAK IT DOWN

Big goals are achieved much more easily if you divide them into smaller goals you can use as stepping-stones to reach the final goal. For example, instead of trying to make the "good-for-age" qualifying times for the Flora London Marathon before you've even run a half-marathon, aim to finish a 10K within the next two months. As this goal approaches, plan your second goal of finishing a half-marathon in the next three months. Finishing your first marathon might follow in the months leading up to the end of the year, prior to the entry deadline for the 2006 Flora London Marathon. Write down each intermediate goal in your training log, and fill in the long run and speed sessions needed to prepare for them. If any of these smaller goals becomes too stressful, add another stepping-stone goal.

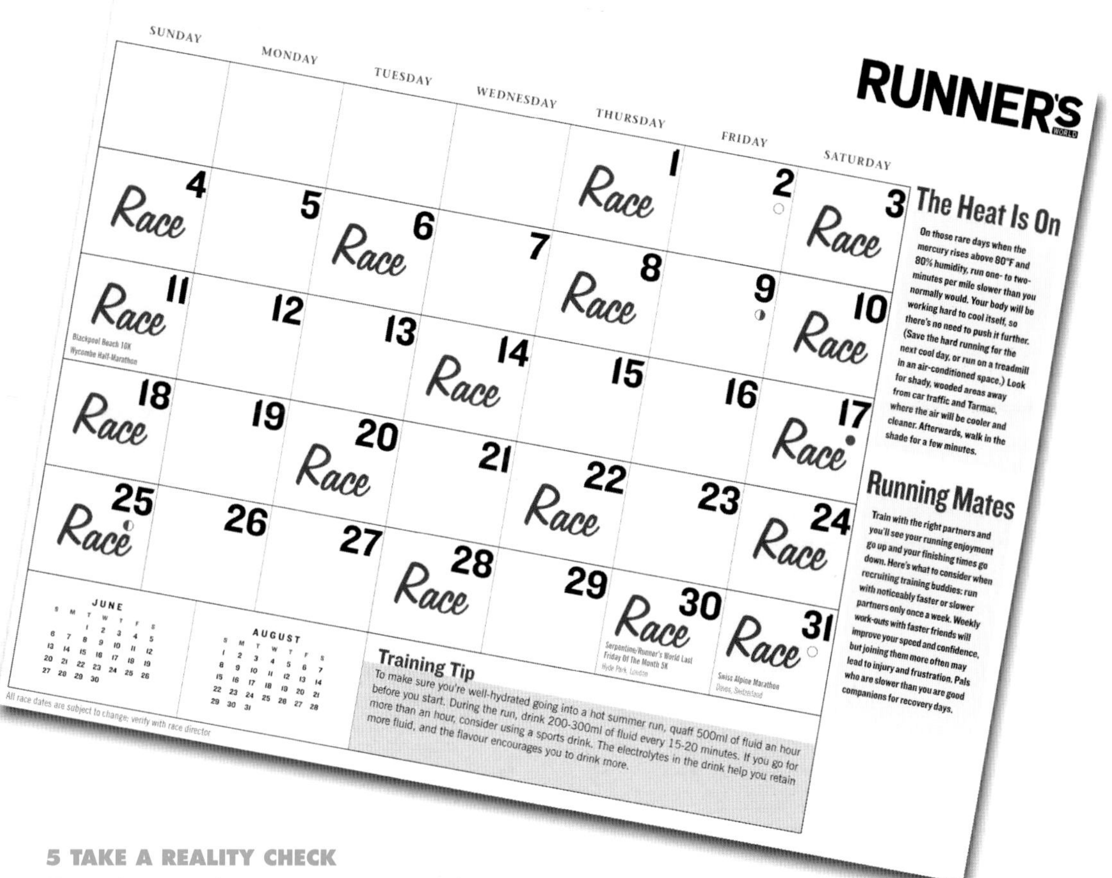

5 TAKE A REALITY CHECK

How do you know your time goals are achievable? By running a 5K, you can predict your potential finishing time in a 10K, half-marathon or marathon. There are a number of prediction charts around, such as those at www.runnersworld.com (just click on "calculators") that will calculate your predicted race time at a given race distance based on your actual time at another race distance. If your goals are more qualitative (eg to enjoy running more), look over the notes in your log every few weeks to see if you're on the right track. If not, make the training adjustments necessary to give you a realistic shot of reaching your goal.

6 PLANNING A RACE SEASON

Once you are used to running, you might want to plan the events you enter so you can make the most of your training, and maintain your interest as the months pass. Each year there are well over 5,000 running races in Britain, ranging from a mile to 100Ks and more, with options over trail, countryside, fell, track and road. Some people may manage 100 races in a year, including 30 marathons, but it isn't advisable if you want to maximise your performance and keep injury and boredom at bay. Variety and recovery should be your keywords. It's also valuable to decide what, for you, are going to be the three or four most important races of the year. This not only helps focus your training, but also affects the way you approach the other races in your year.

Here's what we'd consider a classic racing year, using some of the best races in the country as examples. We'd recommend not racing more than twice in most months, and after your race allowing one day of easy running per mile raced. (The dates we've used are normal for the race examples we've given, but you should check the Race Diary to see whether they've been confirmed yet for this year.)

April

The classic marathon month in the UK. Ever heard of a little race called the Flora London Marathon, for instance?

May

London Marathoners should be gently easing their way back into training and racing, and others should be focusing their energies on speed. Try an unusual race distance, such as the Waterloo 15K, in Merseyside, this month. It's also the start of the track season and the women-only Race For Life 5K series.

June

Make this a month for shorter racing and training distances, to rediscover your fast-twitch muscles. If you make a 10K your main aim (or the famous 5.7-mile Nike Blaydon Races, around Newcastle), you'll also have plenty of energy left for track races, 5Ks or mile races.

July

With two months of short, sharp speedwork under your belt, make this a 5K month. You could easily do two if you can find them, or tackle a 5K plus the 3.5-mile, 20,000-strong Chase Corporate Challenge in London.

August

August's race scene is a lull before the autumn storm. For variety, try one of the good five-milers on offer, such as the Thorney 5.

September

September is a crucial training month if you want to be racing well in October and November, so don't overdo it. A 10K – for example, the famously fast Swansea Bay 10K – will be an ideal bridge between short summer races and tougher winter events.

October

This is a good month to focus on competition – races are less plentiful after this and you might want to make the most of the generally milder race conditions. Tackle a fast 10-miler, such as the BUPA Great South Run in Portsmouth, along with your club cross-countries.

November

Make a good cross-country result your main priority, now that you've had two months of practice. Add any other race from 10K to half-marathon to make the most of your fitness.

December

A flexible month, but do have a goal. The Leeds Abbey Dash 10K is often your last chance for a fast race in the calendar year, or you can get into the festive spirit with a Christmas-themed event.

January

If you're not a member of a club, this is a very light racing month, with very few road options, but join a club and, whatever your standard, the wonderful world of cross-country opens up to you. Whether you are a miler or marathoner, this is also a good month to get some regular and consistent training in. Visit the UK Athletics site to find your nearest club at www.ukathletics.net.

February

A good 10K, such as the quick Puma Dewsbury 10K in Yorkshire, will come naturally once you've spent a couple of months of cross-country racing.

March

Flora London Marathon runners will be touching 20-milers in training this month, but if you're only going to do one race, make it a half-marathon, such as the Bath Half-Marathon. There are many other good options. ■

YES COACH

Goals signpost your improvement as a runner, but when your burgeoning development slows or ceases altogether, a little coaching could be the spur to take you to the next level... and don't for a minute think you're not worthy

Every runner reaches a point where their times plateau, training runs becomes harder and harder to bother with, and the snug in the local pub seems a far more attractive proposition than an evening of fartlek training. Sometimes these times pass thanks to the purchase of a new pair of trainers or an unexpected PB, but if your results and motivation don't seem to be picking up of their own accord, it could be time to turn to a coach for help.

We know what you're thinking: running coaches are just for runners like Paula Radcliffe or those skinny blokes that knock you off the pavement on Tuesday nights. Wrong. Running coaches can benefit any runner, whether you're just starting out and want to build up to 20 minutes, or if you want to go sub-2:30 for a

marathon, and nowadays you're spoilt for choice. Long gone are the days of the coach as the fearsome man with the manic glint in his eye, booming, gravelly voice, draconian methods, 1980-issue CCCP tracksuit and matching houseclock-sized stopwatch. (Though you can find coaches of this description if you really want.)

Head to your local club and you'll more than likely find an approachable and knowledgeable coach ready to help, or perhaps search the Internet for an online trainer, or go for one-to-one coaching from a personal trainer. Read on to discover which breed of coach could be for you.

THE CLUB COACH – BUD BALDARO

Club Coach – Birmingham University Athletics Club
UK Athletics Squad Marathon Coach

It would be easy to be intimidated by Bud Baldaro's coaching CV. He has guided Marion Sutton to two Chicago Marathon victories and the 2000 Sydney Olympics, and set the programme for the current British women's 3,000m steeplechase record holder Tara Krzywicki, but, like club coaches up and down the country, Baldaro derives as much pleasure from helping new runners as he does from seeing his charges battling for major medals.

"As long as a runner is committed to their goal – be it breaking an hour for 10K or making the Olympic squad – then I'll train them," says Baldaro. He is typical in that he takes two club sessions a week, offering a variety of work-outs at different speeds and distances, but his involvement with his runners doesn't end there. "I talk to many of my runners two or three times a week. I help them set goals, advise them on injuries and talk them through their weekend races," explains Baldaro, "but joining a coach's group isn't just about running. There's always loads of banter. It's a great social occasion."

ONLINE COACH – JOE BEER

Online coach with his own company: www.jbst.com
Coach for 12 years, after studying sports science at university; international triathlete

British age group international triathlete Joe Beer is based in north Devon, but don't worry if you don't live in the south-west of England. Beer currently has 37 athletes on his books in locations as diverse as Ireland, Sweden and the Middle East. His location, and your's, is irrelevant, as Beer's coaching advice is available with a few simple taps on your computer keyboard.

"Runners and triathletes sign up at my website, and I then get in touch with them by email," explains Beer. "The first thing I do is send them a 10-page-long questionnaire, which gives me an idea of their fitness, their goals, their diet, and even their strengths and weaknesses."

Using this information, Beer sets email schedules for his runners, and provides them with detailed, scientific coaching advice. "I send my runners their schedules, and they fill in all the details – mileage, heart rate, what they've eaten and the like – and send it back to me. This gives me a great idea of what's working, what isn't and what needs to be done."

"One of the most satisfying things for me is seeing completely new runners learning more about themselves," he says. "They start off asking me loads of questions, but as they become fitter and more confident, I find they need me less and less as they learn to depend on themselves."

PERSONAL TRAINER – LOUISE JORDAN

Personal trainer for three years with her own studio – www.smithsyardstudio.co.uk. Completed Marathon des Sables, and has a marathon PB of 3:45.

The best personal trainers have sports science degrees, UK Athletics coaching qualifications or have trained with a reputable and intensive training company such as Premier Training International. Anyone can call themselves a personal trainer, so ask to see qualifications.

Ask friends, running shop employees or health-club staff to recommend a trainer who runs. Contact the National Register of Personal Trainers – www.nrpt.co.uk; 0870 200 6010 – or the Register of Exercise Professionals – www.reps-uk.org; 020 8686 6464 – to find running-friendly, qualified and insured trainers near you, and check your personal trainer has an up-to-date first-aid certificate.

"I have a huge range of clients," says south London-based personal trainer Louise Jordan. "Some want to start running to get fit, others are serious runners who want to beat personal bests." The training she recommends is as varied as her client base. "There's no typical session for my clients. I see most of them more than once a week, and I try to provide them with a realistic programme that fits into their life," explains Jordan. "Some clients I have doing hill sessions and speedwork, others simply pay me because they just want someone to run with."

Jordan, like other personal trainers, can offer more than some "traditional" coaches. Because of her training, Jordan is also able to offer her clients advice on cross-training disciplines that'll improve their running. "I can set them core stability exercises, weight programmes and stretching routines," she says. "In fact, for many of my running clients, this is where they need the most help. They have no trouble getting out running, but need me to motivate them and guide them with other activities." ■

CHAPTER 4
Nutrition

If you don't put petrol in your car, you'll soon be standing at the side of the road trying to thumb a lift. It's the same story with a runner's body: don't put in enough fuel and you're heading for a breakdown. Good nutrition means more than just pigging out on a big plate of pasta the night before a long run or race: eating and drinking right every day will help you make the most of all of your training miles.

FUEL'S **PARADISE**

As with most forms of production, low quality inputs equal low quality outputs. So if you want to produce good running, be good to yourself and consume foods that will favour your best running efforts

Runners are not average citizens. We are different to the sedentary folk for whom dietary recommendations were created. We need more calories and protein. More carbohydrates. We need more nutrients in general. And runners covet foods that never figure in government recommendations – like carbohydrate and protein drinks and energy gels.

That's why we've designed this food plan, aimed specifically at runners, that, as well as being tasty, will help keep you on the move.

EATING AND TRAINING: HOW TO TIME IT RIGHT

Many runners know exactly what they should eat and when they should eat it. It's the practical application of this theory that messes them up. You are either ravenous when you don't want to be – during training – or not hungry when you should be – immediately after training. The problem is when you are planning your run around a busy work schedule, your brain, leg muscles and stomach aren't always in sync.

An early morning run, for example, can leave you feeling fatigued during your working day. A midday training session may become no more than an afterthought if hunger overrides your motivation. And an after-work jaunt may press your dinnertime perilously close to bedtime.

If you are looking for ways to get back into sync, read on. The following advice will help coordinate your meals with your training schedule, based on the time of day you run.

DAWN PATROLLING

To eat or not to eat? That is the eternal question of those who like to run as the sun is coming up. The answer is, if you can, you should fuel up before your morning run. This performs two functions. First, your muscles receive an energy supply to help you power through the run. Second, your entire body, especially your brain, receives the fuel and nutrients it needs for optimal functioning. It shouldn't be a surprise that studies support this and that eating before a run boosts endurance compared with fasting for 12 hours. People who eat before working out rate the exercise as being better yet less rigorous compared with non-eaters.

That said, not everyone can eat before a morning run. If you're the type of person who sleeps until the minute before you head out the door, you might not be able to fit in a meal before you run. Also, eating too close to your run may spoil it by causing cramps and nausea. On the other hand, if you're a true early bird, you may have the time to eat breakfast, read the paper and wash up before you head out of the door.

Here are a few refuelling strategies for both types of morning exercisers:

Early risers

Choose high-carb foods that are low in fat and moderate in protein. Aim for about 400-800 calories, which will fuel your training without making you feel sluggish. Drink about half a pint of water two hours before your run to offset sweat loss.

Try these 400- to 800-calorie pre-run breakfasts:

- Two slices of toast, a yoghurt and a piece of fruit
- Cereal with skimmed or semi-skimmed milk and fresh fruit
- A toasted bagel topped with low-fat cheese and tomato slices

Late sleepers

Most runners fall into this category and don't have time to eat and digest a full meal before they head out the door. If you fall into this camp, experiment to see what you can stomach before you train. A few suggestions:

- Half a pint of a carbohydrate drink
- An energy gel washed down with water

Evening meal specialists

If none of these sits well with you just before a run, then fuel up the night before with a large dinner. As long as you don't plan a long or intense run in the morning, a high-carbohydrate evening meal should power you through your pre-breakfast run.

ON THE RECOVERY

Whether you're an early or late riser, your body needs calories from carbohydrate, protein and other nutrients after you have finished running. A recovery meal will help fuel your morning at work, preventing post-run fatigue. Eat within an hour of your training and be sure to include both carbs and protein. Some options:

- A fruit smoothie made with a tablespoon of protein powder
- Eggs on whole-wheat toast, juice or fresh fruit

■ Leftovers from dinner – pasta, soup, chilli or even vegetarian pizza are proven winners

THE LUNCHTIME CROWD

People who run during lunch hours sometimes find hunger gets the better of them. That's because if you ate breakfast at 6am, you've gone six hours without food. By noon, your fuel from breakfast is long gone and your blood sugar may start to dip. Rather than increasing the size of your breakfast (which may just leave you feeling sluggish), you should bring a light, pre-run snack to work.

Eat one to four hours before your run to allow enough time for food to leave your stomach, and consume 100-400 calories, depending upon your body size and how much you had for breakfast. Select foods that are rich in carbohydrate, low in fat and moderately high in nutrients. Try these mid-morning snacks:

■ A breakfast or energy bar with five grams of fat or less

■ One slice of whole-wheat toast topped with fruit spread

■ A 75g serving of dried fruit with a can of vegetable juice

■ One packet of instant oatmeal made with skimmed milk

Post-run lunch

The obvious problem with lunch-hour exercise is that you don't have time for lunch. But you need fluid and food to recover and fuel your brain for the rest of the working day. Packing your own lunch becomes a must – unless you have a work cafeteria where you can grab food for desktop dining. A well-rounded packed lunch can be put together in less time than you might think. Try these tips:

■ Opt for convenience and shop for lunch items that save time, such as yoghurts, raisins, nuts and health bars

■ Always add fruit. Toss one or two pieces of fruit in your lunch bag for a reliable source of nutrient-packed carbohydrate

■ Make the most of leftovers. Choose any food from the previous night's dinner that you've already packed in a sealed container ready for transport, reheating and eating. Of course

EVENING EXERTIONS

After a stressful day at the office, there's nothing like a run to burn off tension. The problem is you don't always feel like heading out the door if you're hungry or just exhausted. If you do manage to run, sometimes you return home so ravenous

» SERVING SENSE

When we recommend 8-15 daily servings of high-carbohydrate food, you may think you'll have to gorge yourself day after day to get the necessary nutrients. But a serving in each of the food groups isn't as hefty as most people think (or hope). Here are a few examples:

GROUP	SERVING SIZE
Carbohydrate	100g of cooked pasta, beans, couscous or other grains (about the size of a computer mouse); one slice of bread; 25g of cereal.
Vegetables	200g of raw leafy vegetables (about the size of a cricket ball).
Fruit	One medium piece of fruit (about the size of a tennis ball); 250ml of juice; 100g of chopped fruit.
Calcium	One pint of milk; 200g of yoghurt; two slices of cheese.
Protein	200g of soybeans; 50-75g of fish or lean meat (about the size of a deck of cards); two eggs.
Healthy foods	25g of nuts (about 20 almonds); an eighth of an avocado; two teaspoons of olive oil.

you'll gorge yourself on anything in sight as you make your evening meal. Then you might eat dinner as late as 9pm and end up going to bed with a full stomach. Not so good.

What to do?

It's very simple – if you can stick to the following two principles:

■ Eat healthily during the day to avoid any intestinal upset that might thwart your training plans. Also eat often and enough that you're adequately fuelled for your session to avoid the "I'm too hungry" excuse.

■ Eat lightly after exercise to recover well without causing digestion to interfere with your sleep.

Better late than never

Evening exercisers may also want to keep the following in mind:

■ Never skip breakfast. Try to eat at least 500 calories for your morning meal. For example, throw together a fruit smoothie made with yoghurt, fruit and juice while you are preparing your toast. Or try cereal topped with nuts, skimmed milk and a piece of fruit

■ Make lunch your main meal of the day. Focus on high-quality protein, such as fish, tofu, lean beef or lamb, chicken or bread with cooked grain, along with fresh fruit. A smoothie, juice or natural yoghurt drink are also great, healthy lunch foods

■ Always eat a mid-afternoon snack. Around three hours before your run, have some fruit or an energy bar together with half a pint of water

■ Drink more fluids. Grab a drink as soon as you step back through the door after your run. And keep drinking as you prepare your meal. This helps replace sweat loss and may prevent you trying to eat everything in sight

■ Eat moderately at dinner. Some people worry about eating too close to bedtime because they fear the calories will go straight to their fat cells. That's simply not true. Your body will use those calories to stockpile fuel in your muscles. On the other hand if you eat more calories than your body needs – no matter what time of day or night – your body will eventually store the excess as fat. ■

SUPERFOODS

Become a fan of these super food groups and watch your running fly

CARB-PACKED FOOD

Grains, beans and potatoes supply the carbohydrate you need to fuel your muscles. Grains also contain important riboflavin and niacin, which your muscles need to convert the carbs you eat into energy. While enriched refined grain products do supply these B vitamins, you should focus on whole-grains, which also provide the fibre you need for a healthy heart and digestive tract.

Amount needed: 8-15 daily servings, of which at least half should come from whole grains; at least five weekly servings should come from beans.

FLUIDS

Simply put, the more you run the more you sweat. If you don't replace those lost fluids, you'll become dehydrated. Apart from hurting your performance, chronic dehydration also increases your risk of kidney stones and bladder cancer. If

you're concerned about your weight, make water your fluid of choice. During long runs, however, you may need a carbohydrate drink for fuel.
Amount needed: About 10-12 250ml servings a day of water, or other fluids such as fruit juice and rehydration or carbohydrate drinks.

VEGETABLES

Dark, leafy greens, tomatoes, peppers, carrots and other colourful vegetables supply vitamin C, carotene and antioxidants. These protect you from the kind of free-radical damage that can occur during heavy training, which, in turn, prevents muscle soreness. Choose fresh, frozen or canned vegetables, as these all supply a wealth of vital nutrients.
Amount needed: Four to six servings daily. Include two or more antioxidant-rich selections, like spinach or Brussels sprouts.

FRUIT

Brightly-coloured fruits such as kiwi fruit, berries, watermelons and oranges are rich in antioxidants and other phytochemicals. Fruit juice does contain some of these properties, but you'll obtain more cholesterol-lowering fibre and other nutrients from whole fruit.
Amount needed: Three to five servings a day, at least half of which should be brightly-coloured antioxidant abundant fruits like mango, pineapple or cantaloupe.

CALCIUM-RICH FOODS

Eating dairy products is the easiest way to ensure

you're consuming plenty of bone-strengthening calcium. Dairy products also offer a good dose of protein. If you don't eat dairy products, then select calcium-fortified soy products. (Aim for at least one soy product daily which supplies 10g of protein.) Other dairy substitutes include calcium-fortified products such as fruit juice or breakfast cereals, but these won't contribute significant amounts of protein.
Amount needed: Two to three servings daily.

PROTEIN POWERHOUSES

As a runner, you need 80g or more of protein a day. This macronutrient is especially important after your work-outs, when you need to repair muscle damage and speed recovery. So include soy foods, fish, eggs or lean meat in your post-training meal.

Lean meat, especially beef, is loaded with zinc, a mineral most runners lack. Soy products, along with fish and other types of meat, provide iron and other trace minerals, such as copper and manganese, which your body needs, especially during heavy training.

Try to eat oily fish once or twice a week for its protein and healthy omega-6 and omega-3 fatty acids – essential oils many runners should have more of. Omega-3s protect the heart and are also believed to benefit brain health, foetal development, psoriasis and certain cancers.
Amount needed: Two to four 60-70g servings a day.

HEALTHY FOODS

The fat found in nuts, avocados, olives and olive oil is actually quite good for your heart. However, your total number of fat servings depends upon your calorific needs.

Substitute these healthy fats for saturated and trans-fats whenever possible. For example, snack on a handful of nuts instead of crisps, use avocado as a spread on bread instead of butter or low-fat spread, cook with olive oil instead of margarine or butter, and if you can find it, use flaxseed with seasonings on salad dressings. Flaxseed oil also supplies a healthy dose of omega-3 fats, the same ones found in fish.
Amount needed: Three to five servings of nuts per week.

HEALTHY SNACKS

If your runs last longer than an hour, you'll want to consume energy bars, gels or carbohydrate drinks and other performance foods to boost your energy levels. Because these foods contain easily digestible carbs, they make great pre- and post-run snacks as well. Consume about 30-60g of carbs during each hour of running (most bars contain 30g or more of carbs; most gels contain about 25g). Foods such as jelly babies, fig rolls, dried fruit and honey also supply fast, digestible carbohydrate.
Amount needed: One to two servings on a long run (up to 60g per hour of running).

NON-VITAL EXTRAS

Foods such as crisps, cakes and doughnuts offer too few nutrients and too many calories. Plus, these types of snacks often contain saturated or trans-fats, two of the biggest artery cloggers. But to be honest, one of the reasons you run is so you can eat the foods you love. So munching on a couple of Hobnobs or drinking the odd can of cola is not a major problem, so long as they don't become dietary staples.
Amount needed: Don't go overboard.■

›› TOP TIPS

- If you run in the morning, try to eat at least an hour before you begin. If you don't have time to prepare and eat food, experiment with carb drinks and energy gels, or eat a large meal the night before
- If you run at lunch, have a mid-morning snack and pack your own lunch to eat afterwards at your desk. Always eat fruit
- If you run in the evening, eat well during the day to prevent post-work slothing. Make lunch the main meal of your day and eat morning and afternoon snacks
- Eating junk food occasionally is not the end of the world. If it's not out of control, don't beat yourself up. Enjoy the treat

TASTY **TIPS**

You don't need a magic potion if you want to shift some weight, fight colds, boost your endurance, protect yourself against major illnesses or run faster and better – all you need is good food

We've put together some of the best nuggets of nutritional know-how – some weird, some wonderful – that'll help make you healthier, fitter and even happier. Incorporate some of these ideas into your daily eating plan, and you'll be eating smarter and running faster.

COLOUR YOUR DIET

Buy the brightest vegetables you see. Vibrant colours usually correspond with more vitamins. This means going easy on iceberg lettuce and cucumbers, and loading up on carrots, tomatoes, red peppers and sweet potatoes – which are higher in vitamins A and C. Or go for darker shades of greens. Romaine lettuce for example, has nearly seven times the vitamin C and twice the calcium of its paler, iceberg cousin. The same holds true for fruit. Pink grapefruit, for instance, has more than 30 times the vitamin A of its yellow-coloured cousin.

FORK OUT ON CHINESE

Eating Chinese takeaway with chopsticks isn't just a way of showing off – it's much healthier than shovelling your chow mein down with a spoon. Scoop your takeaway out of the carton or bowl with chopsticks – or a fork – and you'll be more likely to leave behind the fatty, artery-clogging sauce.

DRINK GINGER ALE INSTEAD OF COLA

Besides packing too many empty calories, colas (including the diet kind) are high in phosphorous, a mineral that can prevent the absorption of calcium. Ginger ale is a better carbonated drink. It has no phosphorous and as many as 30 fewer calories per glass than regular cola.

BLOT YOUR PIZZA

By blotting the grease on top of a pizza with a kitchen towel you'll eliminate at least a teaspoon (4.5g) of fat per slice.

STERILISE YOUR OYSTERS

The next time you order oysters it may help to add a dash of Tabasco sauce before you gulp them down. Researchers found spicy sauce kills dangerous bacteria found in raw oysters. Infection is rare but it can be fatal, especially in people with impaired immunity. Tabasco killed the bacteria in less than five minutes.

EAT COW, DRINK COW

Make that occasional juicy steak even better for you by washing it down with a glass of skimmed milk. According to research, calcium may help reduce the amount of saturated fat your body absorbs. Like fibre, calcium binds with fat molecules and helps flush them out through the intestines.

INSTEAD OF SECONDS, CHEW GUM

When sanity dictates you stop shoving food into your face at the buffet or dinner table, pop mint-flavoured gum into your mouth. It changes the flavour of everything, and makes that extra helping of lasagne almost impossible to swallow.

PRESS YOUR LUCK

The fact your beef is brown doesn't necessarily mean it's safe to eat. Meat that's old or has been exposed to too much air can brown prematurely, making it appear properly cooked. Press down on your burger and note what colour liquid emerges. If the juice is nearly yellow, with no trace of red, it's safe. If not, send it back.

FREEZE SOME MELON BALLS

Substitute frozen melon balls for ice cubes in fruit drinks; 110g of honeydew melon has 230mg of potassium and 20g of vitamin C.

MAKE A BETTER FISH FINGER

Fish fingers are the seafood version of hotdogs – delicious, easy, but not too healthy. Here's a healthier, DIY version: cut a salmon or tuna steak into finger-size portions. Dip the sticks into an egg-white batter and roll them in a bowl of breadcrumbs. Stick a few in the freezer, and when you're feeling peckish simply bake in the oven.

USE HEALTHY GARNISHES

One secret of weight-loss is making bland foods taste great. Smear mustard on a low-fat turkey sandwich and it becomes delicious. Use Worcestershire sauce to spruce up broccoli and other healthy foods. Lightly brush barbecue sauce on grilled vegetables, and you'll find yourself craving that aubergine.

HALVE YOUR BEEF AND EAT IT

Here's a way to make meaty chilli, pasta sauce or meatballs with a good deal less fat: start with extra-lean minced beef. Crumble your meat and brown it in a frying pan. Watch it sizzle. Next, dump the browned beef on to a dish covered with a double thickness of kitchen paper. Place another paper towel over the meat and blot up the grease. Presto! Fat goes into the towel. Then, to remove even more fat, toss the cooked beef into a strainer and rinse it with hot water. Then squeeze out the water and add the meat to your bolognese. Blotting and rinsing can knock about 50 per cent of the fat from your beef. And you won't taste the difference.

SWEET NURTURED

Jelly babies are one of the best secret weapons a runner can pack. A handful of low-fat sweets will help keep your blood glucose stable during long runs and races. (Low blood glucose causes the dips we see in performance as the body switches from carb to fat burning.)

PUT A LID ON IT

You can reduce the amount of oil needed to pan-fry foods simply by keeping the lid on the wok. The lid catches and returns moisture that would usually escape, thus preventing the need for more oil.

SHAKE IT, DON'T BAKE IT

To cut back on salt, don't add it to food during cooking. Instead shake it on when the plate reaches the table. Research shows people given totally unsalted food – but a free hand with the shaker – put in one fifth of the amount originally called for in the recipe.

DRINK LEFTOVER MILK

Your favourite breakfast cereal may be fortified with a veritable alphabet of vitamins, but that doesn't mean you're getting all the nutrients listed on the side of the box. Up to 40 per cent of the vitamins in the cereal quickly dissolve into the milk. To make sure you obtain the most vitamins from fortified breakfast cereals, pick up the bowl and slurp all the milk down – just don't do it in front of the servants, it may raise challenging points of etiquette.

OBSERVE THE THREE-QUARTER RULE

Three-quarters of your dish should contain fresh produce and grains, with the last quarter saved for fish, meat or chicken. This combination will supply longer-lasting energy and fuel for many hours.

MAKE A HEALTHIER MARINADE

When grilling chicken, try this oil-free marinade: combine three small glasses of apple juice and two cloves of crushed garlic with a cup of reduced-salt soya sauce.

POKE THE CHICKEN

Barbecued or grilled chicken is tasty, but there's a catch-22: leave the skin on and the bird will be as fatty as beef; peel the skin off, and it'll be drier than the Gobi Desert. A quick solution: poke a few dozen holes in the skin with a fork before cooking. This will let the fat drip out, but will still keep the meat moist.

FREEZE!

One of the easiest ways to improve your diet is to stock your freezer with bags of frozen vegetables. Not only do they provide a variety of nutrients, they're also convenient. Throw a handful in soups, stews, stir-frys and instant rice dishes. Frozen vegetables are usually frozen within a few hours of harvest, so their nutritional value can actually be greater than their fresh cousins.

JAM THE JAM

Fruit is good for you, so the best yoghurt must be the kind with fruit in it, right? Not necessarily. For the most nutritious yoghurt, skip the "fruit on the bottom" varieties. The fruit will be mostly jam, which packs the equivalent of eight or nine teaspoons of sugar per pot – nearly as much as a can of fizzy drink. Instead, choose plain low-fat yoghurt or flavours such as lemon, which don't contain fruit, and add your own berries. Fresh berries will also provide a healthy dose of fibre.

CHANGE YOUR DIPS

Instead of buying fatty sour cream-based dips to drag your nibbles through, think black-bean dip or go Middle Eastern and buy some hummus. It's made from chickpeas, which are high in fibre, and it's great with raw vegetables like celery and carrots.

BE A BREADWINNER

Shopping in the bread aisle, you naturally grab a loaf of something brown – it must be higher in fibre than the white stuff, right? Well, no – that dark complexion may be courtesy of molasses or food dyes. Likewise, a loaf with seeds or oatmeal flakes gracing its top isn't necessarily high-fibre either; they could just be decoration. To be sure you're a breadwinner every time, look for the phrase "100 per cent wholewheat or wholegrain" on the package.

FEEL THE BURN

Spicy food makes you eat slowly, fills you up more quickly and increases your metabolism so you burn more calories – three reasons to put some cayenne on your chicken.

MAKE SOME COURGETTE CHIPS

Fancy some chips to go with that burger? Try courgette chips. Slice two courgettes into chip-sized pieces. Sauté the chips in half a teaspoon of oil in a large pan over medium-high heat until lightly browned. Sprinkle with basil.

MINE'S A PINT

Drinking one beer a day has been associated with a 40 per cent lower risk of developing kidney stones. One explanation is that the hops in beer help prevent calcium leaching out of bones and taking up residence in your kidneys.

BUY THE BEST BERRIES

Before you buy strawberries or raspberries, turn the carton over. You're looking for nature's expiry date: juice stains. Dripping fruit is one step away from rotten fruit. If you've already bought berries that are going soft, place a single layer of them on a baking sheet and freeze for 20 minutes.

CELERY INCREASE

Celery is pretty much the answer for anyone whose doctor has told them, "You have high blood pressure; cut down on salt." Celery's natural salty flavour can help quash your sodium urges, whether noshed raw or added to a wide variety of dishes. And as a bonus, it contains potassium, a mineral that's been shown to help fight hypertension.

LAST LONGER WITH COFFEE

Plenty of bad things have been written about coffee, but treat yourself to a strong cup an hour before a race and the caffeine will help you burn fat more efficiently. That means your carbohydrates will last longer allowing you to race longer and harder.

HAVE A BIT OF GINGER

You should try to get a bit of ginger every day. Ginger root has natural anti-inflammatory properties, especially if you take it regularly. So, slice half a teaspoonful of the root and eat it with vegetables, or mix it with boiling water for a pain-relieving ginger brew.

POT LUCK

A pot of low-fat yoghurt provides half the recommended daily allowance of calcium, and as studies have shown the dietary calcium intakes of athletes with bone injuries such as stress fractures are abnormally low, you should eat more yoghurt. You don't have to just spoon it from the pot, though. Why not add it to your favourite low-sugar cereal; or use plain yoghurt instead of sour cream on top of baked potatoes.

BRAIN JUICE

A slug of orange juice first thing in the morning will make you faster. That's because fruit juice is the best source of energy for the brain. Overnight the brain's fuel – blood glucose and liver glycogen – drops so we feel sluggish come morning. Fruit juice is packed with fructose, the sugar that restocks liver glycogen supplies, and as it's liquid, it's absorbed quickly.

THE MISSING ZINC

Another way to keep your bones healthy is to load up with zinc. This mineral helps manufacture healthy bone and cartilage cells. We need about 15mg a day and the easiest places to get it are from red meat and zinc supplements. Or you could start necking the oysters. As well as – allegedly – doing wonders for your love life, these little shellfish are mega zinc-givers – down five and you'll consume 41mg of the mineral.

NOBODY DOES IT BETA

It's long been known that the beta-carotene found in carrots protects against diseases such as cancer and can protect against muscle damage and soreness, but this antioxidant can also make you faster. In one US study, 5K runners were given the equivalent of five carrots worth of beta-carotene a day. At the end of the 30 days, the runners ran on average 30 seconds quicker than before. If you don't fancy becoming Bugs Bunny, other good sources of beta-carotene include peaches, apricots, and red and yellow peppers.

RIDE THE CHOCOLATE CARRIAGEWAY

Obviously, stuffing 12 Mars Bars down your throat every day might lead to weight (and pimple) gain, but every now and again a chunk of chocolate is quite a healthy treat. Chocolate, especially the darkest varieties, contains the same phytochemicals found in red wine that have been shown to fight heart disease. In fact, some studies have found chocolate contains more phytochemicals than other powerhouses such as tea and strawberries.

PAMPER YOUR PRODUCE

Cut and wash fruit and vegetables just before cooking or eating them. This keeps vitamin levels at their maximum. And don't cut them into tiny pieces. The more surface area exposed to oxygen, the faster vitamins lose their potency.

DO SOME PORRIDGE

A true wonder brekkie, not only is porridge a great source of carbohydrates – it's also a great weapon in the battle of the bulge. It contains a high amount of water-soluble fibre so it keeps you full for longer – hence the saying "it sticks to your ribs". Oats also lower blood cholesterol.

RAISIN THE BAR

Sprinkle raisins into yoghurt, on your cereal or just snack on them throughout the day, as they are a fantastic energy snack. Four tablespoons of raisins contain 79g of carbohydrates, 302kcal as well as potassium, iron and phytochemicals. And they're virtually fat-free, too.

THE GOOD GOO

You'd think something that tasted as good as honey would have to be bad for you. Nope. Honey is a mixture of glucose and fructose, so it's great for a quick energy boost. Pure honey also contains a huge range of vitamins such as B6, thiamine, riboflavin and patothenic acid, as well as calcium, copper, manganese, phosphorous potassium, sodium and zinc. Added to that, it also contains several different amino acids and antioxidants. So go on, smear it on your toast.

MARK THE ALMONDS

All nuts are good for you, but almonds are among the best. A 30g serving gives 160kcal, with about two-thirds of those calories coming from heart-healthy fats. Almonds have been

EAT ME

shown to lower heart-disease risk thanks to their healthy fats and phytochemicals. They're also a great source of vitamin E, an antioxidant that's hard to find in food sources. Almonds are great on their own but also add flavour to cereals, yoghurts, salads and even stir-frys.

DON'T BE A GUTS

After a run, it's easy to stuff food down without it touching the sides. By not rushing your meals, though, you'll actually lose weight. US researchers found people who extended their meal times by an average of four minutes, simply by chewing more slowly and enjoying their food, burnt up considerably more body fat than greedy guzzlers.

NO BANANA DRAMA

Bananas are chock full of vitamin B6, which helps boost your body's production of the feel-good chemical serotonin. This helps elevate mood, giving you a calm, positive feeling. Slice a banana over cereal or eat one as a mid-morning snack.

CHEERS FOR TEARS

Onions might make you cry, but they'll also stop your nose weeping. Along with other vegetables from the allium family (such as garlic or leeks), onions contain quercetin, an antioxidant that smothers invading bacteria. So if you want to avoid the sniffles, add onions to everything.

PACK TWO LUNCHES

Not an excuse to gorge yourself on two Big Mac meals a day, instead a rather clever nutritional trick. We tend to feel hungry every four hours, but most of us don't eat to that timetable. Instead, we scrimp on breakfast and lunch before stuffing our faces in the evening. Instead, eat two 600kcal "lunches" a day. Have one at 12pm and the next at 4pm and you'll boost your energy and "ruin" your appetite so that you don't stuff yourself in the evening.

GUZZLE GRAPE JUICE

The best health drink for people with heart trouble is a glass of purple grape juice after a daily aspirin. The aspirin protects your heart by preventing bloodclots, but this effect can be blocked by the adrenalin that exercise and stress produce. Flavonoids in grape juice may stymie that response.

HEAL WITH HALIBUT

Fish, especially cold-water species such as tuna and halibut, are rich in Omega-3 fats, which contain a fatty acid called eicosapentaenoic acid (EPA). This reduces both inflammation and the pain-causing prostaglandins it triggers. Fish is also a great source of muscle-repairing protein, so try to eat at least three servings of fish a week to beat aching muscles.

CRUNCH BUNCH

Between meals snack on crunchy foods to wake up your mouth and your mind. Fresh vegetables such as radishes, broccoli and cauliflower dunked in a spicy dip – such as chilli, lime and low-fat yoghurt – will stop you flagging at your desk mid-morning.

MAKE IT AN ORANGE

Any fruit is good, but oranges are the king. They offer a massive dose of immune-system boosting vitamin C – over 130 per cent of the RDA. They also contain a good helping of potassium, folic acid and pectin – a fibre that helps balance blood sugar levels and keep hunger at bay. If that's not enough, there's a big bunch of cancer and heart-disease-risk-reducing flavanoids, too. So if only one fruit makes it into your bowl, make it an orange.

TEA'S UP

A brew doesn't just provide you with vital fluids, it also helps protect against a number of age-related ailments. Tea, especially the black and green varieties, contains catechins and flavanols, phytochemicals that fight the free-radicals that lead to illnesses such as cancer, Parkinson's and osteoporosis. ■

TO YOUR **HEALTH**

We all know staying well hydrated is important, but few of us are aware we can have too much of this particular good thing

As she passed her coach and friends at the 15-mile mark of the 2002 Boston Marathon, Cynthia Lucero smiled and waved cheerily. It was typical behaviour for the petite woman from Ecuador. According to all who knew her, Lucero loved life, loved to help others and loved running. Seven miles later, however, something went horribly wrong.

It should have been the best of times for Lucero. The previous week she had defended her doctoral dissertation to become, in effect, Dr Cynthia Lucero. The dissertation studied the positive effect of marathon training on cancer victims and their families.

Lucero was running her first Boston Marathon. She had trained well, and eagerly anticipated the day. Things seemed to go swimmingly until about the 22-mile mark, where she stopped to drink a cup of fluid. Another runner remembers hearing Lucero say that she felt dizzy and disoriented.

A few steps later, Lucero staggered briefly then fell to the pavement, unconscious. She never regained consciousness, becoming just the second runner ever to die in the Boston Marathon, and the first to die of hyponatraemia, which is caused by excess fluid consumption.

We live in a water-obsessed society. Water bottles have replaced orange segments as the half-time refreshment at football and rugby matches; water coolers are as pervasive as tea bags in office kitchens, and schools increasingly encourage you to send your child to school with their own drink bottle. Why? At least in part because every fitness article in every newspaper and magazine insists you absolutely, positively must drink eight big glasses of water a day.

But where's the proof? Amazingly, there isn't any. Even in marathons, the available evidence indicates overhydrating is as potentially dangerous as underhydrating, with Cynthia Lucero's story serving as an unfortunate exclamation mark. Yes, we runners need to drink generously – no one questions that – but we need to drink with a fuller understanding of the facts, the medical science and the potential risks.

WATER, WATER EVERYWHERE

Water is by far the largest constituent of the human body, making up about 60 per cent of total bodyweight. This large pool of water performs many crucial functions, including nourishing the cells, carrying food throughout the body, eliminating waste, regulating body temperature, cushioning and lubricating the joints, and maintaining blood volume and blood pressure. Inadequate levels of fluid consumption have been associated with kidney stones and higher rates of urinary tract infections, bladder and colorectal cancers, and even heart disease in one or two studies.

Given this information, all experts agree an adequate water supply is crucial to the body's optimal functioning. But how much water and other fluids are adequate?

THE EIGHT GLASSES MYTH

Most adults – at least those that read the health pages of newspapers or magazines – have come to believe that they should drink eight 250ml glasses – that's two litres – of water a day, but there's little to no evidence supporting the eight glasses rule.

Last summer, Heinz Valtin, the Professor Emeritus of Physiology at Dartmouth Medical School, USA, published a compelling article in the *Journal of the American Physiological Society*.

Basically, Valtin committed himself to searching out medical-scientific verification for the eight glasses rule. He couldn't locate any. "I have found no scientific proof that we must drink at least eight glasses of water a day," concluded Valtin,. "The published data strongly suggest that we probably are drinking enough, and possibly even more than enough."

Ron Maughan, Visiting External Professor of Loughborough University and the foremost researcher on hydration in the UK, agrees with Valtin. "You hear this advice from magazines, but where is it actually coming from? Not the Department of Health."

Tim Lawson, director of Science In Sport, a UK-based sports nutrition company, believes the eight glasses rule might only apply if "you were eating dehydrated food". He says the figure is misquoted as it fails to take into account the moisture content from food (especially fruit and vegetables) and the fluid intake from other drinks.

Of course, Valtin was researching the hydration habits of average, non-exercising people. Runners sweat heavily and need to drink more than non-exercisers, and the heavier and more muscular you are, the hotter the weather and the faster you run, the more you will sweat.

AWASH IN WATER

Meanwhile, a survey of 2,818 adults in the year 2000 by the American-based International Bottled Water Association (IBWA) revealed an average adult drinks 4.5 litres of fluid a day. The IBWA argues that 1.5 litres of this amount is alcohol and caffeine drinks (both considered diuretics, meaning they increase urine production), and should be subtracted from the total.

THE TRUTH ABOUT CAFFEINE

However, research conducted in the last two years has reversed the age-old wisdom that caffeinated beverages are diuretics. Actually, to be more precise, the research confirmed that caffeinated beverages are diuretics but only to the same degree as plain water. If you drink a lot of water, you need to go to the toilet. It's the same with caffeinated beverages, no more, no less.

"The research indicates caffeine stimulates a mild diuresis similar to water," says heat and hydration expert Larry Armstrong, author of *Exertional Heat Illnesses*. Armstrong reached this conclusion after analysing 10 medical articles on caffeinated beverages, and published his

» YOUR DAILY DRINKING REQUIREMENT

The old formula – everyone needs eight 250ml glasses of water a day – is out.

It has been replaced by formulas based primarily on your gender and bodyweight.

Here are the formulas for moderately active men and women:

Male Drinking Requirement
Bodyweight (lbs) x 10.36

Female Drinking Requirement
Bodyweight (lbs) x 9.176

Example A 132lb women needs to drink 1,211ml of water a day – 132 x 9.176 = 1,211. She'll get the rest of her daily water supply from food and metabolic processes. Runners need to drink extra to cover daily sweat losses.

report last year in the *International Journal of Sport Nutrition and Exercise Metabolism*.

In 2001, Maughan also reviewed the literature to find a diuretic effect occurred only when high caffeine doses of over 300mg were given to research subjects whose caffeine intake had been restricted for a few days prior to the test. He also noted the same myths surround alcohol – especially beer – which isn't, he claims, that much of a diuretic.

BEATING A PATH TO THE BATHROOM

Other experts agree with Valtin, Armstrong and Maughan that there's no dehydration epidemic sweeping the country. If anything, we're overhydrated. This isn't necessarily a bad thing. It's probably just adding to your daily mileage and calorie burn, with all those trips to the bathroom, but there's little evidence for the list of dehydration ills – fatigue, headache, dry skin, lack of concentration and so on – put forth by some.

"Without any convincing data, I remain sceptical of all these so-called dehydration problems," says researcher Barbara Rolls, author of *Thirst*, and a leading expert on hydration. "It's a myth that's being perpetuated. The thirst mechanism is exquisitely tuned to keep us in fluid balance."

Maughan confirms the view that thirst is a useful mechanism, maintaining that it is simply a learned behaviour. Unlike children, who demand a can of cola as soon as they feel like it, but then only have a sip and are unable to finish the drink, adults learn to restrain the immediate impulse to drink, and to wait until they are thirsty enough to finish the entire can.

MARS AND VENUS

When it comes to sweat rates and fluid-replacement needs, men and women come from different planets. Because men are, on average, significantly heavier than women and have more muscle mass, they sweat more than women and need to drink more. Or, to turn things around: women don't sweat as much as men, so don't need to drink as much.

They also have a smaller blood plasma "tank" than men, which is easier to overfill. Many women are new marathoners who are happy to finish in five hours or more. They reach the 20-mile mark exhausted, and think, "If I can force myself to drink more I'll feel better." It's a recipe for disaster.

For the reasons just stated, a woman's hydration need can be up to 30 per cent less than a man's. This essential fact has been largely overlooked in most articles on hydration needs, and it's particularly important for female runners, because most of the marathoners who suffer from hyponatraemia (excessive water drinking), including a number who have died from marathon-related hyponatraemia, have been women.

HYDRATION, PERFORMANCE AND RISK

Dehydration diminishes performance, because it thickens the blood, decreases the heart's efficiency, increases heart rate and raises body temperature, but a modest dehydration is a normal and temporary condition for many marathoners, and doesn't lead to any serious medical conditions. Extreme fluid consumption, on the other hand, can be deadly.

THE LONG AND SWEATY ROAD

The first dehydration studies with marathoners were done at the Boston Marathon in the 1960s, an era when runners were advised to avoid water-drinking because it caused stomach cramps. At any rate, race organisers provided no fluids en route. The result was that the runners lost five to six per cent of their bodyweight through sweating, but apparently suffered no particular harm.

A FULL TANK

Since then, a substantial body of research has shown that anything more than a two per cent dehydration will worsen performance, and everyone agrees that it makes sense to limit dehydration as you run. Some runners can even train themselves to drink more. Studies have also shown that the more fluid there is in your stomach, the more will reach your blood, where you want it. Hence the good advice to run with a comfortably full stomach and to "top up your tank" frequently.

OUT OF THE LAB, ONTO TO THE ROAD

Nonetheless, in the real world, most runners who finish a marathon in three to four hours will sweat about twice as much per hour as they can drink. This can easily lead to greater than two per cent dehydration. Why this scenario? Because the body doesn't like to run hard and drink hard

>> WATER IN, WATER OUT

Your daily water supply comes from three sources, and you lose water in four principal ways. The percentages shown here are averages for non-exercisers. Runners sweat more, and need to drink more, than non-exercisers.

Actual percentages will vary considerably depending on the weather, your diet, the amount you exercise and other factors.

Water Intake	Per cent	Water Loss	Per cent
Fluids	60%	Urine	50%
Food	30%	Sweat	35%
Metabolism	10%*	Respiration	10%
		Faeces	5%

*Approximately 10 per cent of your daily water supply comes from metabolic water – fluid that's "liberated" within the body when you burn fats and carbohydrates.

at the same time. (At about four-hour pace, it seems, runners are going slow enough, perhaps with walking breaks, to drink sufficiently to avoid most dehydration. Those athletes completing five- and six-hour marathons, and Ironman-type triathlons that last twice as long, can actually overhydrate.)

With regards to the often-quoted warnings to avoid greater than two per cent deydration, Maughan emphasises that, "there is no sudden cut off point – dehydration depends on performance and the individual." He does however acknowledge that even one per cent dehydration is enough to have a negative effect on performance.

THE SWEAT-RATE PARADOX

As we get fitter, we sweat more. This means we dehydrate faster – a cruel blow, it would seem. In any given marathon, in fact, the winners are probably the most dehydrated runners on the course. At sub-five-minute pace, they produce tremendous amounts of heat and sweat, and have no time for drinking. Of course, the body is clever. It knows it can cope with modest dehydration. Heatstroke is the serious danger. So the body increases your sweat rate as you get fitter, because sweat promotes cooling, which helps keep heatstroke at bay. Dehydration can certainly contribute to heatstroke (which is one of the prime reasons why all athletes are admonished to drink regularly), but it doesn't cause it.

RISE OF HYPONATRAEMIA

As marathon running has boomed, and particularly as it has attracted more women and recreational runners, hyponatraemia has intruded on our sport. It means "low blood sodium", but it's caused by excessive fluid consumption, which lowers the concentration of sodium in the blood. As we've seen, in extreme cases, hyponatraemia can lead to brain seizures and death. Maughan describes the condition as "a significant danger for a small number of people".

In 2002, America's Boston and Marine Corps Marathons had their first-ever fatalities attributed to hyponatraemia. Hyponatraemia is also beginning to appear in other endurance athletes, including ultramarathoners, Ironman triathletes and long-distance walkers. So far, there are no known cases of death from hyponatraemia in endurance events in the UK, although there have been cases associated with psychiatric illness.

WATER RATES

The hyponatraemia issue has forced sports and medical groups to take a new look at their hydration guidelines, and several have already adjusted their recommendations. Last autumn, the International Marathon Medical Directors Association (IMMDA) issued the first fluid-consumption guidelines from a medical organisation completely focused on runners.

IMMDA, which represents some 150 major

marathons on all seven continents, suggests marathoners should consume 385-800ml of fluid per hour (you'll need more the hotter it is, the harder you run or the heavier you are), with an absolute ceiling at 800ml. See www.aims-association.org/immda.htm.

That's just over half the fluid requirement proposed since 1996 by the widely-quoted "Exercise and Fluid Replacement" stance of the American College of Sports Medicine, which calls for 590-1,180ml per hour. Clearly the scientific jury is still out when it comes to appropriate water consumption.

For the first time in its 107-year history, the Boston Marathon last spring provided all 20,000 runners with a fold-out pamphlet from the American Running Association and the American Medical Athletic Association. It advised runners to stay hydrated but not to over-drink, to maintain a salty diet, to favour sports drinks and to recognise warning signs.

The Gatorade Sports Science Institute (www.gssiweb.com) has recently published one of the most comprehensive advisories on hyponatraemia, *Hyponatraemia in Athletes*. It reinforces the idea that hydration is important, and that each of us sweats at a different rate, produces varying amounts of sodium in our sweat and reacts differently to heat stress.

WATER FORESIGHT

We also believe it's a good time to review your hydration practices. Runners need to pay more attention to their daily fluid consumption than most people, but we don't need to be obsessive. Given half a chance, the body will self-regulate to a normal, healthy state of fluid balance.

If you drink a lot of water and get a little overhydrated during the day, that's okay. Your body will simply send you to the toilet. Conversely, if you can't drink quite enough during a marathon, that's also okay. Sit down with a sandwich and carbohydrate drink after the race, and your body will soon soak up the water it needs. Don't rush and don't over-drink. After a race, you've got plenty of time to rehydrate.

HYDRO THERAPY

Keep the following in mind and water consumption should never become an issue for you:

Drink generously, but appropriately Know yourself and your needs, and make adjustments for the weather. A runner training while away on holiday in Greece may well need to drink more during and after a slow 10-mile run in August than during or after an all-out marathon effort on a cool spring morning. You should listen to your body.

Use carbohydrate drinks Before, during and after training and races, drink carbohydrate drinks made with electrolytes. These contain the water you need, appropriate amounts of carbohydrates and small amounts of sodium, all of which are essential.

Pay particular attention to post-exercise rehydration You're likely to become dehydrated during a long, hard run, so make sure you drink enough afterwards. The sooner, the better. The same goes for food. Take your fluids, take your carbohydrates, take a little sodium, take a little protein – and you'll be fine.

Weigh yourself daily during periods of intense training If you're losing weight, make sure it's from fat loss, not chronic dehydration. Maughan's recommendation is to restrict actual weight loss to one per cent of body mass. You can also check your urine colour. It should be clear or light yellow (unless you have recently taken some B vitamins, which can turn the urine bright yellow).

When running long and slow – three or four hours or more – monitor your fluid consumption Be sure you're not drinking more than you need. Also, consider running with a salty snack that you consume at the 20-mile mark. If you're a woman, pay particular attention to these recommendations.

Drink when you're thirsty While it's true that your thirst doesn't kick in until you're one to two-per cent dehydrated, there's nothing wrong with that. Remember that your body has an "exquisitely tuned" water-balance mechanism. Use it. ■

FUEL ON THE MOVE

You probably know that your body can only hold about 18 miles-worth of easily useable energy, but did you know that unless you top up your fuel reserves on the run, it starts trying to conserve that energy after as little as nine miles, which will affect your performance?

Here's why: when your body senses that your easily accessible reserves of carbohydrate energy have fallen to 40 or 50 per cent, it starts to increase its use of fat as a source of fuel. It simply cannot let your blood sugar reserves empty completely, because your brain relies on them. The trouble is that fat can't be turned into energy nearly as fast as blood sugar can, so your body becomes forced either to slow down, or to increase its effort dramatically to maintain the same speed. In both cases, you'll find yourself breathing more heavily, because fat conversion requires more oxygen.

The simple solution is to take in fuel on any run over 80 or 90 minutes (and also fluid on any run over an hour, in normal weather conditions). There are three main choices for on-the-run fuelling: energy drinks, bars, or gels. Here's a run-down of each sort, with advice on which work best for particular running situations, but, as always, the best thing to do is to experiment a little – during training, not racing – and find what suits your palate, and your wallet.

ENERGY DRINKS

It's easy to become confused when it comes to choosing what to drink when you're exercising. There are dozens of brands, each producing different types of "sport drinks" – rehydration drinks, energy-replacement drinks, recovery drinks, drinks that give you an energy kick, waters with added vitamins and even added oxygen – and if that isn't enough there are the flavours: strawberry, mango, Devon toffee...

In fact, if you're new to running you might wonder why you need a sports drink at all. You can, of course, simply drink water.

Surprisingly, though, water isn't the best way to rehydrate. Firstly, water will often fill you up before you've actually consumed enough to replace the fluid lost during exercise. Second, water doesn't contain electrolytes – the minerals such as sodium, potassium and magnesium that you lose through sweat during exercise, and that also assist fluid absorption.

Sports drinks are designed to rehydrate you quickly, and supply you with a readily available and easily digestible source of carbohydrates. You have to factor in the price, the ingredients, the uses, and the taste of each when deciding which to use. Although subjective, taste is often the most important factor when choosing a drink. If you can't stand the flavour, all the maltodextrins, glucose polymers, vitamins or minerals in a drink won't convince you to use it.

IN THE MIX

Different drinks are suited to different runs and different conditions. A drink that's suitable for a three-day adventure race in the cold of winter might not be suitable during 400-metre repetitions when you're warm-weather training.

Rehydration When it's hot, or you're just sweating heavily, you need a rehydration drink. These contain electrolytes – minerals such as sodium and potassium – which, as well as replacing those sweated out, actually help speed up the absorption of fluid into the body. Dehydration through fluid loss can adversely affect your performance after just half an hour in hot conditions, while your muscles shouldn't start to get low on energy for at least an hour. Having said that, most also contain carbohydrates (sugars such as glucose and maltodextrin).

How much liquid? A two per cent drop in bodyweight through sweating can lead to a 20 per cent decrease in performance, but if it's cold and you're hardly sweating, you can run for three to four hours before fluid loss becomes a serious issue. Weighing yourself before or after a run will show you exactly how much fluid you've lost, but drinking 150-250ml of fluid every 15-20 minutes is a safe rule to follow in average conditions, and after a run, drink up to twice as much fluid as you've lost.

Energy Our muscles can only store 16-18 miles worth of carbohydrate. So if you're running for a long time, or performing hard, short, fast runs, you definitely need to top up the energy stored in your muscles before, during and after the run.

If the weather is cool, all you have to worry about is basic liquid replacement and keeping your energy reserves topped up during long runs, so you can get away with a higher concentration of carbs. In hot weather, rehydration becomes much more important. You'll need more fluid, electrolytes and the same quantities of carbohydrate as in cold weather (but diluted with more water for rehydration).

Work out the carbohydrate concentration of a drink by finding how many grams of carbohydrate it has in a litre (eg Lucozade Sport contains 66g per litre. So, 66/1000 x 100 = 6.6 per cent).

How much energy? As a rough guideline, aim to take on board one gram of carbohydrate per kilogram of bodyweight per hour of exercise. So, if you weigh 70kg you need 70g of carbs for an hour-long run. If you're using a drink at six per cent solution, that's more than a litre per hour, or 500ml at 14 per cent. Drinks that need to be diluted at up to six per cent contain simple sugars (eg glucose, fructose). These empty from the stomach slowly, and if you mix them too strongly they can even contribute to dehydration – as they can draw water from the stomach. For a more potent energy hit, look for drinks whose main ingredient (the first on the list) is a complex carbohydrate (maltodextrin, glucose polymers). These can be taken in much higher concentrations without compromising the rate at which they're absorbed.

BEHIND THE BARS

The next alternative is energy bars. Yoghurt-coated banana, caramel chocolate, wild berry, cinnamon roll crisp, strawberry whip... they might sound as though they should be gracing the dessert menu of a restaurant, but they're actually just some of the flavours that can now be found in the energy bar section of your local health-food shop, supermarket or specialist running store.

This choice of tempting flavours simply highlights that there is now a massive choice facing runners when they come to choose an energy bar. To make the decision a little easier, here's a rundown of the information you need to know when choosing a energy bar to suit you.

Bar examinations

When you're running for long periods, you need to supplement your energy by replacing the calories you burn, and, as you already know, carbohydrates are the most effective and useful source of those calories. A great way to get that essential fuel is to eat an energy bar that supplies you with between 30g and 60g of carbohydrate.

The carbohydrates in different energy bars tend to come from similar sources. You'll find complex carbohydrates in the form of rice, oats and, in a few products, maltodextrin. Any simple carbohydrate is commonly derived from dried fruit or fructose and glucose syrup.

As well as carbohydrates, energy bars contain plenty of other ingredients, and these can have a significant effect on the bar's effectiveness. Fibre, fat and protein can all slow down the digestion of the bar, which in turn slows down the fuel as it heads to your blood stream. Ideally, an energy bar should contain less than 5g of fibre, 4g or less of fat and 10g or less of protein.

Washing it down

Something else to bear in mind is that you'll also need to drink something with your energy bar. Not only will this help you to swallow it – especially when you have a dry mouth during a run – but it will also speed up the digestion. So aim for 350-500ml of water with each bar you eat. You don't have to – and probably won't be able to – eat the whole bar at once. Just nibble on it during your run.

ENERGY GELS AND THE ALTERNATIVES

While bars are easy to carry, and energy drinks can meet both your fuel and fluid needs, if you have access to water on your run – such as race drinks stations, or park water fountains on training runs – gels are more practical. Essentially, they're concentrated drinks of about 100kcal each, so nearly all require you to drink water in order to create a digestible solution in your stomach.

What's The Alternative?

Because most gels and bars are pretty sweet, sticky and relatively expensive, it's natural to wonder whether solid food could be a realistic alternative. The answer – we found – is that bite-sized chunks of sweet snacks are not inedible in training, but they are inferior in that they don't get converted into energy as quickly, and require more water for digestion.

Dried Apricots Approx £1/100g

Per 100g: 165kcal; 36g carb; 3.9g protein; 0.6g fat; 6.3g fibre

Cost per 100 calories: 60p

Main ingredients: Apricots

Munchability: Tasty and soft, especially the partially re-hydrated ones. Not over-sweet, which is a bonus if you have to face a lot of on-the-run fuelling.

The science: Fructose is a useful fast-release sugar, though too much of it can cause digestive problems. Also, the fibre content of dried apricots is not ideal for runners looking to avoid mid-run pit-stops. Best combined with other snacks or eaten post-run.

High5 Energy Gel (26g) 79p

Per 100g: 272kcal; 68g carb; 0g protein; 0g fat

Cost per 100 calories: £1.12p (also mix your own powder, £6.99 per 600g, 30p/100kcal)

Main ingredients: Maltodextrin, fructose, dextrose, natural flavouring, sodium chloride, potassium chloride, preservatives

Munchability: The jammy blackcurrant and

strawberry High5 flavours are the best on test. Very thin syrup, not hard to swallow and fractionally less sweet than the Leppin and Maxim gels. Comes in sachets or as powder that you mix using a special small bottle (this can be mixed to a thin, isotonic solution).

The science: Designed so that one sachet of gel needs only 75ml of water to produce an isotonic mix in the stomach. Contains a blend of fast- and sustained-release carbohydrates.

Leppin Squeezy (125ml) £2.99 or 80p (25g)

Per 100g: 251kcal; 63g carb; 0g protein; 0g fat

Cost per 100 calories: 77p/£1.27

Main ingredients: Enzymatic hydrolysate of maize (maltodextrin), water, fructose, sodium chloride, preservative, flavour, vitamin B1

Munchability: Fine. Very sweet, and a similar syrupy texture to the Maxim gels. Not the most natural-tasting flavours, but a there is a wide range to choose from. Comes in 65kcal sachets or 387kcal squeezy bottles. The bottles are very easy to use but the tops aren't always screwed on properly at first.

The science: Maltodextrin is the standard way of providing a high energy content in a relatively digestible form. Fructose content helps to provide faster-release energy, though too much can cause gastrointestinal upset.

Mars Bar (65g) 35p

Per 100g: 477 kcal; 73.6g carb; 4.5g protein; 18.3g fat

Cost per 100 calories: 11p

Main ingredients: Milk chocolate, glucose syrup, sugar, hydrogenated vegetable fat

Munchability: You might find yourself fighting the temptation to eat chocolate when you're sitting around doing nothing, but the reality of swallowing it on the run is very different, as it leaves you with a sticky mouth, and can go down a little heavily if your stomach is feeling at all fragile.

The science: The sugar and glucose in a Mars Bar are fine, but the 18 per cent fat makes it hard to swallow and hard to digest. (And although its energy count is very high, over 40 per cent of the energy comes from fat, which is processed very slowly.)

Maxim Energy Gel (100g) £1.35

Per 100g: 310kcal; 77g carb; 0.1g protein; 0g fat

Cost per 100 calories: 44p

Main ingredients: Glucose syrup, water, acidifier, flavourings, vitamin B1

Munchability: Very acceptable, with a genuinely convenient, re-sealable top. Eye-wateringly sweet, as you'd expect from glucose syrup. Nonetheless, not hard to swallow. Flavours quite strong and sharp.

The science: Designed to provide energy as fast as possible, by using only glucose, which does not need to be broken down by the body. However, it must be taken with plenty of water to be moved from the gut quickly and comfortably. (Simple sugars such as glucose are associated with a sugar high followed by a sugar low, but this effect is suppressed during exercise.)

PowerBar (65g) £1.25

Per 100g: 342kcal; 65g carb; 15g protein; 3.1g fat

Cost per 100 calories: 56p

Main ingredients: High fructose corn syrup, oat bran, maltodextrin, milk protein, brown rice, vitamins and minerals

Munchability: Surprisingly not bad, for a bar with a reputation as a chewy monster. Carry it in small chunks, and as you chew, the bar dissolves in your mouth. It's fairly easy to swallow, and leaves you with a cleaner mouth than the Mars Bar or Joosters. Bite off too much, though, and you half-suffocate.

The science: A good mix of fast- and sustained-release energy, plus useful vitamins and minerals. Deliberately designed to dissolve into a thick fluid that sits easily in the stomach, though the 15 per cent protein content means it's better after high-intensity exercise than during it.

PowerBar PowerGel (41g) £1.25
Per 100g: 270kcal; 67g carb; 0.3g protein; 0g fat
Cost per 100 calories: £1.13
Main ingredients:
Maltodextrin, water, fructose, dextrose, sodium, potassium, vitamins C and E, amino acids

Munchability: More of a paste than a gel – too thick to swallow easily without water. Still, the consistency reduces messiness, and most of the flavours are rich and tasty. Like any gel, it can be diluted in small bottles to make it easier to swallow.
The science: Contains a mix of fast- and sustained-release carbohydrates (80:20). The added antioxidant vitamins and amino acids are useful for the diet in general, but you don't particularly need top-ups during normal exercise.

Science in Sport Go Gel (70ml/87g) £1
Per 100g: 116kcal; 29g carb; 0g protein; 0g fat
Cost per 100 calories: 99p
Main ingredients:
Water, maltodextrin, natural flavouring, gelling agents, sweetener, preservative
Munchability: A big hit, even though the packs are relatively large and heavy for their calorie value, and the mild flavours have a faint aftertaste. By far the easiest to swallow; the thin, clean gel goes down more easily than water. Also, because it's the only isotonic, ready-mixed gel on the market, it's easy to digest, even without water.
The science: An isotonic gel is easy to swallow and easy to digest. It makes the pack size big, but at the end of the day, the easier a gel is to eat, the more likely you'll use it. The use of maltodextrins and gelling agents mean this is a sustained-release energy gel.

Starburst Joosters (45g) 36p
Per 100g: 355kcal; 88.6g carb; 0g protein; 0.1g fat
Cost per 100 calories: 23p
Main ingredients:
Sugar, glucose syrup, starch, fruit juices (five per cent), citric acid

Munchability: Pretty good, as lively debate on the runnersworld.co.uk forums testifies. Mouth-watering and very manageable one at a time – though they turn into a gloopy, hard to swallow mass if you give in to the temptation of eating a handful at once.
The science: Simple sugars make for good quick-release energy, and they'll keep your levels topped up if you eat little and often. Joosters are fat- and protein-free, so their digestibility is high, provided you sip water regularly with the aim of keeping the mixture in your stomach isotonic. ■

›› TOP TIPS

Refuelling Rules

◆ Consume 200-300 calories per hour – that's two to three normal gels. Your body uses approximately 1g of carbohydrate per kilogram of bodyweight per hour.

◆ Refuel regularly from the first half-hour of your run – it's hard to kick-start your body once it's started to slump.

◆ To avoid developing cramp, take water with your gels as instructed – usually from 75-200ml per pack. Solid food requires even more water.

◆ Don't try a gel, bar or energy drink for the first time in a race.

◆ Whatever you eat, do drink 150-250ml of water per 20 minutes in normal conditions.

◆ Dehydration affects performance as much as energy depletion does.

CHAPTER 5

Weight Control

If you want to shed a few pounds, then look no further. No other exercise comes close to running in the weight-loss stakes. Minute-for-minute, it burns more calories than any other activity. Of course, if you're serious about dropping a dress size or fitting into smaller trousers then you need to combine running with sensible eating. This chapter will show you how to train smart, and eat smart so that you'll soon see your love handles and bulging tummy simply melt away.

FAT AND FICTION

Fat's not bad for you per se, but will eating more of it really speed up your running? That's just one of the questions we answer as we investigate the facts, and the fiction, surrounding the world's most misunderstood nutrient

Perhaps because its collective waistline is expanding, the British public (including many runners) is becoming obsessed by fat. People want to eat less of it and carry less around on their bodies. To achieve these goals, they're willing to try all manner of weird and wonderful foods, systems and exercise routines.

THE ISLE OF WEIGHT

The problem is that nothing seems to be working. The Department of Health recommends no more than 35 per cent of total calorific intake coming from fat, but some estimates put the figure closer to 40 per cent. Furthermore, ever-increasing numbers of British people are becoming chronically overweight – one in eight men and one in seven women is currently diagnosed as being clinically obese. Many more are simply overweight according to recognised norms.

Of course, that just makes us more desperate for weight-loss programmes that claim to work miracles, no matter how unproven they may be. The fat battlefield is a major industry in this country, and it is an industry in which confusion, misinformation and quackery run rampant.

In this section, we aim to set the record straight. We'll take a look at some of the more persistent fat-burning claims made in the past few years, then we'll give our recommendations.

First, though, let's explode a couple of common myths:

MYTH 1: EATING LOW-FAT FOODS ENSURES WEIGHT-LOSS

If you take nothing else from this chapter, remember one fact: if you routinely consume more calories than you expend, you will gain weight – and that is irrespective of the composition of your diet. Even if you eat less than 30 per cent fat calories and limit your consumption of saturated fat to 10 per cent (both are standard recommendations) you'll still gain weight if you take in more calories than you burn. It's a bedrock principle.

If you are surprised, you're not alone. Many people believe the myth that as long as they eat low-fat or fat-free foods, they won't gain weight. That is rubbish. If you eat a whole bag of low-fat savoury snacks in one sitting, you're consuming several hundred calories. Most of them are carbohydrates, but carbohydrates can be stored as fat too, if you eat enough of them. So can protein, and obviously, so can fat.

We're not saying that carbohydrates, protein and fat are all the same. Clearly, fat is the real bad guy if you eat too much of it, and that's the case for a variety of reasons. High-fat diets are associated with obesity, high cholesterol levels, cardiovascular disease and cancer. Fat is much higher in calories than protein or carbohydrates (nine calories per gram versus four per gram for proteins and carbohydrates), and dietary fat is stored as body fat more efficiently than either protein or carbohydrates, but fat consumption is not the only culprit.

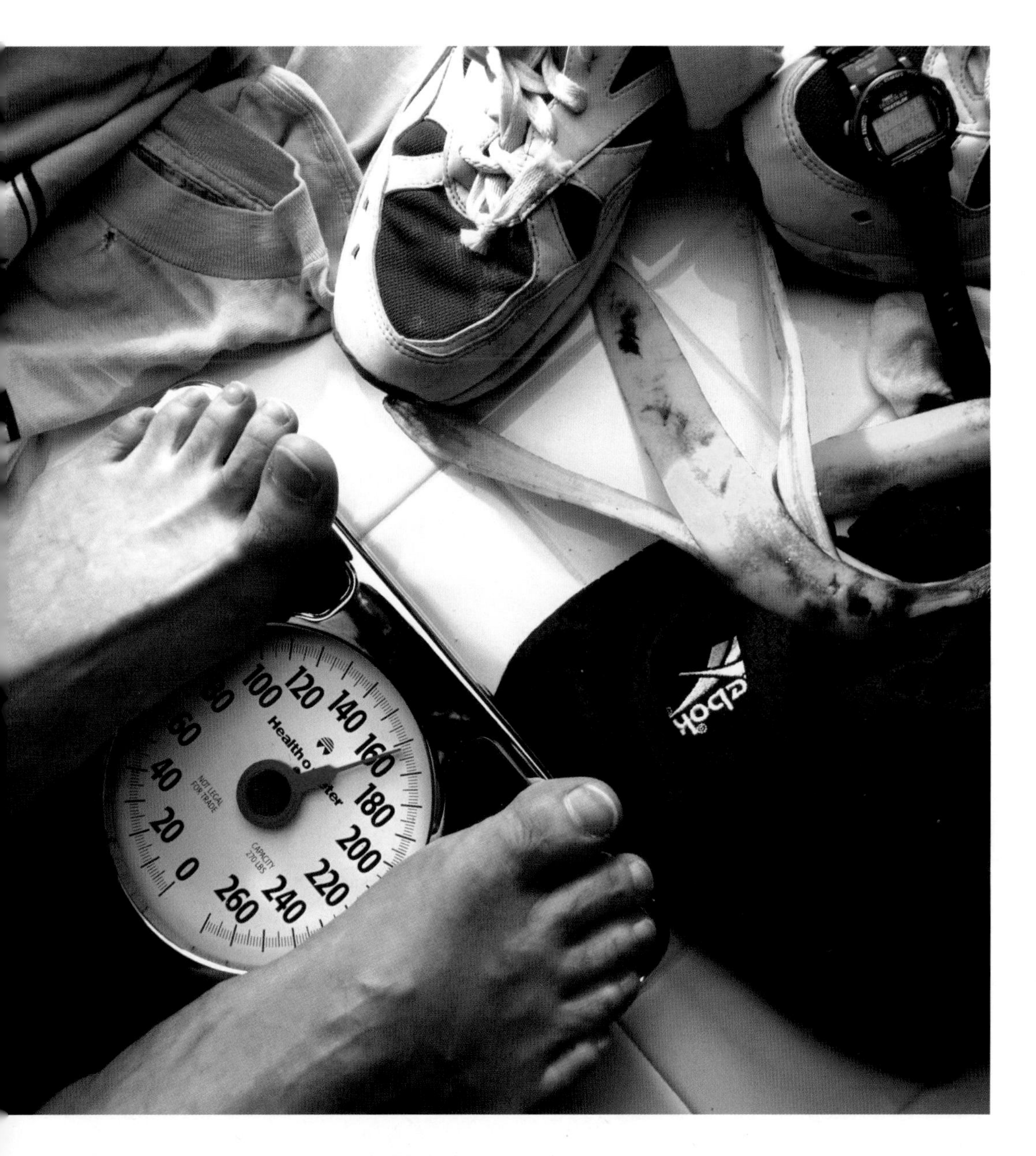

MYTH 2: SLOW-INTENSITY WORKOUTS ARE BEST

This myth maintains that the optimal exercise intensity for fat burning is slow intensity – comparable to walking. Not true. The physiological fact of the matter is that running burns more fat (and calories) than walking. At 65 per cent of VO_2 max (easy running pace) you can burn significantly more calories per unit of time than you do at 25 per cent of maximum (walking).

A study in Quebec showed an aerobic exercise programme that included occasional 90-second bursts at 95 per cent of maximum heart rate burned three-and-a-half times more body fat than a steady-state, moderate-intensity programme did. What's more, the interval trainers achieved this high rate of fat loss while expending less than half the calories of the steady runners during exercise.

One explanation for this startling result is that resting metabolic rate can stay elevated for hours after a session of intense exercise. One Norwegian study found significant fat-burning occurred for 15 hours after exercise at 70 per cent of VO_2 max. Low-intensity exercise does not cause a comparable boost in metabolism.

Running may make you a better fat burner but this is because habitual endurance exercise increases the activity of certain muscle enzymes involved in fat burning. These enzymes enable you to spare glycogen (your short-term energy supply) while you burn more fat. In other words, endurance exercise teaches your body to burn more fat at a given exercise intensity compared to a sedentary person, but it doesn't follow that low-intensity workouts are better – though, as with most myths, there is a degree of truth in it. You do burn a higher percentage of fat calories versus carbohydrate calories at lower intensities. It's also true that as you increase intensity, the percentage shifts in favour of carbohydrate, at the expense of fat calories. Nevertheless, at higher intensities you are still burning more fat calories in absolute terms – the percentage of fat versus carbohydrates may be lower, but it's based on a much higher total of expended calories.

In the end, if the "low intensity is best for fat burning" myth gets people to exercise, we're all for it, but the point is that low-intensity exercise isn't the best way – the fastest way – to burn fat: high-intensity exercise is, and what's the best, no nonsense, high-intensity exercise going? Running, of course.

ARE CARBOHYDRATES BAD FOR YOU?

Much of the criticism levelled at carbohydrates originates from a book called Enter the Zone, by biochemist Barry Sears. Sears argues people are getting fatter because they eat too much carbohydrate and too little protein.

Sears and his followers put insulin at the centre of this problem. They believe high-carbohydrate diets raise insulin levels higher than they should be, and that high insulin levels inhibit fat-burning. The answer, says Sears, is to eat more protein and less carbohydrate, which will keep insulin levels down and promote fat-burning. The famous low-carb Atkins diet is based on similar principles. Sears created the 40-30-30 diet, whereby you consume just 40 per cent of total calories from carbohydrates, 30 per cent from fat, and 30 per cent from protein.

Unfortunately, the vast majority of sports nutritionists and exercise physiologists disagree with him. Glen Gaesser, a fat-burning expert at the University of Georgia, says: "Sears misconstrued the facts. He says there are more fat people than ever because of high-carbohydrate diets. The real point is they're simply eating too much."

Scientific debate notwithstanding, the 40-30-

» 10 LOW-FAT TRICKS

Low-fat living – the cunning way:

1 Remove the skin from poultry. This simple tip will save you as much as five grams of fat in every serving. Also, roast meat on a rack so excess fat can dribble out on to a tray below.

2 Skim the fat off gravy and sauces. Gravy is particularly high in fat, containing around 10g per serving. The best way is to prepare it a few hours before you need it and refrigerate it. The fat will naturally settle on the surface and can be skimmed off easily when cool.

3 Intensify the taste of butter by heating it until it is brown before adding it to your ingredients. You'll use less.

4 Normal croutons in soup or salads add as much as eight grams of fat. Make low-fat alternatives by coating cubes of bread with a water and oil mix and sprinkling with fresh or dried herbs.

5 Avoid eating thin, frozen chips. Fried in saturated animal fat, they typically contain 15 per cent fat. Because they are thinly cut, they have a greater surface area and absorb more fat than thick chips. Frozen chips take in more fat too. Try the oven variety which typically contain around five per cent fat.

6 Make sure oil is heated well before you add anything to it. If you put food into cold oil the food absorbs most of the oil before it gets hot and you'll probably have to add more.

7 Avoid mayonnaise-based salad dressings. A large portion of crunchy green salad contains around 80 calories with no fat. Two tablespoons of blue-cheese dressing sends the calorie count rocketing to 280 calories with 90 per cent fat. Make your own or opt for a fat-free vinaigrette instead.

8 Watch out for high-fat soups. Soup entrees have been shown to reduce fat consumption in ensuing meals, but not in the case of creamy soups. Opt for low-fat skimmed milk versions or vegetable-based broths.

9 Pizza toppings can turn a low-fat, high-carbo meal into a high-fat feast. Avoid olives, bacon, salami and too much cheese. Go for piles of fresh vegetables.

10 When buying snack foods, read the labels for fat content. Many snacks in health food stores are labelled as containing "purely vegetable oils" which sounds healthier than saturated fat, but is not necessarily the case. Often this vegetable oil is coconut or palm oil, which consist of 86 and 49 per cent saturated fat respectively. Coconut oil is even more saturated than beef fat and lard. Even labels that claim a product is cholesterol-free can be misleading. Vegetable oils such as coconut and palm oil don't contain cholesterol but can raise cholesterol levels in the blood.

30 approach has attracted many proponents. Peter Snell, 800m and 1500m gold medallist in 1964 Olympic Games and now an exercise physiologist in the USA, began following the programme and lost 20 pounds in two months. His wife, a serious orienteer, also had some luck with the method. "We've been enjoying our success," he says, "I'm nearly back to my racing weight. A high-carbo diet clearly doesn't work for everyone."

CAN FAT IMPROVE PERFORMANCE?

In 1994, a couple of well-publicised studies indicated high-fat diets could improve exercise performance and, in the process, not cause weight gain. In a New York study, researchers found six well-trained runners significantly increased their VO_2 max and time to exhaustion on a treadmill by following a high-fat diet (38 per cent fat, 50 per cent carbohydrate) instead of a typical training diet (24 per cent fat, 61 per cent carbohydrate). The researchers theorised that more dietary fat may boost fat-burning, which would enhance performance.

Also in 1994, a team of researchers in South Africa found two weeks of fat loading – at 70 per cent fat calories – improved the performance of five trained cyclists exercising at walking intensity. This was compared against a regimen of carbo-loading for two weeks. At high intensity – comparable with running – there was no difference in performance between those following the two diets; fat loading did just as well as carbo-loading.

The New York lab did another study a few years later, showing that four weeks on a high-fat diet (43 per cent fat) produced performance gains in well-trained runners, and concluded that for this type of athlete, fat-loading may be the way to go.

THE FAT OF THE MATTER

What should we make of all these studies? After all, carbo-loading has been with us for so long we can hardly conceive of an alternative. Should we be attending pre-race fat-loading parties instead? Ought you order a plate of steak and chips the night before your marathon?

In short: no. The results of the two New York studies are intriguing to say the least, but many question their protocol, which didn't include enough random factors. In fairness to the researchers, the work does indicate more fat may benefit some runners.

As for the South African study, the researchers maintain fat-loading may improve the body's ability to burn fat, though they still believe in carbo-loading in the three days prior to an endurance event. However, other studies have shown performance gains with high-carbo diets not accompanied by fat-loading. Above all, a high carbo diet ensures you'll have plenty of carbs in store when you need them.

Another point about high-fat studies is the possibility subjects received a performance boost from consuming more calories. Serious, high mileage runners exercise so much they have a hard time meeting their energy needs, and so when they switch to a higher-fat diet they may finally meet their high calorific needs.

THE **FATS** OF LIFE

The Department of Health recommends consuming no more than 30-35 per cent of our total calories from fat in food, but in reality we consume nearer 40 per cent. Both so-called invisible fats – those hidden in foods – and visible oils, spreads and meat fats contribute equally to our consumption.

Because fat is so rich in calories – there are 700kcal in 25 grams of fat, which is more than four times the amount in the same weight of carbohydrate or protein – too much of it can result in obesity. Additionally, certain types of fat are more unhealthy than others and can increase the risk of some of the biggest killer diseases in the UK, such as heart disease and cancer.

WHERE DOES OUR FAT COME FROM?

In the UK, cakes, biscuits and desserts provide 19 per cent of our fat intake, along with dairy foods (15 per cent), soups and sauces (three per cent), chocolate and fudge (three per cent), oily fruits such as olives (one per cent), meat products (24 per cent), spreads such as butter and margarine (17 per cent), fish oils (three per cent) and eggs (four per cent).

WHY DO WE NEED FAT AT ALL?

In spite of its unhealthy reputation, some fat is necessary in the diet to keep us in good shape. For instance, the body requires a minimum of

25g of fat to allow the absorption of the fat-soluble vitamins A, D, E and K and also beta carotene. Fats are especially important in the diets of children, who should never be advised to follow a reduced-fat diet.

There are different types of fat, which vary nutritionally. The two main types of fatty acid are saturated and unsaturated. The unsaturated fats are found in vegetable oils, fish and nuts and can be categorised as either monounsaturated or polyunsaturated; saturated fats come mainly from animal foods – examples are butter, lard and fatty meats.

The body can manufacture certain types of fat itself, but it cannot make some of the polyunsaturated fats – these must be obtained from food. For this reason they are called essential fatty acids. Omega-6 fatty acids are one of these, and they are needed to stay in good health, although too much can be harmful.

The other essential fatty acids are Omega-3 which are found mainly in vegetable oils and oily fish. The body generally requires less of these oils. They are needed for brain function and in research have been shown to help prevent blood from clotting, and therefore are thought to be important in the prevention of heart disease.

WHICH FAT SHOULD WE CUT OUT?

The Government recommends cutting the saturated fat content of our diets to around 10 per cent of our calorie intake. Saturated fats are found mainly in foods of animal origin, although palm and coconut oils also have a high saturated fat content. A high intake is known to increase the risk of heart disease, so try to replace them with healthier, unsaturated fats.

Some fats are hardened artificially in the manufacturing process, which requires changing unsaturated fats into saturated. These are called trans, or hydrogenated, fats. Research has suggested these are unhealthy and can be as big a risk for heart disease as a high intake of natural saturated fats.

WHAT'S GOOD ABOUT FAT?

Before you throw all the fat in your diet out with the bathwater, we should point out that it does some good things, too. Take its talent for keeping us energised, for example. Fats are capable of storing more than twice as much energy per gram as the same amount of carbohydrates.

We also need fat for healthy skin and hair, and without fat, we'd have a hard time regulating our body temperature. Fat deposited just below the skin acts like a thermal blanket to keep our body temperature constant.

Fat also surrounds vital organs, such as the kidneys and the heart, protecting them from blows and trauma, and fat is important to the nervous system because it insulates the nerves in a protective covering. ■

›› TOP TIPS

◆ If you're looking to lose a few pounds, and perhaps improve your running in the process, you must create a calorie deficit. That means burning more calories than you consume

◆ Simply eating low-fat and fat-free foods does not mean you can eat lots of them and not gain weight. Read nutrition labels to track total calories as well as fat calories

◆ High-protein diets such as the 40-30-30 protein plan won't hurt you, but there's no fat-burning magic to the ratio. You still need to burn more calories than you are taking in

◆ Light exercise is not best for fat-burning. Some exercise – any exercise – is better than nothing, but a good run will burn more than a walk will. It might not be much more but it will be more

◆ Don't try fat-loading – at least, not yet. It's an intriguing concept, but there's not enough evidence to support it. As it stands, eating fat at the expense of carbohydrate is thought to put the average person at risk of obesity and cardiovascular disease

◆ Do some strength work. Firstly, it's a good calorie burner: lifting weights with the legs can burn up to 12 calories per minute, a comparable rate to running. Secondly, muscle tissue burns more calories than fat tissue, so your resting metabolic rate will increase as you increase muscle mass.

BURNING DESIRE

Feel like you're not receiving profitable physical returns on your energy expenditure? Maybe it's time you maximised your metabolism

It's a familiar scenario: you run three or four times a week, and you watch what you eat, but lately you've noticed you have a little less energy and a little more "meat" around the waistline. You've tried running more, which is good, and eating less, which is not so good, but the result is you have even less energy and you're really, *really* hungry. Worse, it's as-you-were around the midriff, and your "unformed" thighs are refusing to reinvent themselves. At this point, you throw in the towel and stuff your face because you're dying of hunger.

We're willing to bet your metabolism – your calorie-burning furnace – is stuck on low. Especially if you're older than 30 years, after which your metabolism begins to drop by about one per cent a year. You don't have to take this lying down; you can fight back. You can boost your metabolism in several ways, as you're about to find out.

First, though, a quick physiology lesson. Your metabolism is the rate at which your body burns calories. It's broken down into three parts; the three burners on your metabolic stove top.

Basal metabolism (sometimes called your resting metabolism) is the largest burner. It accounts for about 60 per cent of the calories you expend each day. You burn these calories simply to exist, including when you're sleeping.

Activity metabolism is the second burner. It makes up about 30 per cent of your daily calorie burn. These are calories you burn during running, as well as doing other activities, such as sweeping the floor, walking upstairs or chopping firewood.

Thermic metabolism is the final burner. It accounts for the calories you expend digesting food, and since certain foods take more energy (calories) to digest, you'll want to emphasise them whenever possible.

If you work it right, a good metabolism-boosting programme will turn up the heat on all three burners. Best of all, a few simple changes to your exercise routine, eating habits and supplements intake will have you on your way to becoming a leaner and faster runner.

RUN FAST

Adding speed sessions to your programme is one of the best ways to crank up your metabolism. Hard running burns lots of calories (activity metabolism), and comes with an afterburn dividend (raised basal metabolism) – but it has to be hard. "It is becoming fairly clear that metabolism does remain elevated for at least a couple of hours after the session – assuming the training was somewhat taxing," says physiology researcher Dr Greg Crowther.

Indeed, proof of the fat- and calorie-burning power of fast running comes via Canadian research undertaken at Laval University in Quebec. It showed runners who employ speed training burn several times more fat than runners engaged in slower, steadier running.

In addition, fast running stimulates production of Human Growth Hormone (HGH). Try one of these fast-burn work-outs at least once (preferably twice) a week: six to eight 400s at your best one-mile pace; four or five 800s at 5K race pace; three or four mile repetitions at 10K race pace. These sessions will incinerate calories and rev up your metabolism in the process.

RUN TWICE

It may sound somewhat over the top, but twice-a-day training can be profoundly rewarding. It'll raise your metabolism for extended periods of time thanks to two afterburn peaks during

the day. Your body will also manufacture more HGH, boosting your muscle mass not to mention the fact you'll burn more calories because of the extra exercise. On the days when you lift weights, why not run for 20-30 minutes in the morning or at lunchtime, then hit the gym in the evening? You'll feel energised by the first session thanks to your increased metabolism. Just make sure you eat and drink steadily through the day to ensure you're still energised going into your strength training.

BURNING FUEL

To boost metabolism by way of the foods you eat, think protein, calcium, fibre and spices. Therefore eat a whole-grain, corn-fed chicken sandwich topped with hot peppers and a long glass of semi-skimmed milk to wash it all down three times daily. Well, not really, but almost.

SEEK PROTEIN

Protein generally takes longer to digest, meaning you're burning more calories while your body is breaking it down. Try to eat some protein at every meal and snack-time. It doesn't have to be a steak or chicken breast – it could be something like poached eggs on toast for breakfast, or cottage cheese or low-fat yoghurt instead of a bagel. This will increase your thermic metabolism by as much as a third during the day.

MILK THE SYSTEM

Studies show calcium boosts basal metabolism and can aid fat burning by making your body prefer fat as fuel. Calcium in foods is preferable to calcium from supplements, but don't go overboard and drink gallons of milk. There is no added benefit in drinking more than about two large glasses per day (equivalent to 1,200mg).

HIGH-FIBRE ALL ROUND

Just like protein, high-fibre foods increase thermic metabolism because the fibre slows digestion, resulting in a higher calorie burn rate. Healthy, high-fibre foods to eat throughout the day include beans, fresh fruits and vegetables and whole-grain breads and pastas.

GO FASTER WITH SPICES

Spicy foods do more than make you sweat. Research shows capsaicin, the spicy ingredient in hot peppers, can temporarily speed up your resting metabolism.

GO GREEN

Unlike black tea (the tea-bag kind) and other teas, green tea contains a phytochemical called ECGC researchers say can significantly boost your basal metabolism. In fact, the action of ECGC seems to work best when it's in brewed green tea, rather than pill form.

ALCOHOL AWARENESS

Alcohol dehydrates you, slowing your thermic metabolism. It can also keep fat from metabolising, which can reduce your basal metabolism, and it can cause you to eat like every day is Christmas Day. This slows down both your thermic and activity metabolism.

EAT EARLY AND OFTEN

Skipping breakfast further decreases your thermic metabolism (already low, because you haven't eaten since the night before). It also tends to slow your activity metabolism because you have less energy making you more likely to use the lift instead of taking the stairs and so on. A good breakfast should include protein, carbohydrates and some fat, and contain enough calories to keep hunger at bay until your mid-morning snack.

STAY FLUID

Dehydration slows your thermic metabolism because your stomach needs water to digest food. It also causes fatigue, which will definitely hamper your activity metabolism. Try for at least eight glasses of water a day, and more on hot, sunny days. Remember the runner's standby: carry a water bottle around with you, and sip from it often.

AFTER BURNERS

There's a lot of quackery surrounding supplements these days, so be careful. Supplement quality can vary greatly between manufacturers. Other supplements have little scientific support. Some of the best and safest supplements for boosting a runner's metabolism include:

Chromium

Taking a chromium supplement may help some runners by normalising their blood-sugar levels, which in turn can boost metabolism. Chromium works with insulin to metabolise fats and carbohydrates. A chromium deficiency can cause blood-sug ar levels to soar (not good) and fat and carbohydrate metabolism to plummet (even worse). Therefore sourcing adequate chromium is particularly important for those with type II diabetes or hypoglycaemia.

CLA

Research suggests taking Conjugated Linoleic Acid (CLA) supplements can help reduce body fat. CLA is a naturally occuring fatty acid, found most commonly in meat and dairy products, but it is thought modern farming practices have resulted in our diets containing less CLA than in the past.

Caffeine

Taken in small doses (such as in coffee or tea), caffeine can make you more alert and energetic – and more likely to get up off the couch, which will boost your activity metabolism. (Caffeine tablets, which can cause the jitters, are not recommended.) Research has also shown caffeine can improve performance. So if you normally drink coffee first thing in the morning, continue to have a cup before morning runs or races.

» HEAVY LIFTING

Weight lifting is an excellent four-in-one attack on your lazy metabolism. It not only burns calories, elevating your activity metabolism while you're lifting, but can also cause an "afterburn" (the period of time your basal metabolism remains stoked by the weight session) that can last for 48 hours. Plus, weight training builds muscle and muscle increases your basal metabolism permanently (by 50kcal per day for each pound of muscle you gain). Finally, it stimulates your body to produce more HGH, which helps increase muscle mass and burn fat.

To design a strength-training programme specifically aimed at burning fat, we consulted strength expert Lou Schuler of Men's Health magazine. The seven exercises he suggests here work the large muscle groups of your shoulders, torso, buttocks and upper legs, since these areas are where you can make the most gains.

If you're completely new to strength training, start by doing only one set of each of these exercises; otherwise do two to three sets per session. With each exercise, lift enough weight to tire you out after 10-12 repetitions. Work this programme into your exercise schedule two or three times per week, always allowing at least one day of recovery between sessions. Exercise caution on all lifts if you have a history of back problems.

1 Bench press

Be careful not to arch your back when you lift, as arching can cause injury. To guard against this, simply position your feet on the end of the bench while you lift.

2 Standing row

Keep your torso in a "fixed" position, with knees slightly bent, to decrease the stress on your back. Lean forward at the waist until your upper body is at 45 degrees to your thighs. Keep your back straight and pull the weight in to your ribs.

3 Shoulder press

Keep your shoulders in line with, and directly above, your hips – don't hunch forward. When you lower the bar, bring it to chin level in front of your head, not behind it – as this can strain your neck and shoulders.

4 Pull-up

Place your hands shoulder-width apart on the pull-up bar. As you pull yourself up, keep your body as close to vertical as possible. Don't rock back and forth or pull your knees up to your torso. If you can't pull yourself up to the bar, step on a bench to assume the "up" position, hold it for 10-20 seconds and then slowly lower back down (that's one rep).

5 Crunch

Before doing the crunch, pull your stomach muscles in as far as you can, as if you're pulling your belly-button to your backbone. Then do the crunch. (Harder, isn't it?)

6 Split Squat

To assume the proper starting position for this exercise, do a standard lunge while holding dumbbells. Then raise and lower yourself by pushing with your thighs and glutes, keeping your torso vertical.

7 Single Dumbbell Deadlift

With this squat-style exercise, you come all the way up until your legs are straight, and down until the dumbbell hits the floor. As you lift and lower the weight, keep your back "fixed" and straight (no hunching forward) and keep your arms fully extended but close to your body to guard against back strain.

Muscle Burns

If you still need further incentive to train with weights, read this: on average, one pound of muscle burns 40-50kcal per day while at rest, whereas one pound of fat burns just two calories. Which means if you gain just one pound of muscle through strength training, you'll burn an extra 350kcal a week – automatically. This is about 1,500kcal a month, or 18,000kcal a year.

Of most interest is the fact that burning 18,000kcal a year translates to losing five pounds of weight. Which all means if you gain just two pounds of muscle, you'll actually burn off 10 pounds of fat in a year. So get yourself to a gym and start squeezing some steel.

» TOP TIPS

- ◆ Your metabolic rate determines how quickly your body burns calories. It can be increased with simple diet and exercise changes
- ◆ Speed training increases both your active metabolism (while in the act) and your resting (basal) metabolism for long post-exercise periods. It is a proven fat burner
- ◆ Go twice. Twice the activity, twice the afterburn. Variety is the key.
- ◆ Protein, calcium, fibre and, capsaicin (found in peppers) are known metabolism boosters. Make sure you're getting plenty
- ◆ Don't skip breakfast. You need the energy to fund the morning's activities
- ◆ Drink coffee. It can help kick you into action
- ◆ Lift weights. It's a great way to switch your resting metabolism to max

USE IT AND **LOSE IT**

Run faster, eat better and lose 10lb in the next month

You're a runner; so the chances are pretty high that you're not one of the growing number of obese people in this country. You're probably one of the healthiest specimens your doctor sees on any given day, but this doesn't mean you're entirely satisfied with your current weight and that you're not interested in losing a few pounds in order to become healthier, feel better and run stronger.

To demonstrate how easy that could be, we've set out a plan. The goal: lose 10lb this month. The modus operandi: run a series of fat-burning workouts each week; watch what and how much you eat. It couldn't be easier.

Now let's look at the numbers. To lose a pound, you have to burn roughly 3,500kcal and not replace them, which forces your body to burn a pound of stored fat to compensate. Ten pounds a month is 2.5lb a week. So you need to create an 8,750-calorie deficit each week – or a 1,250kcal deficit each day.

Wait! Before you throw up your hands in despair over these impossible-sounding targets (and reach for the Haägen Dazs for comfort), remember that daily calorie input and output is a big numbers game.

Your body burns thousands of calories each day just sitting around or driving to work, not to mention exercising. For instance, a 12-stone man burns 1,850kcal a day at rest and another 1,600 through normal daily activity. That's a total of 3,450kcal burned each day. Then, if he runs 30 minutes at a good clip (seven-minute mile pace), he burns another 540kcal, which brings the total up to 3,990 a day. If the same runner were to eat 3,990kcal worth of food, he'd neither gain nor lose weight. But if he follows our weight-loss guidelines to create a 1,250kcal deficit each day, he can still consume 2,740kcal, which amounts to 16 bagels or 27 bananas or 34 apples or 14 servings of pasta. The point is, you can eat a lot of food if you're exercising and eating sensibly.

All these principles apply to women, too, but on a smaller scale. Because women weigh less and generally have slower metabolisms, they burn fewer calories than men over the same activity. Now that the numbers aren't so daunting, let's take a closer look at how to lose those 10lb.

RUNNING STRATEGIES THAT BURN CALORIES

Running is the most efficient way to shed weight. For our 12st man, running for 30 minutes at a 10-minute mile pace will burn about 385kcal. Leisurely cycling for 30 minutes will burn 231kcal; relaxed swimming, 308kcal; and walking (at three miles per hour), a mere 135kcal. But even in running, some work-outs are better than others for burning calories and fat.

Of course, there's the time-proven long run, which puts the body in the fat-burning zone, but these days, the shift is towards faster paced sessions, which burn calories and fat much more efficiently. A recent study at the University of Texas showed that fast running burns 33 per cent more fat per minute than slower running. That can be a big help when you're trying to lose weight and are pressed for time.

We've selected some of the best calorie-consuming, fat-burning training sessions. Do two or three a week. On the other days, run easy for 20-30 minutes or do some relaxed cross-training such as cycling, swimming or stair-climbing.

Long Runs

Run slowly for at least 45 minutes to an hour; one-and-a-half to two hours would be ideal. The slow pace – which puts your metabolism in the

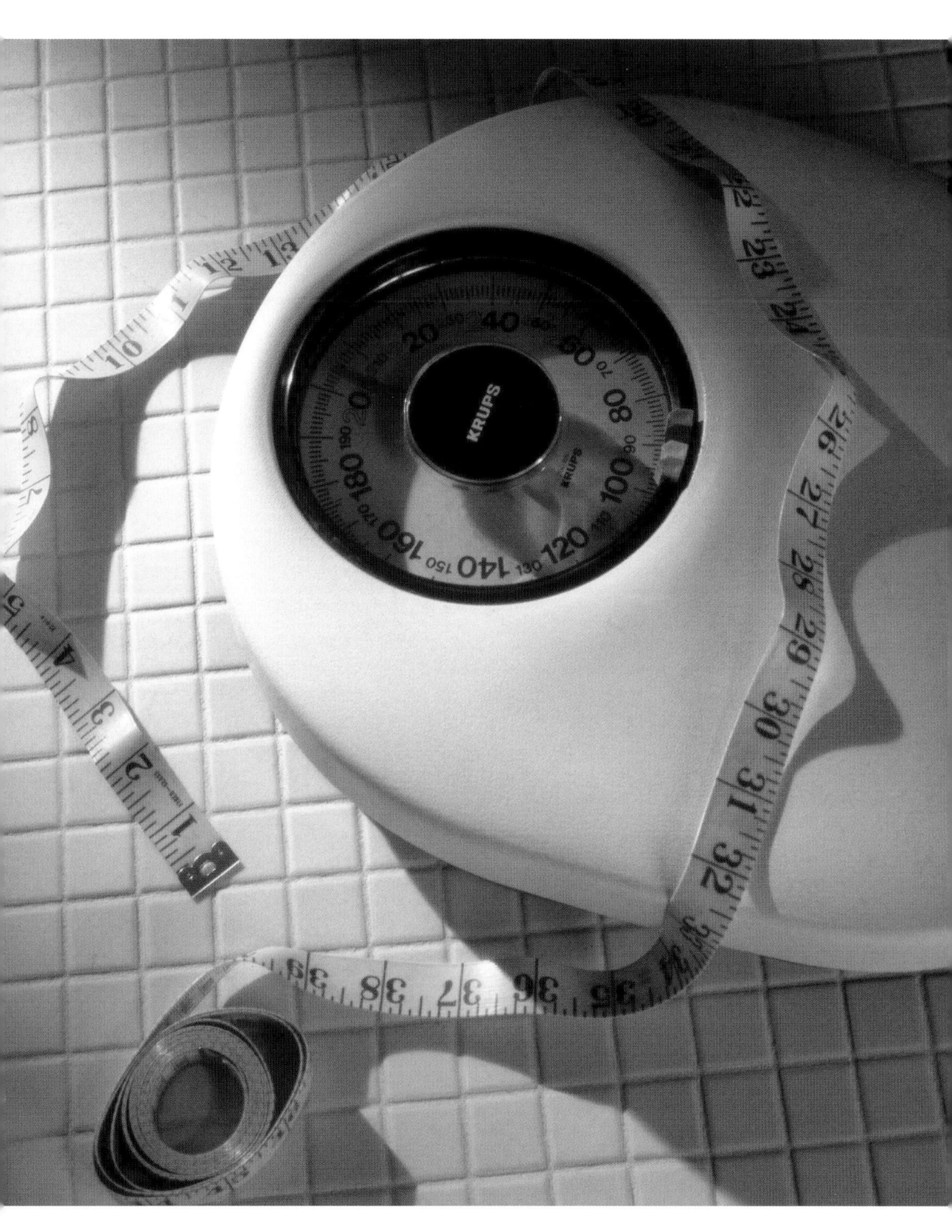
KRUPS

fat-burning zone – coupled with the long period of time maximises total fat burning. A 90-minute long run for a 12-stone man can burn more than 1,000kcal.

Tempo Runs

Long, slow runs are great, but you can't do them every day. If you have just 20-30 minutes to run, your best bet is to pick up the pace. The faster you run in those 20-30 minutes, the more fat you'll burn, because your total energy cost is up.

Run 20-30 minutes at between 10K and 10-mile race pace – an effort that should feel hard but controlled. You'll cover more distance and burn more calories during a 30-minute tempo run than during 30 minutes of slow running. A 12st man on a tempo run of this duration can burn more than 450kcal

Speed Sessions

Speed sessions are always great calorie-burners. After a five-minute warm-up, try running one to three minutes at 85-95 per cent effort, then walk or jog for recovery. Do five to 10 of these fast intervals in a session, then finish with a five-minute cool-down. Speedwork also produces an "afterburn" effect. That is, you keep burning calories at a high level even after you've stopped running. This can sometimes amount to as much as 200 extra calories, according to a recent Scandinavian study, and fast running suppresses your appetite for an hour or two, so you'll eat less and lose more.

A speed workout that includes 8 x 2 minutes at 90 per cent effort (with a five-minute warm-up and cool-down) can burn more than 700kcal (including afterburn) for a 12st man.

Evening/Morning Runs

A few hours after your evening meal, go for an easy run of 20-30 minutes and don't eat any more before going to bed. This will deplete your glycogen stores. The next morning, before breakfast, run 45 minutes to an hour at a steady pace. Your carbohydrate-depleted body will turn to fat-burning more quickly and more intensely.

This workout will stimulate fat burning, but psychologically and physiologically, it will be hard. So we suggest doing this dual workout with a friend who is also trying to lose weight. You'll motivate each other. A 30-minute evening/45-minute morning run will burn more than 1,000kcal in total for a 12st man – and many of those will be fat calories.

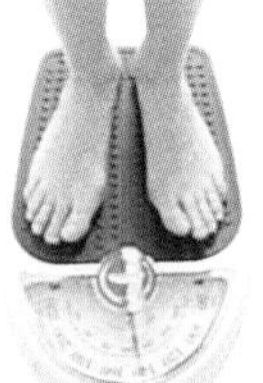

PUMP UP THE WEIGHT LOSS

By adding a once- or twice-weekly weight-training session to your schedule, you not only burn more calories when you are working out (115 every 30 minutes for our 12st runner) – but also when you are just sitting around. That's because as you add muscle, your resting metabolism rises. So you'll burn more calories when you do taxing work like watching TV and reading RUNNER'S WORLD.

A good weight workout is circuit training – essentially "laps" around the weight room, doing all the standard machine exercises, one right after another. When you can lift a weight 15 times easily, set it at a higher level. Five pounds is a good increase for upper-body exercises; 10lb for the lower-body.

EATING STRATEGIES THAT BURN CALORIES

While you're revving up your running, ease back a little on your eating. Don't worry, you don't have to starve yourself. In fact, taking in too few calories

WEIGHT LOSS TIPS

Seek a dietician's help

It's not easy to determine what foods to eat to achieve the right ratio of carbs, protein and fat, so consider calling in a professional. A registered dietician can guide you in your food choices and fine-tune your weight-loss programme. For a list of registered dieticians in the UK, write to the British Dietetic Association, 5th Floor, Charles House, 148/149 Great Charles Street, Queensway, Birmingham B3 3HT.

Avoid fad diets

Weight-reducing plans that have you radically changing your eating habits usually don't work – at least in the long run. Sure, you can lose weight quickly, but most of the time it just comes right back.

Don't use diet pills

They don't even work well. Unless you're clinically obese and at high medical risk (you have diabetes or high blood pressure, for example), you should not take diet pills. They don't eliminate the main reasons people overeat, which are often psychological.

Record your progress

Mark your weight loss on a calendar or in a diary. A visible record of your success can help to motivate you to continue. It will show that, despite occasional ups and downs, you're making steady progress.

Understand genetics

Your family history frequently dictates your physique. If your parents are big, you'll probably be big. You can't change this. You may never be as skinny as the featherweight runners who win races, but you can maintain a reasonable and healthy weight for your particular frame.

Shop with a list

Avoid impulse purchases and impulse eating. Impulsive food choices often prove to be high-calorie ones. If you shop with a list, you'll be less likely to grab high-calorie foods off the shelf. In the same vein, don't go to the supermarket when you're hungry.

slows your metabolism and makes it harder to lose weight. By simply making a few adjustments to your usual diet, you can cut calories quickly. Here are a few ways to do just that.

Make Healthy Choices

You don't need a calorie counter to plan low-fat meals, just some common sense. A simple meal plan for the day could be the following:

Breakfast Cereal with fruit and skimmed milk.

Lunch A chicken or turkey sandwich with lettuce, tomatoes and spicy mustard.

Dinner Pasta with vegetables and a pinch of grated parmesan.

Drink water with every meal, and if you want a snack between meals, have fruit or half a bagel.

Make Substitutions

One of the easiest ways to reduce your calorie intake is to find low-fat or low-calorie substitutes for some of the rich items in your diet. Using mustard instead of mayonnaise cuts 85kcal off your turkey sandwich. Skimmed milk saves 90kcal per glass over full-fat milk. Lemon juice or wine vinegar on your salad saves 100kcal over ordinary dressing.

Eat Less Food

Your battle isn't against food, but against too much food. Learn to be polite but firm at Sunday lunch when your mum passes the roast potatoes the second time. When you eat at home, cut your serving size. "It's the number one way to cut calories," says John Allred, co-author of *Taking The Fear Out Of Eating: A Nutritionists' Guide to Sensible Food Choices* (Cambridge University Press). If you usually have two slices of bread with dinner, eat one. If you have 170g of pasta, have 110g.

Allred also suggests using smaller dinner plates. "That way, you still have a full plate of food in front of you, but you'll be eating less," he says.

Eat More Often

Many sumo wrestlers skip breakfast on purpose. They want to drive up hunger and slow their metabolism so when they dive into a fat-filled lunch, it sticks to their ribs (and bellies and sides) like glue. You, of course, don't want to look like a sumo wrestler, or you wouldn't be reading this. By eating three small meals a day, plus healthy snacks, you keep hunger on an even keel (avoiding overeating, the real enemy), and your metabolism runs at an even burn.

First, don't skip breakfast. Nancy Clark, author of *Nancy Clark's Sports Nutrition Guidebook* (Human Kinetics), says a good breakfast is one of the most potent weapons for losing weight. It keeps your metabolism turning over, prevents hunger and overeating at lunch, and makes you more likely to eat higher-quality foods throughout the day. A good breakfast should be hearty but not heavy (about 500kcal). Examples include: cereal with skimmed milk and a banana, or a bagel and yoghurt.

And don't neglect the afternoon snack. A bagel at 3pm can be the difference between running a hard seven-mile run after work (which will burn lots of calories and help you to lose weight) or calling it quits after a slow two miles (which doesn't burn lots of calories). The main reason people don't feel like running after work is because they're hungry. The afternoon snack gives you energy to burn.

After you've burned that energy, replace some of it right away. A high-carbohydrate snack after a workout speeds your recovery by replenishing muscle glycogen. It also staves off hunger so you don't overeat at dinner. A sports drink or energy bar is fine, as are bagels. Orange juice is a great recovery fluid. It's got vitamin C, potassium, no fat and only 140kcal per 300ml serving. Plus, you're replacing lost fluids. Ideally, your post-workout snack should be consumed within 30 minutes of your exercise, and your meal no more than 90 minutes later.

Tempting Fat

You know your weak spots (ice cream, croissants, pizza, whatever). Set up a defence. If you crave ice cream, don't have it in the freezer. If it's a croissant on your way to work, find a route that avoids the coffee shop. If pizza is your passion, throw away those leaflets from the pizza delivery companies.

It's okay to indulge once in a while, but try some of the low-fat treats available, and consume them in moderation. Reduced-fat crisps and tortilla chips are available at most supermarkets. The same goes for biscuits and cakes. Choose reduced-fat or fat-free varieties. But remember, despite the "healthy" labels and marketing, these snacks do still have plenty of calories, so eat them sparingly.

MAKE NEW HABITS

There are plenty of little things you can do with your diet that will make a big difference in your weight-loss efforts. Here are five of them.

Don't mix fat and sugar

A burger, large fries and cola is a pretty bad combination to begin with, but it's doubly unhealthy because it acts as a hidden invitation to your body to pack on fat. The simple sugars in carbonated drinks cause a release of insulin into your bloodstream, which makes fat cells more prone to storing fat. So, by the time the burger and fries get to those cells, the door is wide open, and they come right in.

Man cannot live by carbs alone

Protein and a little fat help to keep you satiated for longer and prevent you from overeating. "Fat and protein stay with you longer," says Nancy Clark. For example, if you have a plain toasted bagel and a glass of fruit juice for breakfast, you'll be hungry again an hour later, but if you spread a little peanut butter on the bagel, you'll be fine until your morning snack.

Eat a complex diet

So you want loads of energy to burn all day? Eat lots of complex carbohydrates: fresh fruits, vegetables, whole grains and legumes. Complex carbohydrates take longer to burn than simple sugars, giving you energy and staving off hunger at the same time.

Trim your meat

Cutting visible fat from meat or the skin from chicken before cooking will eliminate more than 65 per cent of fat calories from your meal.

Hold the mayo

Fish is a healthy option, right? But mixing tuna with mayonnaise adds hundreds of fat calories to a tuna salad sandwich. Instead, try mixing the tuna with chilli sauce, lemon juice or a little mustard.

ONE STEP AT A TIME

According to sports nutritionist Kris Clark, you'll have the most success changing a dietary habit if you take the simplest approach. "When I spot a problem in an athlete's food record, I work on just one food at a time," she says, "two at the most. It can be as basic as telling the person to buy a nutritious breakfast cereal and eat a bowl of it every morning."

Clark believes people need at least three or four weeks to break old dietary patterns and establish new ones. "I have my clients stay with one dietary change for as long as it takes to become a matter of habit," she says. "Once we are successful with the first change, we can go on to the second."

It's like the way you learned to run. First one mile, then two, then... It's the same thing with improving your diet. Take your time. Don't expect too much or set unattainable goals. Just stay focused on the task and let patience and discipline work their magic. ■

» WHEN IS THE BEST TIME TO BURN CALORIES?

If you're trying to lose weight through running and gym workouts, is it better to burn calories by working out before eating, or afterwards?

A Running and gym work are definitely the right way to go, because exercise is crucial for a successful weight-loss programme, but the timing of your meals won't change the number of calories burned during a workout (for running, that's about 100kcal per mile).

However, timing will affect how you feel and perform when you train. If you're not properly fuelled going into a work-out, it can leave you feeling tired and shaky, and this will compromise the intensity and duration of your exercise. Whether that happens in the middle of a run or a weights workout, it's no fun, and it's certainly going to compromise any weight-loss efforts.

To make sure you have plenty of fuel in the tank, eat two to four hours before your workouts. Include easily digested foods that are high in carbohydrates – such as pasta, cereal, yoghurt, and fruit and vegetables. To speed recovery, refuel immediately after your workouts with more carbohydrate-rich foods, plus a bit of protein from foods such as lean beef, chicken or fish, and skimmed or soya milk.

For optimum weight loss, it's also important to balance calorie intake with physical activity level throughout the day. Eat more when you are more active, and less when you are less active. You should also try to avoid eating large evening meals and late-night snacks. Most importantly, if you're trying to lose weight, keep exercising. The combination of cardiovascular workouts through running and resistance work through weight training should produce excellent results.

Burning Options

Here's how many calories you'll burn during 30 minutes of the following activities. (Note that the calorie totals represent a moderate intensity for each activity.)

Activity	Calories Burned
Running	300
Swimming	280
Skating	260
Cycling	245
Stair climbing	245
Rowing	240
Aerobics	220
Weightlifting	205
Walking	200

CHAPTER 6

Health and Injury

There's an old saying that as a runner you're either injured, recovering from an injury or just about to become injured. It's time to add a new category to this list: the runner who's injury proof. Okay, we can't promise that you'll never turn an ankle out on the trails, but by following the advice in this chapter you can go a long way to making sure that sore shins, pulled hamstrings or throbbing knees never trouble you again.

BITE BACK AT INJURY

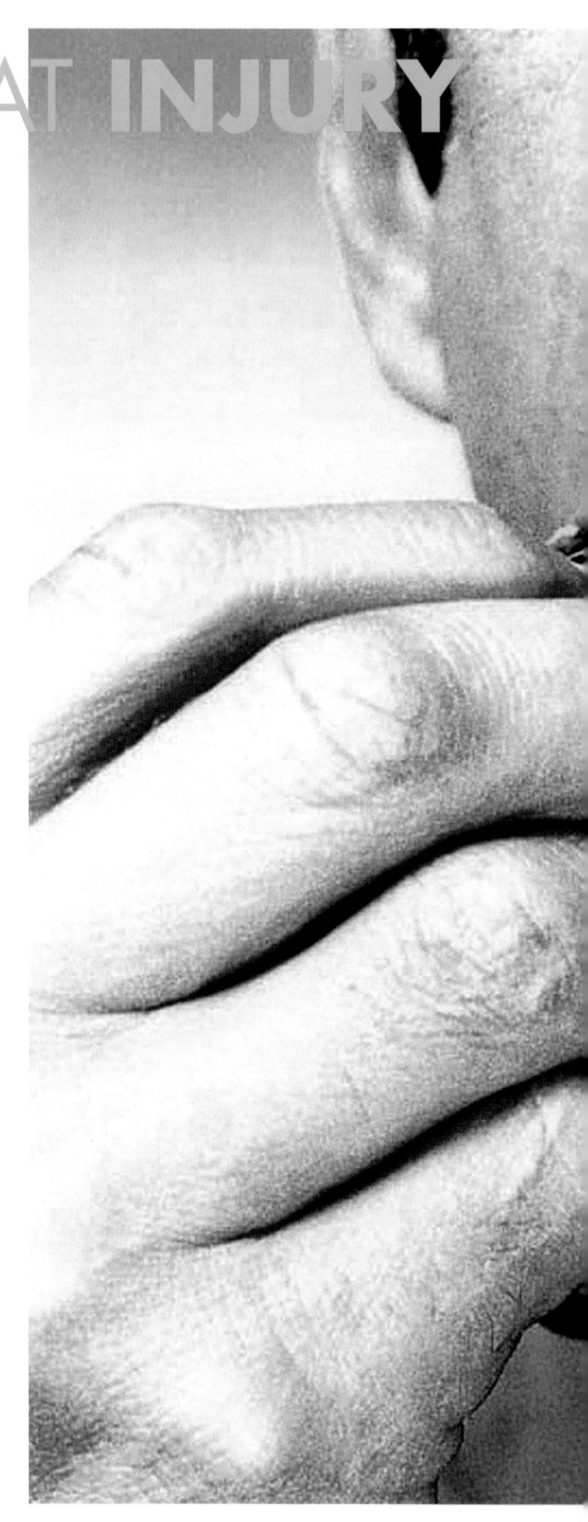

When running begins to take its toll on your body open the pantry and let food be your medicine

Injury is undoubtedly the most frustrating part of running. Tear your patellar tendon, and you are likely to miss several weeks of running, cycling and almost every other activity requiring knee movement. Not fun. If surgery is required, you will enter a rehabilitation programme that will include icing and physical therapy.

But what about a food-rehab programme? Surely feeding an injury such as a patellar tendon tear with the right foods will help nourish the knee and rebuild new, healthy tissue. Given your regular exercise programme is on hold for several weeks, you do of course want to heal as quickly as possible. Well take heart because the foods you choose to eat, and those you omit, can significantly influence your rate of recovery.

Although different injuries, and the fact every runner has a unique physiology mean no nutrition programme fits all, we've highlighted five remedies that should help keep you healthy, keep the weight off and have you back in your running kit before you can say, "A glucosamine-fortified kiwi fruit juice please?"

ANTIOXIDANTS

You can blame much of the swelling and soreness you feel when injured on substances called free radicals. These highly reactive molecules damage tissue as they search for missing electrons. Antioxidants, such as vitamin E and beta carotene, stop this damage by providing free radicals with the electrons they need, thus ending their destructive search. This, in turn, prevents unnecessary swelling and pain.

To be sure of consuming a complete array of antioxidants, including flavonoids and carotenes, eat several daily servings of fruits and vegetables,

such as kiwis, apples, oranges, winter squashes and dark leafy greens. You might also consider taking 268mg of vitamin E a day, since it's difficult to consume that amount from food alone.

GLUCOSAMINE

In the past few years, sports doctors and other physicians have increasingly advised patients to take the amino acid glucosamine to ease the inflammation and pain of osteoarthritis, a degenerative joint condition caused by overuse, traumatic injury or simply old age. One of the hallmarks of osteoarthritis is an erosion of the cartilage that cushions your joints.

Chondrocytes (the cells in your joints that make up cartilage) need glucosamine to function optimally. According to several studies, supplemental glucosamine – about 1500mg daily – helps soothe pain, possibly by stimulating cartilage growth. Animal studies suggest supplemental glucosamine may speed up the healing of injured joints as well.

Glucosamine also helps produce glycoproteins, which are substances in ligaments, tendons and joint fluids. So it may speed healing in those areas as well, though research has yet to test that theory. "I find that glucosamine does work in some of my patients who are active, giving them better mobility," says Eric Heiden, an orthopaedic surgeon and former Olympic speed-skating gold medalist.

If you want to give glucosamine a try (it's sold over the counter), then consult your GP. Glucosamine is considered safe, though long-term use has not yet been evaluated.

PROTEIN

Every day, your body busily makes millions of new proteins to replace worn-out proteins in your muscles, red blood cells and connective tissues. When you damage your muscles, tendons, ligaments or joints, many of these proteins break down more rapidly than usual. Your body struggles to pump up production by forming new proteins from dietary amino acids (the building blocks of protein). To do so, however, your body needs these amino acids in abundant supply. Without them, you slow the repairing process, just as a Tarmac shortage would slow a road project.

As a runner, you need about 60-100g of protein daily – a bit more than a non-athlete – to keep up your body's normal protein-building schedule. Once you throw an injury into the mix, you need to concentrate on protein even more. As you recover, keep your protein intake in the 80-100g range.

Also, don't skimp too much on calories. If you're like me, you cut calories to avoid gaining extra weight during your couch-bound recovery, but this may actually delay your recovery. If your muscles, brain or other organs don't have enough fuel to function, they will raid your body's protein stores, dwindling those supplies. So if you start losing weight, be wary. It could mean you're not feeding your body enough protein to heal.

Feed your injury top-quality protein by incorporating eggs (or egg whites), soy products, lean meats and non-fat or low-fat dairy products into your normal meals. These foods contain all the amino acids your body needs. Beans also provide protein, but you must combine them with a grain (such as lentil soup with bread) to produce a complete supply of amino acids.

VITAMIN C

When you're injured, an adhesive-like protein called collagen forms scar tissue which glues your cells back together. Without adequate vitamin C, your body can't make this important substance.

In a classic study conducted more than 30 years ago (such studies aren't done today for ethical reasons), a group of men were fed a vitamin C-deficient diet, with no fruit and vegetables, for several weeks. The researchers then made a small incision on one leg of each man and monitored his healing process. Scar tissue failed to form because little collagen was present. Fortunately the men recovered from their disastrous diet – and their cuts – as soon as they resumed their vitamin C intake.

While this experiment is extreme, it shows the value of vitamin C for optimal healing. The recommended daily requirement (RDA) for vitamin C is 60mg, but that amount is widely regarded as being too low. Aim for 100-250mg. Taking in extra vitamin C is easy, as just one orange supplies 80mg. Other fruits and many winter vegetables, such as broccoli, cabbage and even potatoes, are also good sources. Or take a supplement.

ZINC

Your body needs this mineral to manufacture healthy bone cells (osteoblasts), and cartilage cells (chondrocytes). If you suffer a stress fracture or tear some cartilage, these cells work overtime to repair the damage. Without enough zinc, your body can't make enough osteoblasts and chondrocytes to do the job.

Unfortunately, many runners are already zinc-deficient. If you don't eat meat or don't take a multivitamin, you're probably not consuming the daily 15mg your body needs. Besides red meat, zinc-rich foods include clams and oysters. Good vegetarian sources include wheatgerm, whole-grain cereals and breads, and zinc-fortified cereals. Along with loading up on zinc-rich foods during your rehab, multivitamin that contains 100 per cent of the recommended daily dose of zinc. ■

ESCAPE FROM **INJURY**

All runners are taking a bit of a gamble with their health, but if you follow these 10 commandments, you'll stack the odds in your favour.

Most runners know about injuries. They're almost part of the game. Run long enough or hard enough, and you'll probably come down with an ache that will temporarily sideline you.

Fortunately, most running injuries are short-term. After a few days or weeks of rest, you can return to your regular routine. Still, there is a better way: don't get injured in the first place. If you adopt the principles outlined on these pages, you'll have a reasonable chance of running in good health indefinitely. Ignore them, and... well, you know. You reap what you sow.

1 FOLLOW A STRAIGHT AND EVEN PATH

The best surfaces for running are firm but not too hard, relatively flat (without camber) and smooth (without ruts or holes). These are the most common places to run:

Roads If you live in a rural area with low traffic volumes, roads can make fine running surfaces, but keep in mind that most are cambered so that water will run off the centre of the road. If you run down the road against traffic, the slant causes your left foot to pronate (roll inwards) and your right foot to supinate (roll outwards). So map out your routes over the flattest streets you can find.

Pavements The most convenient, and sometimes the only option if you live in town. Concrete is significantly harder than asphalt, and since pavements aren't continuous, you have to jump off and on at every corner. Furthermore, many pavements are cracked and uneven. If you catch your toe on a raised paving slab, the next thing you know, you'll be nose-down against the pavement, so make sure you pay attention to your footing as you go.

Lawns and other grassy areas Because they're soft, you might think that golf courses or wild areas would be ideal places to run. They can be – but too much unevenness on these surfaces will force the muscles and tendons in your feet and legs to work far harder than they would on a flat course and increase the possibility of injury. When you consider that more than half of the population has some biomechanical abnormality, you begin to see why it can be downright treacherous if you head out over terrain where ruts and holes lie hidden in the grass. You're better off running on close-cropped, even grass because you can see any rough spots and avoid them.

Running tracks Tracks offer even surfaces that are firm but not too hard. The one disadvantage is that they force you to turn frequently and can strain your muscles unevenly, but if you change direction often, you'll lessen the chances of injury. Also, run in the far outside lanes, especially during warm-ups and cool-downs.

Beaches Most beaches are poor places to run. Generally, the sand is too soft and causes uneven footing, which strains and stresses your leg muscles. Also, the beach is slanted, and, just as on a cambered road, your legs are forced to work unevenly – one pronating too much and the other oversupinating. If you can't resist a seaside jaunt, run at low tide, when you can run on packed sand and a flatter stretch of beach, and don't run too far in one direction; turn around to reverse the stresses on your legs.

Trails Whether it's a tow path alongside the canal or a bridleway in the forest, trails are great for running. The surfaces are good, and take you away from the traffic. Only run here in full daylight though, and, while it's nice to admire the views, keep an eye on where you are putting your feet in case there are tree roots or rocks underfoot.

2 WARM UP, COOL DOWN

When you first get up in the morning, your muscles and soft tissue are tight. In fact, at that time, your muscles are generally about 10 per cent shorter than their normal resting lengths. As you move around, they stretch to their normal lengths. Then when you start to exercise, your muscles stretch even more, to about 10 per cent longer than their resting lengths. This means you have a 20 per cent change in muscle length from the time you get out of bed until your muscles are well warmed up.

According to the basic laws of physics, muscles work more efficiently when they are longer; they can exert more force with less effort. This means, too, that longer muscles are much less prone to injury.

Make it a habit to warm up before a run or race. Pedal for a few minutes indoors on a stationary bike, or skip with a rope for a few turns before you head down the road. If you'd rather warm up on the run, begin with a walk or a slow jog and gradually move into your training pace.

Cooling down can also help you avoid injury. An easy jog after a hard session or race has been shown to speed recovery by helping to remove any lactic acid that may have accumulated. It also gently brings your muscles back to a resting state.

A good warm-up and cool-down are especially important before and after a hard workout such as an interval session or a race, in which you push your muscles to their limits. The extra time you spend warming up your muscles before a training run or race and cooling down afterwards is worth the effort in improved efficiency and decreased likelihood of getting injured.

3 STRETCH OUT

Without flexibility, you are an injury waiting to happen. Tight muscles cannot go through their full range of motion. Lack of flexibility is probably the biggest cause of Achilles tendinitis and is a major factor in plantar fasciitis and shin splints. Although the muscles in the backs of your legs (the hamstrings) tend to be the workhorses, don't forget to stretch those in the fronts of your legs as well.

Stretching is not the same as warming up. Trying to stretch "short" muscles may cause injury. The best time to stretch is after a run, when your muscles are warm and elongated. Make stretching part of your routine every day.

4 BACK OFF

If you train hard every day, you'll wear your body down rather than build it up. You need to recover after a tough training session or a race – give your muscles a chance to mend and stock up on glycogen for your next hard effort. This is why most experts recommend that you never schedule hard sessions two days in a row. Give yourself at least one day of easy running or rest between hard efforts. If you run fast one day, train slowly the next. If you do a long run one day, plan a short one for the following day. This is the hard/easy method of training.

Just as some people need more sleep than others, some people need more recovery. You may discover that your body performs best when you rest for two days after a hard training session. Or you may even need three easy days. Experiment with various combinations of hard and easy days, and compare the merits of easy running versus rest or cross-training.

5 CHILL OUT

Let your training schedule be your guide – but never your jailer. One of the surest ways to become injured is to train hard on a day when you're tired or feeling soreness or the pain of an injury about to happen. Even if you're following all of the rules – running on a good surface, warming up, stretching, using a hard/easy pattern – other factors of your lifestyle affect your physical wellbeing and level of fatigue. Stress at work or home or lack of sleep can take a toll as well.

If you feel fatigued or overly sluggish, or if you notice twinges of muscular pain, ease up on your training. If you've planned speedwork, run easy instead or take a day off altogether. You will not lose fitness over a day, or even a few days, of rest. Unfortunately, most runners have a hard time following this advice.

Many runners insist on adhering to the printed training schedule as if it were gospel. They refuse to deviate by a single mile from that programme, as they believe that any modification will ruin their chances of running a good race. In fact, the reverse is true. They'd benefit more by giving their bodies a chance to recover.

Remember, a training schedule is built on the assumption that you aren't experiencing any unusual pain before, during or after the run. If pain or fatigue does strike, don't hesitate to modify your work-outs.

6 BRANCH OUT

Runners once took a run-or-nothing approach to their sport, and many still do, believing that other sports cannot benefit their running and may in fact hurt it. The wiser runner explores other options, both to supplement running during periods of good health and as a substitute for running if they are injured.

Participating in another sport a couple of times a week gives your feet and legs a welcome respite from the constant pounding of running and strengthens muscles that running does not exercise. In both of these ways, cross-training can help to protect you from injury.

Replace an easy run or rest day with a cross-training workout. After all, it is often not total rest that your body needs but merely a break from the specialised action of running.

The more muscles you can involve in your training programme, the less likely you are to sustain an overuse injury. Additionally, by working more of your major muscle groups, you improve your overall state of fitness.

If you do become injured through running and have been cross-training regularly, you will have an activity to turn to that will keep you fit while you recover. Overuse symptoms such as soreness or injuries caused by too much shock or jarring can be relieved through swimming or cycling. By using a stair-climber, rowing machine or cross-country ski machine, you can take the stress off an injured area and still get an excellent cardiovascular work-out.

give you an important perspective. With a running log, you can trace your progress and detect errors accurately and objectively. You can see if you've been training too little or too much.

Review your log weekly with a critical eye. Pretend that it's someone else's training programme you're viewing and that you're checking how effective and safe it is. You may be amazed at the training errors you find. Correct these errors, and you'll become a better runner – and one more likely to stay injury-free.

7 SPACE YOUR RACES

Racing pushes the limits of your speed and endurance, and too much racing can push you beyond your ability to avoid injury. Racing is hard on your body, so you must give yourself plenty of time to recover after each event.

The general rule is to take one easy day or rest day for each mile you have raced, and certainly don't race again until that period has passed. For example, allow one easy week following a hard 10K and an easy month after completing a marathon. Top marathoners believe that they can run only two or three good marathons in a year – the gruelling event takes that great a toll.

Occasionally, you may read about someone who runs an incredible number of races – a runner who runs a marathon every week for a year, for example. It's hard to believe anyone can do that without getting injured, but there are always some people who can beat the odds. A few people can smoke three packs of cigarettes a day and live to be 100, but that doesn't mean you can play the odds and expect to avoid the usual painful consequences.

8 WRITE IT DOWN

Keeping a training log of your daily runs may seem compulsive or boring, but charting your distance, pace and course, the weather and how you feel can

9 BUT IF YOU DO GET INJURED...

...come back slowly – much more slowly than you might think necessary.

After a layoff or an injury, your feet and legs, bones and joints are just not ready for any pounding. They have become somewhat soft and lazy, and it takes time to build them to the point at which they can take the forces of running without becoming reinjured.

Furthermore, it's possible that your injury hasn't healed completely. Even though you may not feel any symptoms, the area you hurt will be weaker than it was before your injury and more susceptible to re-injury. If you stress your body too much too soon, the same symptoms are likely to reappear and you could end up with a more long-term problem.

Depending on how long your layoff is, and whether or not you are able to do any cross-training to maintain fitness, you might need to begin your return to your running programme with a walk/jog regime. Although you would rather eat asphalt than be caught walking, do it anyway. You'll still be exercising your muscles and gaining fitness without the hard pounding of running.

If you try to take short-cuts or cheat your body's natural timetable, you're asking for trouble. You simply cannot rush your recovery.

As you become stronger and start to run regularly, increase your weekly distance by no more than 10 per cent. This rule also applies if you're healthy.

10 FINALLY, BE SURE TO EAT WELL

During a layoff, many runners cut back on their diets to prevent weight gain. This isn't necessary. You need extra nutrients to help your body to mend the injured area and to fuel your training once you renew your running programme. If you do gain a few pounds during your recovery period, they'll just melt away when you begin running again.

So eat, and train, wisely and you'll keep running year after year without injury.■

» THE MOST COMMON ROUTES TO INJURY

You don't just need to know what to do to minimise your chances of getting injured – you need to know what to avoid doing, too. These are some of the most common errors made by new and experienced runners alike:

Wearing new shoes on race day This is tempting, because new running shoes have a slipper-like feel from the first fitting. That might remain the case for a short while, but resist it. A plethora of foot and lower-limb problems are just a few miles away.
Prevention Wear them in first.

Wearing old shoes Another big temptation, mainly because new running shoes are so expensive, old ones are so comfortable and it's easy to judge wear by the state of the outsole and the upper rather than (correctly) by the compression of the midsole. Joint or shin soreness is the most obvious result and, in fact, should be taken as a sign that your shoes need replacing.
Prevention Log the miles you've run in each pair of shoes, and change them at least every 500-600 miles. It's cheaper than the medical alternative.

Wearing the wrong shoes This could either be a model unsuited to your gait and foot, or a shoe inappropriate to the type of running you're doing. Either way, you have a problem.
Prevention If you don't know what you're doing, shop at a specialist running retailer. Don't try anything stupid, like doing a fell race in a road shoe.

Ignoring pain Runners accept pain as part of the sport, but not all pain is equal. You have to learn to separate good pain, associated with the positive progression of your fitness, from bad pain, which tends to be unfamiliar, infrequent and generally localised in one particular area of the body. It is an early warning sign of injury, the final severity of which will be determined by how much notice you pay.
Prevention Pay attention to unfamiliar pains. Ease off, and seek medical help where necessary.

Commencing treatment without diagnosis Okay, so you have an injury, you know it's a bad one and you feel you know how to solve it. So you start treatment. The trouble is that you're a runner, not a medical expert. You may have misdiagnosed your problem and started the wrong treatment.
Prevention If there's any chance that you're wrong, see a professional and don't DIY.

Not drinking enough before or during a run This is less of a problem on big race days, when runners are more meticulous in their preparations, than it is in training. Dehydration affects your health and performance whenever you run.
Prevention Drink fluid little and often throughout the day, every day.

Increasing mileage too quickly Many runners insist that patience is more of an impediment than a virtue. When you are building up to a longer race or coming back from injury, the temptation is to do it too rapidly.
Prevention Increase your mileage by no more than 10 per cent per week.

THE BIG FIVE

Preventing these most common injuries will keep you ahead of the pack

Injuries come in many shapes, sizes and places, so it's difficult to make generalisations about how to avoid them or recover from them. Each one is unique, not least because each of us is unique. Still, certain injuries are more common than others. If you can work out how to avoid these, you're ahead of the game.

When the RUNNER'S WORLD editors decided to write about the five most common injuries, we debated them a little. We researched the subject by reviewing the medical literature. We asked each other what we had incurred most often or heard our friends complain about.

In the end, it wasn't very complicated. Five injuries kept coming up over and over again. So we asked the experts how best to avoid these problems. Steering clear of these five injuries is no guarantee that you won't develop others, but it's a big step in the right direction.

Fortunately, many running injuries last only a few weeks, and most are preventable. If you run cleverly and do all the right things to ensure your running health – things you've heard before, such as strengthening and stretching your leg muscles, wearing proper shoes and taking easy days or rest days when you're tired – you can avoid most running injuries, or at least nip them in the bud. That is, if you know what you're doing. That's where this guide comes in. Below are the five most common running injuries: Achilles tendinitis, chondromalacia, iliotibial band syndrome, plantar fasciitis and shin splints. This guide tells you what they are and how to deal with them – everything from whether or nor to run through them, to when it's time to see a doctor, and which doctor or sports-medicine specialist to see.

ACHILLES TENDINITIS

This troublesome heel pain is caused by inflammation of the Achilles tendon. The Achilles is the large tendon connecting the two major calf muscles – the gastrocnemius and soleus – to the back of the heel bone. Under too much stress, the tendon tightens and is forced to work too hard. This causes it to become inflamed (that's tendinitis) and, over time, can produce a covering of scar tissue that is less flexible than the tendon. If the inflamed Achilles continues to be stressed, it can tear or rupture.

Symptoms Dull or sharp pain anywhere along the back of the tendon, but usually close to the heel. Limited ankle flexibility. Redness or heat over the painful area. A nodule (a lumpy build-up of scar tissue) that can be felt on the tendon. A crackling sound (scar tissue rubbing against the tendon) when the ankle moves.

Causes Tight or fatigued calf muscles, which transfer too much of the burden of running to the Achilles. This can be brought on by not stretching the calves properly, increasing mileage too quickly or simply over-training. Excessive hill running or speedwork, both of which stress the Achilles more than other types of running, can also cause tendinitis. Inflexible running shoes, which force the Achilles to twist, cause some cases. Runners who overpronate (their feet rotate too far inward on impact) are susceptible to Achilles tendinitis.

Self-treatment Stop running. Take aspirin or ibuprofen and ice the area for 15 to 20 minutes several times a day until the inflammation has subsided.

Self-massage may also help. "I have every therapeutic machine available for the treatment of Achilles tendinitis and the treatment of choice is massage with a heat-inducing cream or oil," says Marc Chasnov, a physiotherapist. He suggests rubbing semi-circles in all directions away from the knotted tissue three times a day.

Once the nodule is gone, stretch the calf muscles. Don't start running again until you can do toe lifts without pain. Next, move on to skipping with a rope, then jumping jacks and then gradually begin running again. You should he back to easy running in six to eight weeks.

Medical treatment if your injury does not respond to self-treatment in two weeks, see a physiotherapist or orthopaedic surgeon. Surgery to scrape scar tissue off the tendon is a last resort and not very effective. "It usually just stimulates more scar tissue," says Chasnov.

Alternative exercises Cycling in a low gear, swimming and pool running. No weight-bearing exercises.

Preventive measures Strengthen and stretch the muscles in your feet, calves and shins. Wear motion-control shoes or orthotics to combat overpronation. Do not run in worn-out shoes. Ease into any running programme. Avoid hillwork. Incorporate rest into your training schedule.

CHONDROMALACIA

One of the most common knee injuries, chondromalacia is a softening or wearing away and cracking of the cartilage under the kneecap, resulting in pain and inflammation. The cartilage becomes like sandpaper because the kneecap is not riding smoothly over the knees.

Symptoms Pain beneath or on the side of the kneecap. "It's a soreness, a nagging discomfort," says Dr Dave Apple, an orthopaedic surgeon. Pain can worsen over a year or so and is most severe after you run up and down hills. Swelling is also present. In severe cases, you can feel – and

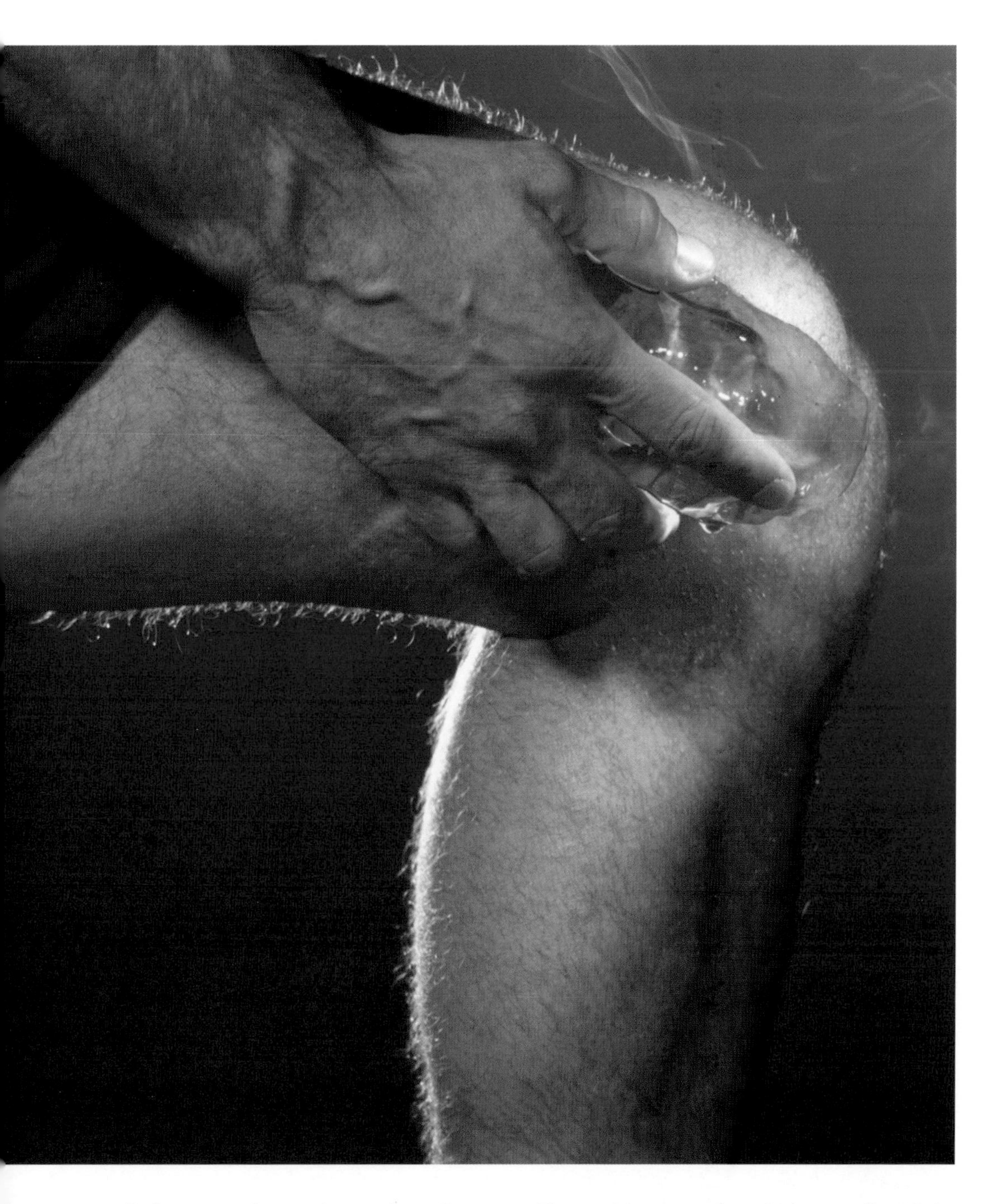

eventually hear – grinding as the rough cartilage rubs against cartilage when the knee is flexed.

Causes Overpronation (excessive inward rolling of the foot) can cause the kneecap to twist sideways. The quadriceps muscles, which normally aid the proper tracking of the kneecap, can prevent the kneecap from tracking smoothly when they are fatigued or weak. A muscle imbalance between weak quads and tighter hamstrings can also pull the

» IT PAIN: GET RID OF IT

The IT band stretch is the most common and effective IT band exercise: stand with your right leg crossed behind your left and put your left arm on your hip. Lean to the left while pushing your right hip to the right. Keep your right foot anchored while allowing your left knee to flex. You should feel the stretch in the iliotibial band from your right hip down the outside of your right leg.

kneecap out of its groove. Hill running (especially downhills) can aggravate the condition, as can running on the same side of a cambered road, or, in general, over-training.

Self-treatment Stop running. Ice the knee for 15 minutes, two or three times a day. Use a flexible, frozen gel pack that wraps around the knee (or, at a pinch, try a bag of frozen peas). Take one aspirin three times a day for 12 weeks. "Aspirin has been found to block further breakdown of cartilage," says Apple. Also, try self-massage on the sore spots around the knee.

Once the pain and swelling are gone, do quadriceps strengtheners. Stand on a step or box at least 10cm high. Keep your right quadriceps tight while you lower your left leg slowly towards the floor. Then raise the leg back up to the box and relax. Repeat 40 times with each leg. Continue increasing repetitions in increments of five every two days, all the way up to 60 reps.

Don't forget to stretch your quadriceps and hamstrings. When you start running again, you also might try wearing a rubber sleeve with a hole that fits over the kneecap, which can help the knee track better. You should be back to easy running in four to six weeks.

Medical treatment If chondromalacia isn't responding to the self-treatment after four weeks, see an orthopaedic surgeon. He may prescribe custom-made orthotics to control overpronation. Surgery to scrape away rough edges of cartilage can alleviate some pain. Despite what you may have heard, cortisone injections won't work. "The problem is, you won't feel pain while you're crunching your knee to bits," says Dr Apple.

Alternative exercises Pool running, swimming and rowing. Anything that doesn't put pressure on the knee.

Preventive measures You should stretch and strengthen your quadriceps, hamstrings and calves. It you overpronate then consider switching to motion-control shoes with firm midsoles. You should never run in worn-out shoes. You may need to wear orthotics. Avoid downhill running, and stay off cambered roads – if you can't, try to run on the flattest part of the road. Incorporate rest into your training schedule. Don't overdo it.

ILIOTIBIAL BAND SYNDROME

This condition results in inflammation and pain on the outside of the knee where the iliotibial (IT) band (a ligament that runs along the outside of the thigh) rubs against the femur, the large leg bone.

Symptoms A dull ache that starts when you're a mile or two into a run, lingers during the run, but disappears soon after you stop. In severe cases, pain can be sharp, and the outside of the knee can be tender or swollen.

Causes Anything that causes the leg to bend inwards, stretching the IT band against the femur, such as bow-legs, overpronation, worn-out running shoes, or workouts on downhill or indoor, banked surfaces. A tight IT band can contribute to the injury, as can stepping up your training too quickly. It sometimes takes just a single hard workout to cause IT band syndrome.

Self-treatment "You usually can't run through IT band pain," says Apple, "but if you do run, back off. Cut back on speedwork, don't run downhill and make sure to stretch the band a couple of times a day. The main thing you have to do is restore the band's flexibility."

Perform the IT band stretch (see panel). In addition to this stretch, ice the knee for around 15 to 20 minutes after running, try some self-massage on the area, and stretch hamstrings and other leg muscles. You should be back to easy running in two to four weeks.

Medical treatment If you feel your IT band problem isn't responding to self-treatment after four weeks, you need to see an orthopaedic surgeon. In severe cases, you may need to have a cortisone injection under the band to alleviate the pain.

» THE GOLF BALL TRICK

To help stretch the fascia, start with a golf ball under the base of your big toe and roll the foot forward over the ball to the base of the second toe and repeat. Repeat the same motion starting from each toe, always exerting enough pressure so you feel a little tenderness.

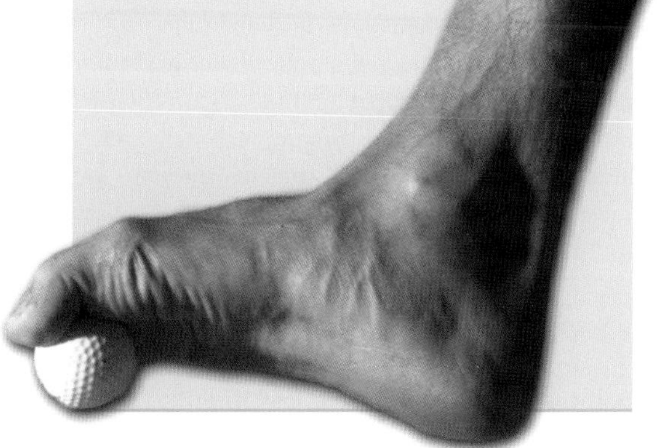

Alternative exercises Pool running, swimming, cycling and rowing, hut not stair climbing. "Anything that doesn't put pressure on the outside of the knee is fine," says Apple.

Preventive measures Make sure you stretch the IT band (after a workout is the best time). Stretch and strengthen your quadriceps and hamstrings. Warm up well before you run. Avoid hard workouts on cambered roads, downhill surfaces or indoor tracks. Ease into any running programme.

PLANTAR FASCIITIS (POLICEMAN'S HEEL)

This is an inflammation of the plantar fascia, a thick, fibrous band of tissue in the bottom of the foot, running from the heel to the base of the toes. When placed under too much stress, the fascia stretches too far and tears, which causes inflammation of the fascia and surrounding tissues. The tears are soon covered with scar tissue, which is less flexible than the fascia and only aggravates the problem.

Symptoms Pain at the base of the heel. "Most people describe it as feeling like a bone bruise or a stone bruise," says Joe Ellis, a sports podiatrist. "Plantar fasciitis is most severe in the morning when you get out of bed or at the beginning of a run, because the fascia is tighter at those times. The pain may fade as you walk or run. Often, a runner will change stride to alleviate pain, but this only provides temporary relief. A bone spur may also develop at the heel, where the fascia has started to tear away.

Causes Stress, tension and pulling on the plantar fascia. Runners with tight Achilles tendons (which put more stress on the fasciæ), or high arches and rigid feet, or flat feet that overpronate are most susceptible. Worn-out shoes, which allow feet to overpronate, or shoes that are too stiff, which stretch the fasciæ, can also make you more susceptible.

Self-treatment Reduce your running. Take aspirin or ibuprofen daily. Ice the area for 15 to 20 minutes several times a day. Ice-massage the fascia. To do this, fill a paper cup with water and freeze. Peel off the paper, place the ice under your foot and roll the foot over it from your heel to the bail of your foot and back again. A frozen-juice can works equally well.

Medical treatment If it hasn't responded to self-treatment in four weeks, see a podiatrist, who may prescribe orthotics, ultrasound or friction massage. Surgery to detach the fascia from its insertion into the heel may be recommended if medical treatments don't help after a year. The success rate is 80 per cent. Surgery to remove bone spurs usually doesn't work. "The spur isn't the problem," says Ellis, "It's a reaction to the problem."

Alternative exercises Pool running swimming and cycling in a low gear. After surgery, only swimming is recommended during rehabilitation.

Preventive measures Stretch your calf muscles. Strengthen muscles of the foot by picking up marbles or golf balls with your toes or pulling a towel towards you with your toes. (Grab some of the towel with your toes and pull, then grab some more.)

Do the plantar fascia stretch while sitting on the floor, with one knee bent and the same ankle flexed towards you, pull the toes back towards the ankle. Hold for a count of 10. Repeat 10 times.

Wear orthotics if you overpronate or have flat feet. Ice the area for 15 to 20 minutes after running. Run on soft surfaces, and incorporate more rest into your schedule.

SHIN SPLINTS

A very common and nagging injury, shin splints are an inflammation of the tendons on the inside of the front of the lower leg. (Sports-medicine specialists don't like to use the term "shin splints" because it commonly refers to several lower-leg injuries. This section uses it anyway, but focuses on the specific problem that is the most common: tendinitis of the lower leg.)

Symptoms An aching, throbbing or tenderness along the inside of the shin (though it can radiate to the outside also) about halfway down, or all along the shin from the ankle to the knee. Pain when you press on the inflamed area. Pain is most severe at the start of a run, but it can go away during a run once the muscles are loosened up (unlike a stress fracture of the shinbone, which hurts all the time). With tendinitis, pain resumes after the run.

Causes Tired or inflexible calf muscles put too much stress on tendons, which become strained and torn. Overpronation aggravates this problem, as does running on hard surfaces such as concrete pavements.

Beginners are the most susceptible to shin splints for a variety of reasons, but the most common is that they're using leg muscles that haven't been stressed in the same way before. Another common cause of shin splints among beginners is poor choice of running shoes or running in something other than running shoes. Runners who have started running after a long layoff are also prone to shin splints because they often increase their mileage too quickly.

Self-treatment Many runners experience mild shin soreness, which can usually be tolerated. "If shin splints hit you at the beginning of a season, a certain amount of running through it will help the body adapt," says David O'Brian, a podiatrist, "but if it's a persistent problem, you shouldn't run through it."

If it does persist, ice the inflamed area for 15 minutes, three times a day and take aspirin or ibuprofen. Ice immediately after running. To hasten recovery, cut down on running or stop altogether. Recovery time is two to four weeks.

Medical treatment If the injury doesn't respond to self-treatment and rest in two to four weeks, see a podiatrist, who may prescribe custom-made orthotics to control overpronation. Ultrasound and anti-inflammatories may also be prescribed. Surgery is rarely required.

Alternative exercises: Non-impact exercises such as pool running, swimming, walking and cycling in a low gear.

Preventive measures You should exercise the tendons and muscles in the front of the leg (see panel). You can also strengthen the lower leg with band exercises. Anchor one end of an exercise band to a heavy object, such as the leg of a sofa. Stretch the band, then loop the free end around your forefoot. Move the foot tip and down and side to side against the band's resistance to exercise different muscle groups. The band can be ordered from a doctor or bought in some sports shops.

Finally, make sure you wear motion-control shoes – and orthotics if your doctor says you need them. Don't run in worn-out shoes. Warm up well and run on soft surfaces. Avoid over-striding, which puts more stress on shins. ■

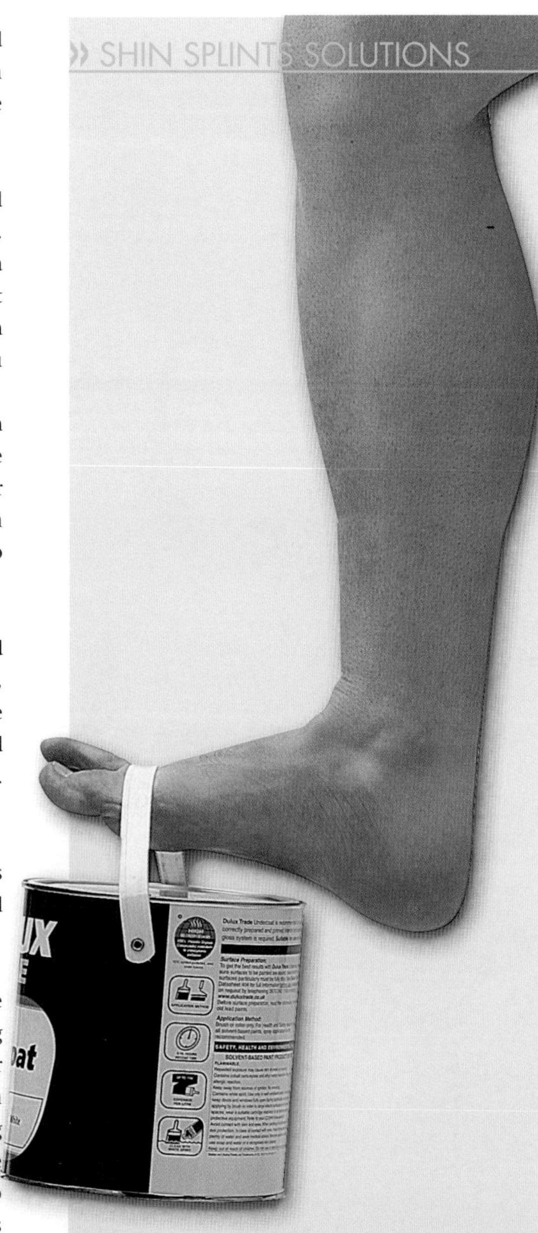

To stretch and strengthen the tendons and muscles in the front of the leg, sit on a table or chair and loop a weight over the front of your foot. You can buy special weights, or use household items – such as a paint tin as shown above. Without bending your knee, move your foot up and down from the ankle.

FLEXIBLE FRIENDS

Stretch your limits and improve your performance with these simple but effective partner stretches

Post-run stretching is something we all mean to do when we "remember" and "have the time". The trouble is, many of us only find the time once every few months.

There are three reasons why you must stretch:

One Tight muscles, tendons and ligaments restrict motion, particularly in the ankle and hip. This will shorten your stride so that you use more energy when overcoming the stiffness to maintain a given speed. Regular stretching will counteract that, improving your running efficiency.

Two Studies have shown that regular post-exercise stretching can be linked to a reduced chance of injury, particularly in the knees, hips and ankles.

Three Other research indicates that stretching stimulates the passage of amino acids into muscles and speeds up repair. So stretching after training will help your muscles repair themselves quicker.

In recent years, one type of stretching has been hailed as particularly effective. Yet it's one many people have never heard of. Proprioceptive neuromuscular facilitation (PNF) has been shown to improve flexibility by 10-15 per cent more than normal stretching, and despite its complex name, PNF stretching is simple to do. In fact, PNF stretching is made even easier to do because it's best done with a partner. So, just as having a running partner will make you more likely to run, having a stretching partner after your run will make you more likely to stretch. Just follow the eight-stretch routine over the page. ■

» ELASTIC FANTASTIC

Your four-step guide to performing a PNF stretch

1 Relax and let your partner gently push you into a stretch as far as is comfortable.
2 Stay in this position for 10-20 seconds – don't bounce or tense up.
3 Push back gently against the pressure of your partner's weight for 10 seconds.
4 Relax again and let your partner re-apply the stretch for 30 seconds (and increase it if you feel comfortable).

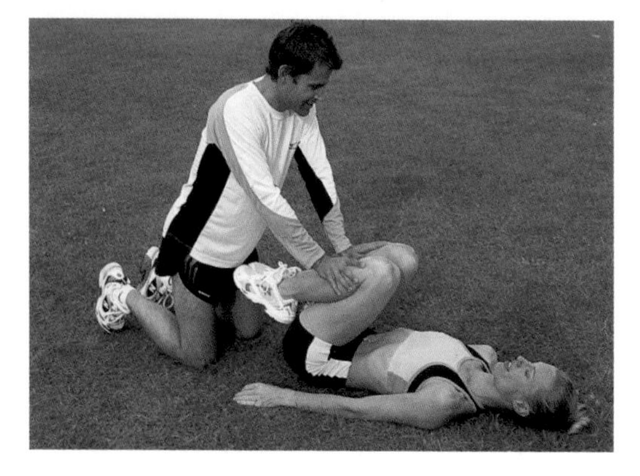

1 Lower back

Stretcher Lie on your back with your arms by your sides. Bend your knees and lift your feet off the floor.
Partner Kneel beside your partner's legs. Take hold of their shins, just below the knee. Gently push the knees down towards the chest. Then perform the PNF sequence (see "Elastic Fantastic", above).

2 Glutes

Stretcher Lie on your back with your arms by your sides. Bend one knee and lift that foot off the floor. Keep the other leg and hip flat on the floor.
Partner Kneel beside your partner's legs. Place one hand below the knee on their bent leg, and the other on the thigh above the knee on their straight leg (to keep it in place). Gently push the bent knee forwards and down towards the chest. Perform the PNF sequence, then repeat for the other leg.

3 Piriformis and hip rotators

Stretcher Lie on your back with your arms by your sides. Bend your knees to 90 degrees. Bring your right leg off the floor and across so that the outside of the ankle rests just above the knee of the left leg.

Partner Lift and support the left leg by resting it against your thigh. Then gently push the right knee towards the left shoulder as far as is comfortable. Perform the PNF sequence, then repeat for the other leg.

4 Hamstrings

Stretcher Lie on your back with your arms by your sides. Lift one leg off the floor as far as you can, keeping the knee as straight as is comfortable.

Partner Kneel behind your partner's raised leg with the back of their calf against your shoulder. Place one hand on the thigh (above the knee). Gently lean forward so your weight increases the stretch on the hamstring. Perform the PNF sequence, then repeat for the other leg.

5 Abductors

Stretcher Lie on your left side with your head supported on your arms. Bend your right leg and bring it across in front of the left leg until the foot rests on the floor (forming an arch over the straight right leg). Keep your hips vertical at all times.

Partner Kneel beside your partner's legs and take hold of their right ankle. Gently lift the ankle straight up as far as is comfortable, supporting the knee if necessary to prevent any strains. Perform the PNF sequence, then repeat for the other leg.

6 Quadriceps and hip flexors

Stretcher Lie on your front with your arms under your head. Bend one knee so that your heel comes up towards your buttock. (Put a folded towel under your abs if you have a bad back.)

Partner Place one hand on the forefoot of the bent leg and gently press the heel towards the buttock. Place your other hand underneath the bent knee and lift it a few inches off the floor. Perform the PNF sequence, then repeat for the other leg.

How not to stretch

◆ Don't stretch cold muscles. Stretching before a run has been shown to increase the risk of injury. Ease into every run, preferably with about 10 minutes of walking and jogging to warm up.

◆ Don't overstretch. Extreme flexibility (such as the splits) is of no real use to runners, so there's no need to force a stretch. Overdoing a stretch to the point of pain, shaking or extreme feelings of tension can cause injury just as easily as twisting your ankle while running.

◆ Don't bounce. It might be what you see the footballers doing at the Saturday morning game, but trust us, it's a sure route to a torn muscle.

◆ Don't just stretch. If you hurt yourself while out running, stretching will not make a bad muscle good. It is a preventative measure, not a quick cure.

7 Adductors

Stretcher Sit on the floor with your legs straight out in front of you and your back straight. Open your legs as wide as they will go, still keeping them straight.

Partner Sit facing your partner and place your feet against their inner calves. Take hold of their arms, and gently press their legs apart (don't push too far) as you pull their torso slightly forward. Perform the PNF sequence, taking care to keep the hip joints relaxed.

8 Chest and shoulders

Stretcher Kneel on the floor. Keep you back straight and clasp your hands behind your head. (Keep your neck relaxed and take extra care if you have a history of shoulder injuries.)

Partner Stand close behind your kneeling partner. Place your arms down in front of theirs and clasp your hands behind their back. Gently pull back with your elbows. Perform the PNF sequence, taking care not to pull your partner's torso backwards.

WHICH **INJURY** SPECIALIST?

If you run enough, chances are you'll pick up an injury at some point. That's when it's vital you take the right advice and the right course of action to have you back on your feet sooner rather than later (and with a lot less pain and discomfort).

Runners pick up injuries. There's no point denying it and no reason to hide it. That's the bad news. The good news is most running injuries are soft-tissue injuries you can resolve yourself with ice, rest and perhaps a dose of cross-training.

Other injuries prove more stubborn. They don't clear up; or if they do, they swiftly recur.

AN ARRAY OF SPECIALISTS

If this happens you may start to think about seeing a medical specialist. But which one? There's a range of specialists all claiming they can help runners. Chiropractors, osteopaths, sports doctors, physiotherapists, podiatrists and sports masseurs can all lay claim to expertise in treating running injuries.

"It can be extremely confusing," confesses John Betser, an osteopath who runs sports injury clinics in Dunstable and Bedford. "There are no absolute guidelines as to which word to use for which treatment. There are seven osteopaths and three physios in our practice, and when we sit down and discuss things we fight a constant battle with nebulous language. It's impossible to pin down exactly what frequently used terms such as 'manipulation' or 'adjustment' actually mean."

So where do you start? We suggest you start with your family GP, although they are by

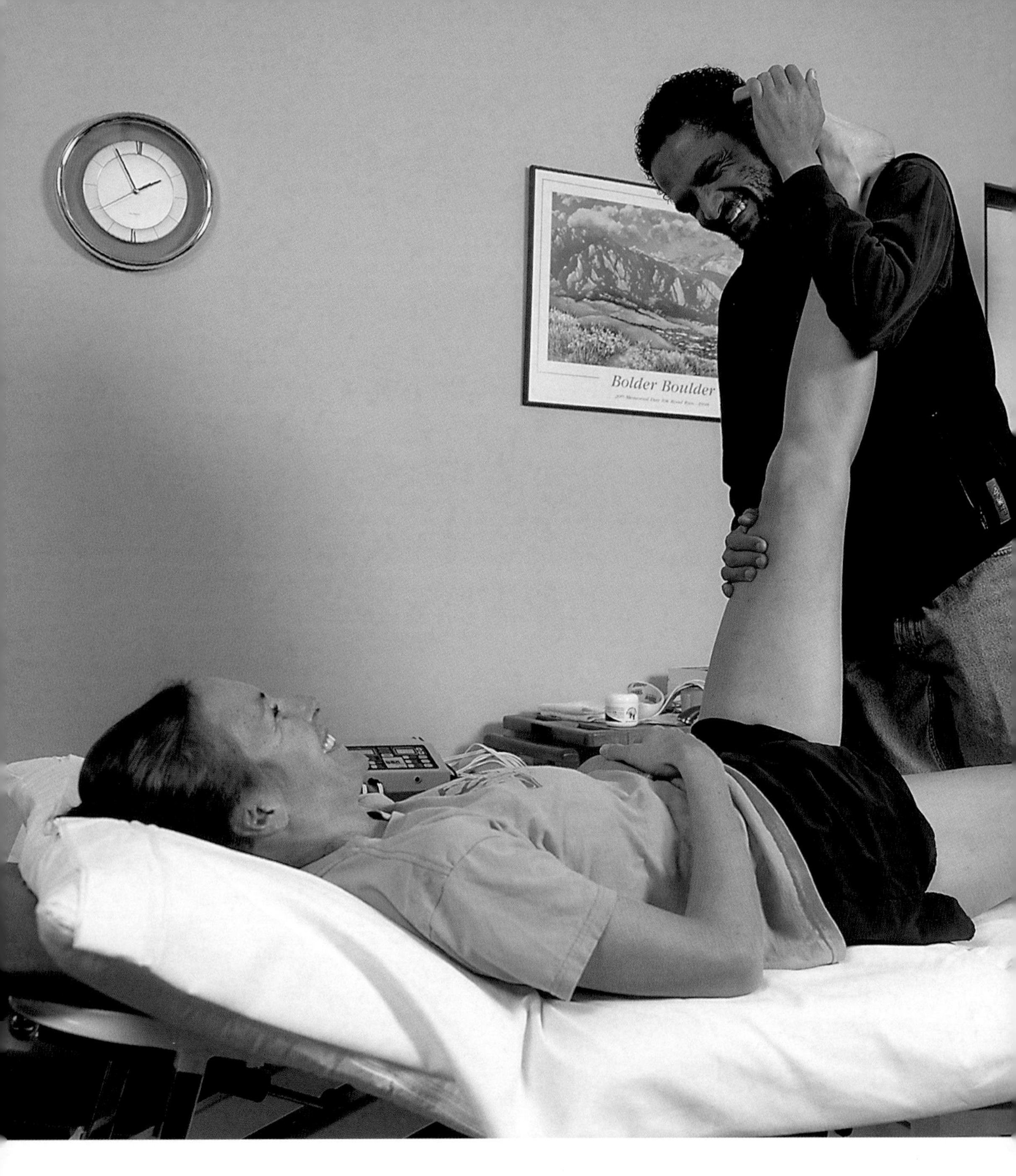

definition generalists, your doctor may be able to cure many of the simpler running problems. If they are unable to help you with your particular problem, they can usually refer you to other medical specialists within the NHS who can; or, depending on the GP, they could also recommend an alternative in the private sector who will see you more quickly. A GP referral is also often required by private medical insurance companies before they will cover treatment costs.

Independent of your GP, you could also seek out a sports injury clinic through your existing

running contacts. Often, practitioners work in close contact with one another, so if you have a club physio they might be able to recommend an osteopath or a chiropractor familiar with running problems. The staff at your local running shop may have information, and each month RUNNER'S WORLD provides details of doctors and specialists all over the country who frequently treat runners.

THE RIGHT ONE FOR YOU

When you visit a specialist, don't be afraid to ask questions. Specialists can be a great source of advice, not just about clearing up injuries, but about preventing problems in the future. Then, as you gain more knowledge and experience, you'll have a more precise understanding of how to avoid injuries and, if you do pick one up, of which practitioner to consult for which injury.

Although the advice which follows should help you gain a better understanding of the medical professionals available, with a rough guide to their area of specialisation, medicine is invariably murkier than its clinical public image suggests. Many of these medical professionals work together and complement each other, rather than being in competition with each other for your custom. Nor, for that matter, do they have strictly defined areas of specialisation.

Indeed, many of them cross over into the same areas and may prescribe a similar type of treatment for the same injury. Finally, it is difficult to assess one medical professional against another, even among those belonging to the same professional body. So, the best practitioner for you is the one that keeps you running injury-free.

PHYSIOTHERAPISTS

The most common variety of specialist in the UK is the physiotherapist. In fact, a recent poll commissioned by the Chartered Society of Physiotherapy (CSP) revealed 88 per cent of people will happily self refer by taking themselves straight to a physio, bypassing the doctor's surgery altogether when they're suffering from a musculo-skeletal injury.

COVERING COSTS: FUNDING YOUR TREATMENT

Of course, at between £40 and £60, trips to private physios can quickly burn a hole in your pocket. So medical insurance might not be a bad idea. And it's not that expensive. "It varies according to

To help you when you're injured, physiotherapists focus on reducing pain and inflammation, and speeding tissue healing. Effective options include:

Cryotherapy A fancy term for ice or other cold treatment, cryotherapy is used in the initial injury phase to relieve pain and swelling by reducing blood flow and nerve conduction. Ice is often used after other physical therapy rehab treatments, such as manual manipulation and stretching, in order to reduce the ensuing swelling.

Deep-tissue massage Although there are specialist sports masseurs out there, many physios use rigorous hands-on stroking and kneading of muscles and connective tissue. "When you injure your tissue, collagen is like a superglue that heals it," explains Jon Lewis, physio and strength coach at Balance Physiotherapy. "But sometimes the body can do too good a job, and the collagen can bind the healthy fibres with adhesions. Then every time you move, it hurts, even though the original injury is healed. The purpose of massage and "friction" treatments is to break up the adhesions. It hurts like hell, but it works."

Interferential treatment Sometimes called "e-stim", this treatment sends low-voltage electrical impulses to the injured area via electrodes. Sounds scary, but the runner only feels a mild twinge when the muscle contracts. Interferential treatment relieves pain in the injured area and can also help heal bone and tissue.

Iontophoresis Iontophoresis is a non-invasive method of delivering healing medication. The drug (usually an anti-inflammatory) is transmitted to the tissues via an electrode with an absorbent pad.

Ultrasound The use of sound waves to produce a deep heat to warm muscle tissues. A wand attached to the ultrasound machine gently massages tissue around the affected area for several minutes, delivering the heat therapy. This promotes healing by relaxing muscles and increasing range of motion.

your age, where you live and so on," explains Ben Falkner at AXA PPP Healthcare. "But a healthy, 30-year-old male runner living somewhere like Brighton could get insurance for about £36 a month. That would include £800-worth of outpatient care, which is what physiotherapy is classed as, as well as hospital care in the event of something major going wrong." This would be subject to a referral from your GP. Though in truth, as Andrew Caldwell, a chartered physiotherapist at the East Midlands Physiotherapy Clinic in Loughborough explains, "most of the time it's simply a case of popping into your GP, telling them what the problem is and that you need a referral for insurance purposes, and they'll write one for you fairly happily." It's also worth remembering that expensive scans, such as MRI and bone scans, would be covered in full with a policy such as that quoted by AXA.

THE LORES OF PHYSICS: TREATMENT AND REHABILITATION

So, you're going to the physio. What will they do? The building blocks of physiotherapy are anatomy, physiology, kinesiology and biomechanics, not medicine and surgery. They can't yet prescribe medications, and not all are able to give injections themselves. And, in addition, most physios can't even order diagnostic exams such as MRIs, bone scans or X-rays (though they should be able to tell you when such things are needed, and may be able to organise them for you. And there are a growing number of extended scope physiotherapy practitioners who can inject and order scans and other tests.)

But what physiotherapists do have is a deep knowledge of the way we move. In truth, the level of specialist knowledge is incredible. As Jennie Edmondson of the CSP explains, "In addition to the obvious areas of sports physiotherapy, back-pain specialists and so on, there are physios whose expertise is treating cancer patients or people with learning disabilities." Whatever your specific problem, there will be a physio for you.

And a good physio will do more than ease your pain. In order to fully cure the overuse injuries that plague runners (tendinitis, runner's knee, shin splints, plantar fasciitis and muscle strains) most physios will first treat the symptoms, and then try to determine the cause. "Physios probably have the best understanding of the mechanics of human movement out of any group of therapists," says exercise physiologist Janet Hamilton, author of *Running Strong and Injury Free*. "They're also one of the best sources for understanding the 'why' of injury onset. Just about any overuse injury will respond to rest and ice, but when you resume running, you may get injured again unless the factors that led to the injury are corrected."

That's why visits to a physio typically involve a lot of detective work. Once the initial healing treatments reduce your pain (see p182), the physio will probably watch you run on a treadmill (and videotape it) to analyse your stride and biomechanics. They may also measure muscle strength and efficiency throughout the body in order to detect imbalances that can pull a stride out of alignment.

After the cause of injury has been determined, a physio can prescribe various steps to correct the root cause of the problem – a stretching and strengthening programme for certain weak or tight muscle groups, for example. A physiotherapist might also check the runner's shoe and add arches, heel lifts or refer them to a podiatrist for customised orthoses.

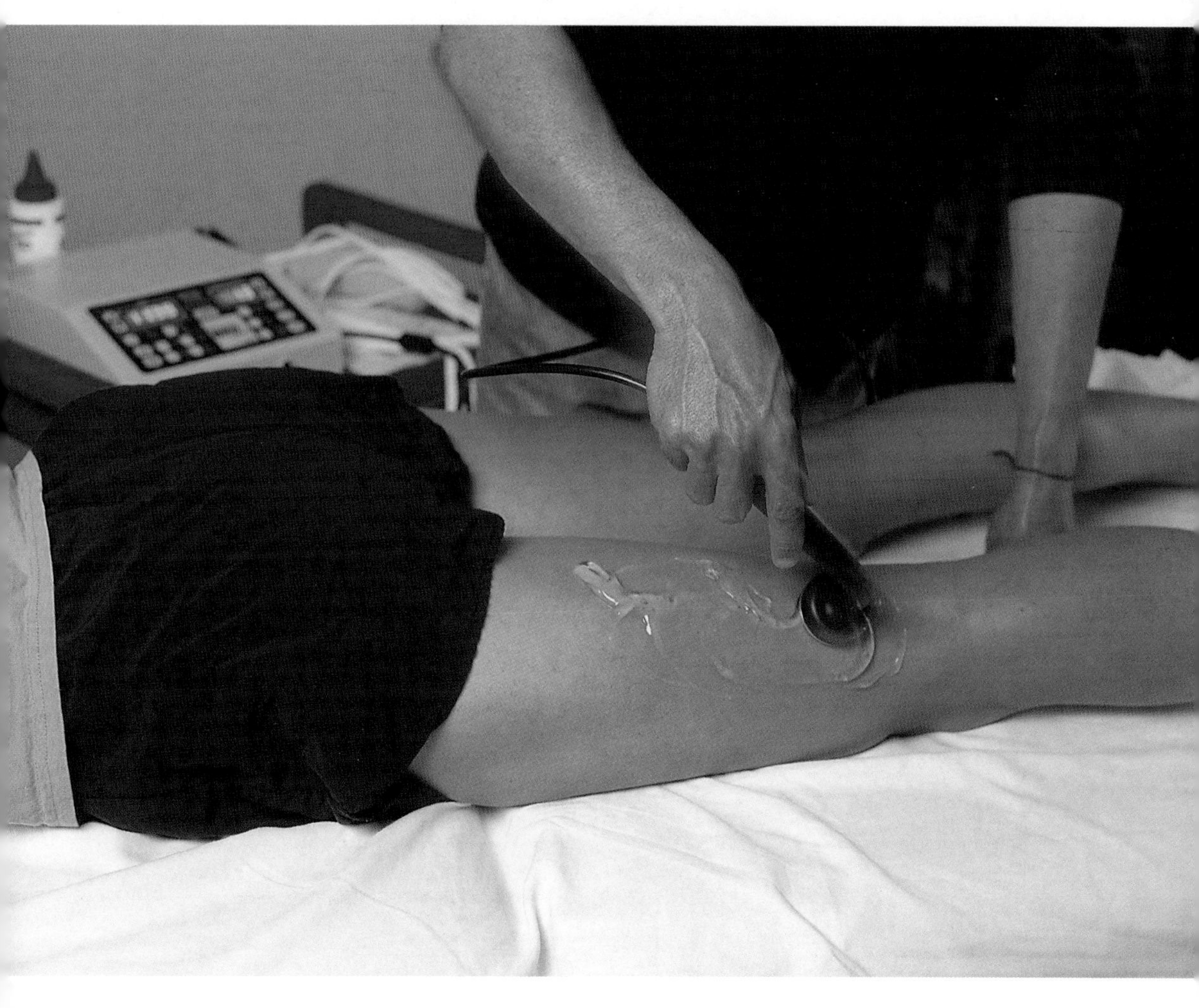

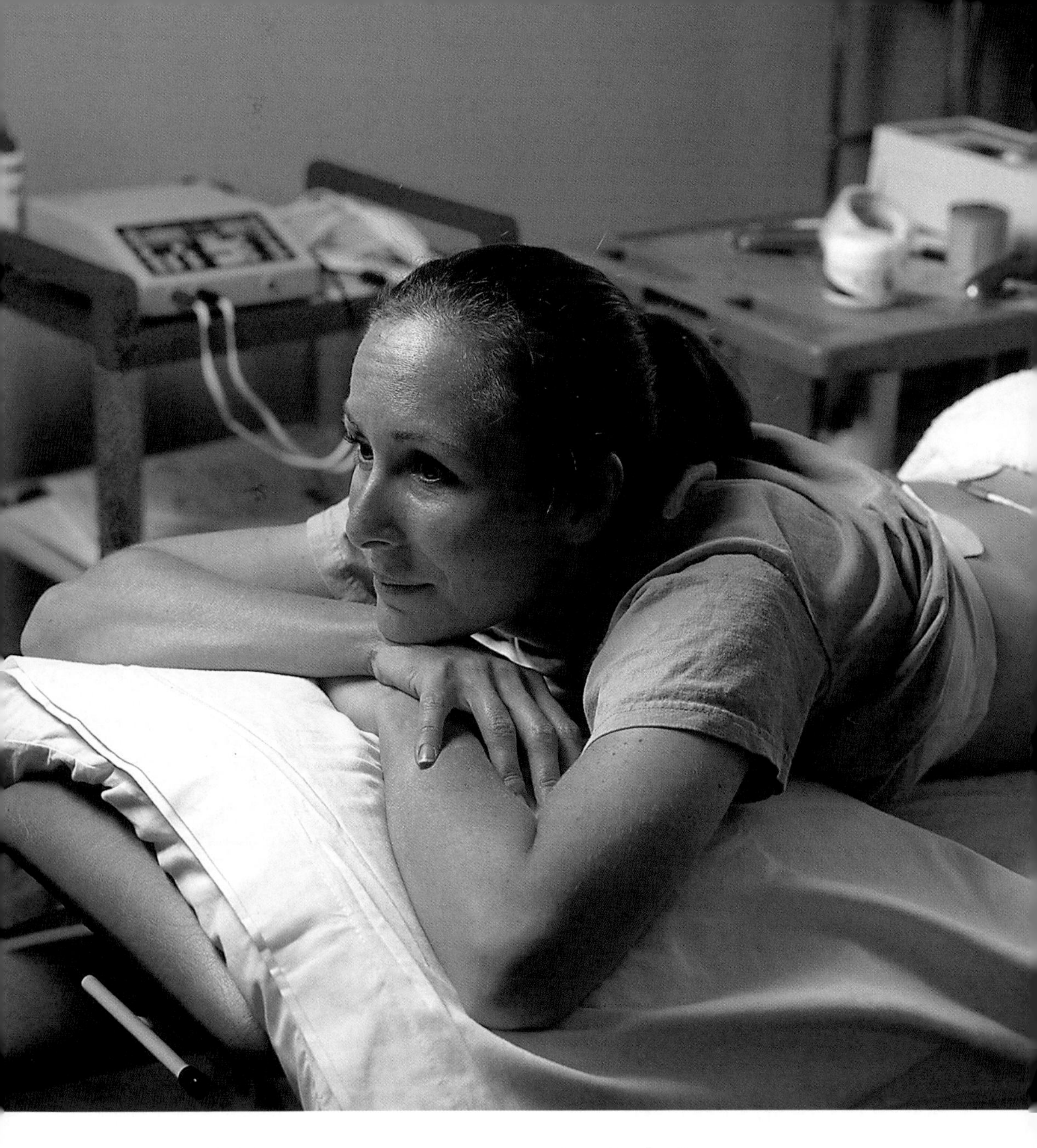

OTHER SPECIALISTS

Chiropractors

Chiropractors are best known for manual manipulations of the spine and neck joints to cure back and neck injuries. However, most chiropractors treat the extremities as well. They concentrate on applying pressure to the bones and joints, characterised by clicks and crunches.

Sports doctors

Sports doctors treat the musculoskeletal system – ligaments, joints, bones, tendons, muscles and nerves. Some treat the entire human body, others specialise in specific areas of the body.

Osteopaths

Whereas chiropractors are likely to crunch and

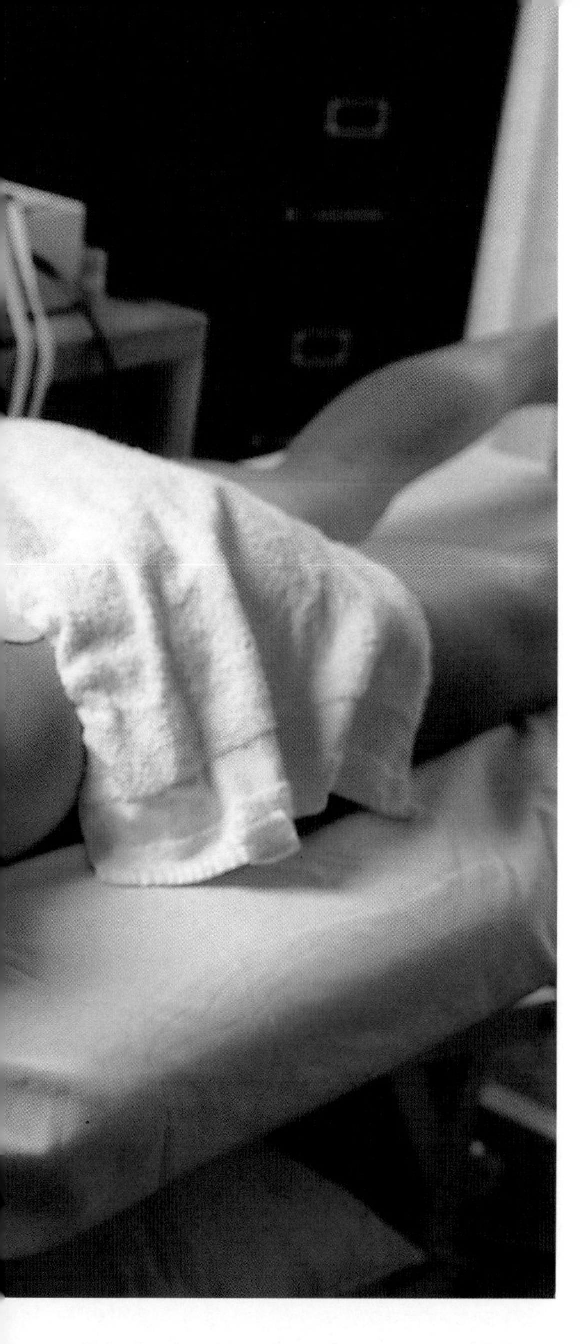

click the bones, osteopaths are more likely to apply pressure to the soft tissue: the muscles, the ligaments, and the tendons.

Chartered physiotherapists

Physiotherapists use a variety of treatments to help muscles and joints overcome injury and work to their full potential. These treatments include: exercise programmes to improve mobility and strengthen muscles; manipulation and mobilisation to reduce pain and stiffness; electrotherapy such as ultrasound to break down scar tissue; acupuncture; hydrotherapy; and sports massage.

Podiatrists

The myth is that podiatrists won't give you a second thought unless you're laid low with foot pain. In actual fact, although podiatrists do specialise in the lower body, podiatry is essentially the treatment of gait and posture problems, which could be located anywhere from your neck to your toes.

Sports masseurs

Sports masseurs knead and stroke the muscles with their hands to relieve muscle tension and improve circulation. Massage can improve flexibility and, for some runners, help to prevent injury, but one of the main benefits is simply relaxation. ■

» TOP TIPS

- When looking for a sports doctor, seek a recommendation from a fellow runner to help find a practitioner who specialises in running injuries
- Don't assume that because a friend has the same symptoms as you they have the same injury – obtain a professional diagnosis
- Don't be tempted to take a pain-killer and keep on running – you'll exacerbate the injury, and could turn a short-term problem into a long-term one
- A simple way to check you are running evenly when you come back from injury: count 1, 2, 3 with each footstep, so the 1 falls on alternate sides. Maintain this rhythm and you know you aren't subconsciously altering your gait to protect a vulnerable knee or ankle
- Ask the specialist what has caused the injury – if it's an imbalance in muscle strength, or tight ITBs she'll be able to give you exercises and stretches to do after it's healed to make sure it doesn't reoccur.

GAIN FROM PAIN

Injury occurs to all but the very luckiest of runners, so you had best be prepared if a niggle comes your way

If you do pick up an injury – and if you run for long enough, you almost certainly will – it can be a miserable experience. It's easy to become bogged down in a funereal gloom at the injustice of it all. Which, of course, does you no good at all – just the opposite, in fact. Recovery is your goal, and what you need is an effective way to bridge that depressing gap between the day you're forced to stop running and the day you can start again.

It up to you. You can wallow in self-pity, lose your aerobic base, put on weight and make yourself and everyone around you miserable – or you can keep in shape so you're ready to go as soon as the niggle clears. Here's the plan...

1 NO WHINING

Keep your running injuries in perspective. Most are relatively minor and will heal in due time. It may seem catastrophic when you can't run, but a bad case of shin splints is nothing when you compare it to friends who have real problems, real illnesses and real pain. Don't moan – no one wants to hear it. Not your partner, not

your children, not even your running friends. Besides, complaining is counterproductive to regaining your health and fitness.

The gain You'll stay positive during the lay-off, thus speeding your recovery.

2 BE PATIENT

There are very few runners who haven't been injured at one time or another, and the vast majority of those runners – even one 72-year-old who broke his hip – was able to run again. Unfortunately, no magic pill will cure you instantly. Nor is a simple change of shoes the right answer. Instead, be confident that regardless of how bad your injury may seem, it's only temporary. You will run again, if you're patient enough to allow the healing process the time it needs.

The gain You'll give your injury time to heal.

3 EAT PROPERLY

When you're running, it's easy to go on a "see-food" diet. Any food you see, you eat – in large quantities. So when you stop running it's easy to stack on the pounds unless you exercise a little dietary control. It doesn't mean going on a crash diet; reduced nutrition lessens the body's ability to repair itself. But by focusing on low-fat goodies and fruits and vegetables and reducing beer and crisps intake you can assist your body's mending process and avoid porking out. When you resume running, any weight gain will come off quickly.

The gain Staying lean will keep your self-confidence up.

4 IF YOU HAVE A ROUTINE, STICK TO IT

That is, if you normally run at lunchtime, continue with some sort of exercise at lunchtime. If you're an early morning runner, go for a walk early in the morning.

Try walking one of your favourite routes, maybe a trail, and take the time to enjoy the landscape, flora and fauna. A two-hour walk followed by typical post-run rituals such as stretching, a session with the ice pack, a shower, warm bagels and the paper will deliver recuperation benefits while keeping your morale at healthy levels.

The gain By sticking with some semblance of your exercise ritual, you'll reap many of its mood-boosting benefits.

5 DO IT OUTDOORS

Fresh air is never better than when you're injured. You can scoop up a lot of it on a bike ride. If it's winter, or if the weather is too foul to cycle, just walk. Processing lungfuls of oxygen is one of the things that make you feel good when running, and you'll achieve a similar effect by doing just about any other vigorous outdoor activity.

The gain Checking out the world around you will take your mind off your injury, and you'll be revitalised by a daily dose of fresh air, fresh scenery and (hopefully) sunlight.

6 SWEAT

If you normally run 45 minutes a day, make sure you do some activity vigorous enough to keep you aerobic for 45 minutes. This is critical for hanging on to your sanity, not to mention your aerobic fitness. It doesn't matter too much what you do, as long as it doesn't aggravate the existing injury.

Hit the exercise bike or use some sort of indoor trainer: a cross-country ski machine, a treadmill, a stairclimber. Putting in 45 minutes on an exercise bike, stairclimber or rowing machine, will drench you with sweat. More importantly, several studies suggest that if you do these aerobic alternatives properly and with enough intensity, they can maintain and even increase your fitness level.

The gain You'll end up with a puddle of sweat and a saturated T-shirt – tangible evidence you've done something to burn calories and maintain your aerobic base.

7 LIFT WEIGHTS

Since you're going to be at the gym anyway, riding a stationary bike or on the stairclimber, it's not a big deal to spend another 20 minutes with weights. And, because you're not running, you're doing more legwork than usual, along with some abdominal and upper body stuff.

The gain You'll burn calories and maintain overall fitness and muscle tone.

8 STAY CONNECTED

One of the worst aspects of *(continued on page 188)*

Correct treatment requires correct diagnosis. Beware of these common running maladies...

Hip: Piriformis Syndrome

Recognise it Dull ache deep within the buttock, often accompanied by "referred pain" in the sciatic nerve running down the back of thigh and in the lower back. Becomes worse as you run.
Avoid it Restrict running on cambered surfaces and practise running downhill in a relaxed, controlled manner. Stretch your piriformis, adductors, hamstrings and ITB, and strengthen your abductors. Shoe choice is very important. Also check for leg-length discrepancies.
Treat it Stretch the muscle, and strengthen when pain has gone. Massage also works – try rolling a tennis ball under the affected buttock.

Knee: Patello-Femoral Pain (Runner's Knee)

Recognise it Possible swelling beneath or on the side of the kneecap. Worse after hill runs. In really bad cases, you'll hear or feel a "grinding".
Avoid it Stretch and strengthen quadriceps and hamstrings, so the kneecap tracks correctly. Practise downhill running, and avoid cambered surfaces.
Treat it Ice for 15 minutes, two to three times a day. Try aspirin (it may reduce the breakdown of knee cartilage).

Lower Leg: Ankle Sprain

Recognise it Initial pain may be mild, but increases as swelling occurs. Visible bruising. In severe cases you may hear the ankle "tear".
Avoid it Take care on uneven ground, as tripping and stumbling are the most common causes. Be extra vigilant if you've sprained an ankle before, as the chances of it happening again are increased. Tape your ankle, or wear a support during runs, and strengthen the ankle using a wobble board.
Treat it Stop running. Employ the RICE method: Rest, apply Ice, wear a Compression bandage and Elevate the ankle. After 72 hours, try heat treatment and gentle massage. If symptoms persist, you may need to have your leg X-rayed.

Foot: Plantar Fasciitis

Recognise it Pain and tenderness radiating from heel to mid-sole. Worst first thing in morning and at start of run. Pain fades with exercise.
Avoid it Only increase mileage or speed gradually. Take extra care if you have flat feet or high arches. Stretch and strengthen Achilles and calves (tightness here places pressure on fasciae). Also strengthen foot muscles.
Treat it Ice massage the area and tape foot thoroughly before running.

Achilles Tendon: Tendinitis

Recognise it Pain, which can be dull or sharp, along back of tendon. Reduced ankle flexibility.
Avoid it Regularly stretch your calf muscles. Only add hills and speedwork gradually. Overpronators are particularly susceptible, making correct running shoes crucial. Avoid shoes with high heel tabs.
Treat it Rest. Ice the tendon for 15-20 minutes several times a day. Stretch calf muscles. Only run when completely pain-free.

Lower Leg: Shin Splints

Recognise it Aching, throbbing or tenderness along the inside of the shin. Painful to touch. Worst at start of run and may ease as muscles warm up. Painful straight after run, but eases until next time.

Avoid it Beginners are particularly susceptible, as doing too much, too soon encourages shin splints. Run on forgiving ground. Again, correct shoes are a must. Strengthen and stretch tendons and muscles in the front of your leg.

Treat it Avoid downhills, run on grass and rest as necessary. If persistent, don't run through pain. Ice sore areas three times a day.

Knee: Iliotibial Band Syndrome (ITBS)

Recognise it Dull ache along the outside of the knee and thigh. ITBS usually only causes discomfort during a run. Vanishes when you stop. Outside of knee may swell

Avoid it Avoid running on cambered surfaces, as this will pull the band tight. Run on soft surfaces and stretch hips and glutes to increase band flexibility. Strengthen quads and hamstrings.

Treat it Don't run through it. Regularly stretch the band and ice the painful area. Gently massage the band too.

Upper Leg Injuries: Hamstring Strain

Recognise it Sudden, searing pain, muscle spasms, swelling, weakness and maybe even a "crackling" sound when pressed.

Avoid it Warm up thoroughly before any sudden, fast running. Strengthen and stretch hamstring.

Treat it Rest, and apply ice regularly. Don't run until the pain has gone – in mild cases this can be as little as two days.

Abdominal Injuries: Stitch

Recognise it Sharp pain, usually below the ribcage. Caused by a spasm of the diaphragm.

Avoid it Don't run too soon after a meal.

Treat it Slow down for 30 seconds. Exhale forcefully every time the foot on the opposite side to the stitch hits the ground. Try deep "belly" breathing, or dig your fist hard under your ribcage, and bend your torso to 90 degrees for 10 seconds.

being injured is not being able to run with your friends. The only time you may see some of them is when you run together. So when you're out of action, make an effort to stay in touch and at least feel like you're part of the running scene. A good way to do this is to volunteer to help out at races.

Take the opportunity to spend more time with your family and non-running friends; you've got no excuse for dropping out of things such as playing football with the kids or going to a late-night party.

The gain Instead of becoming too self-absorbed, you'll keep lines of communication open with your friends, family and the running community.

9 MAKE A DAILY EFFORT

While injuries can be markedly different, most of them respond extremely well to rest and self-treatment. If there are things you can do – see a chiropractor or podiatrist, have a massage – do them, even if they seem like a lot of hassle. If all you need to do is ice the injury or take anti-inflammatories, do it religiously. If muscle inflexibility or imbalance may have contributed to the problem, make a point of stretching carefully twice a day.

The gain By taking action, you'll speed recovery and achieve peace of mind.

10 FOCUS ON TODAY

Don't set an arbitrary deadline for when you'll be ready and then start, whether you're healthy or not. With any luck, you'll only be out of action for a few weeks at the most, but you never know how quickly you'll heal. It doesn't follow that an injury that took four days to heal last time will do so again. As you age, it takes longer for your body to heal.

You may also have to forget about that upcoming race you'd planned on running (especially if it's a marathon). Just because you signed up for it doesn't mean you have to run it. Running a race while carrying an injury is dangerous. Don't do it. There'll be other races. If your injury does heal before the race, be prepared to lower your expectations. Be happy you're on the starting line and in one piece, and enjoy the race.

The gain By not setting strict deadlines, you won't become frustrated when you miss them. More importantly, you won't start running before you're ready. ■

CHAPTER 7

Cross-Training

You can have too much of a good thing, and as running definitely falls into this category it's well worth taking a break from it every once in a while. Including other forms of exercise in your training programme will keep you fresh mentally and physically and will actually make you a better runner. Working out in the gym, going for a swim or a bike ride can boost your endurance, improve your flexibility and even help prevent injury. Plus it gives you a chance to exercise with your non-running friends and family. For a truly balanced weekly programme, a little cross-training reaches the parts that running can't.

CROSS ROADS

Good cross-training can be the best way to run faster

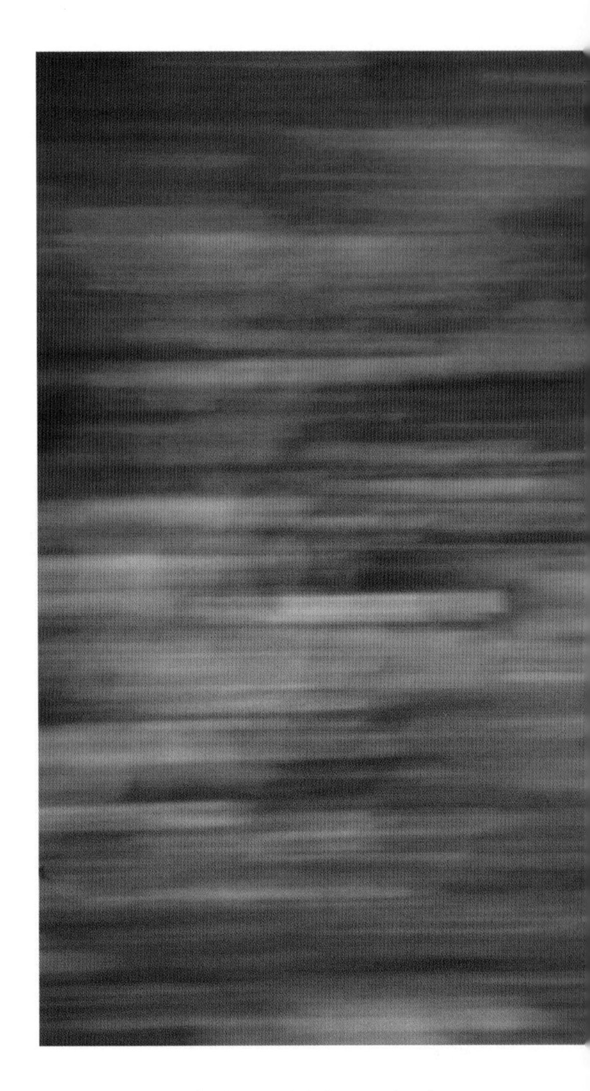

Cross-training can be a tough concept for many runners to grasp. It's not that we don't believe that a variety of workouts is good for us. It's just that we can't work out where the training time is going to come from. Making time for a 30- to 40-minute run is often difficult enough, so how are you going to swim and bike and row and all that other stuff?

Maybe we feel under pressure to put more effort into cross-training because of the increasing interest in triathlons and other multi-discipline events. To be an elite triathlete, some people spend hours every day training. Who needs it?

Fortunately, no one but an elite, multi-disciplinary athlete needs it. The rest of us can benefit from much more realistic doses of cross-training. Still, it's hard to work out how to begin, how much and what kinds of cross-training to do. These are the questions that are answered in this chapter.

Life used to be simple. Runners ran, and swimmers swam. Cyclists pedalled and weight-lifters grunted. Then everything got mixed up. Runners started cycling, swimmers lifted weights, cyclists starting running. Now, it's not unusual to see athletes climbing stairs that go nowhere, or cross-country skiing over a gym floor.

Strangest of all, while these varied activities may look a bit odd, they're actually very good for you. By doing them you'll stretch certain muscles, strengthen others and burn plenty of calories, but what exactly is cross-training supposed to do for runners? And, given all the cross-training choices, which are the best ones for you?

THE "DO MORE, GET FITTER" THEORY

Proponents of this position believe that runners should cross-train with exercises and activities that are as close to running as possible.

The logic The stronger you make your running muscles, the better you'll run.

THE REST THEORY

According to this approach, runners should cross-train with sports that are as different from running as possible.

The logic You can burn calories and get a good workout, and, at the same time, you'll be resting your running muscles and won't be creating the one-sport muscle imbalances that often lead to injury.

THE SPECIFICITY THEORY

Specificity advocates believe that runners shouldn't cross-train – and that's the end of it. It's a waste of time and will only tire you for your next run. When you need a day off from running, take a day off from everything.

The logic Training is sports specific, so the best way to train for running is to run.

No wonder so many runners are confused about cross-training. Who are they supposed to believe, and which theory should they follow? "All of the approaches make sense and could work," says Dr Mike Flynn, an exercise physiologist and one of America's leading researchers in cross-training.

The trick to optimising your training programme, he explains, is to pick the approach that best fits your current running and fitness goals.

To make your decision easier, we've designed cross-training programmes for five different types of runner. Simply find the category that best describes you and follow the suggested advice.

BEGINNERS

This is for runners who run five to 15 miles per week.

The basics If you're running to get into shape, the first thing you need to do is build up your cardiovascular system. A strong heart and lungs will supply more fuel to your working leg muscles, which will allow you to run without constantly feeling out of breath.

If you're switching to running from another sport, you're probably fit enough to run a few miles without much problem, but don't try to do too much too soon. Running involves more pounding than most other sports, and it takes a while for the muscles, tendons and ligaments to adapt.

The programme The best cross-training programme for beginners is one that mixes running and cross-training in equal amounts.

If you're running twice a week, then try cross-training twice a week as well. This will allow you to build your cardiovascular system and muscle strength simultaneously, without undue risk of injury. Another good idea: since your body may not be prepared to handle more than one hard run a week, split your hard workouts between running and cross-training.

The exercises As a beginner, almost any aerobic activity will help to increase your cardiovascular strength. The best exercises are those that also strengthen as many of your running muscles as possible. These exercises will improve the co-ordination of your running muscles and teach them to process and store fuel more effectively.

INTERMEDIATE RUNNERS

This is for runners who clock up 15 to 40 miles per week.

The basics You have developed a strong cardiovascular system through your running. Hence, easy cross-training workouts won't improve your running performance. You need to choose cross-training activities that either provide a very high intensity cardiovascular workout or specifically target your running muscles.

The programme You should be running two to three times as much as you are cross-training. Run for two or three days, and then do a cross-training workout. If you are doing two hard runs a week, select cross-training workouts that allow you to exercise at a moderate pace. You should be using these workouts just to give your running muscles some extra training without extra pounding. If your body can handle only one hard run a week, then one of your cross-training workouts should be an interval or tempo workout (a run that starts off easy, builds to a steady speed in the middle and then finishes at an easy pace).

The exercises Cross-training exercises that provide high-intensity cardiovascular workouts are cross-country skiing, stair climbing and high-cadence stationary cycling. "Grinding away in a high gear on a bike will slow your turnover, but using a high cadence (over 90 rpm) will keep you quick and allow you to get your heart rate up," says Dr Tim Moore. For muscle-specific workouts, stick with cross-country skiing, in-line skating and stair climbing.

ADVANCED RUNNERS

This is for those who run more than 40 miles per week.

The basics You have probably maximised your cardiovascular conditioning, as well as the strength,

efficiency and co-ordination of your leg muscles, so cross-training won't directly do you much good. To improve your running performance, you need more quality in your runs. Running coaches and exercise physiologists generally recommend at least two hard runs a week – a shorter interval session on the track and a longer tempo run on the road or trails.

The programme Since both hard running and high mileage can increase your injury risk, your best bet may be complete rest rather than cross-training. This will allow your muscles to recover completely for your next run. If you don't want to take days off, you can consider low-intensity cross-training with a sport that doesn't tax your running muscles. This will burn calories, and the variety will keep you mentally fresh. Some researchers have even found that very light activity may help you recover more quickly than complete rest.

If you choose to cross-train, replace one or two of your easy runs – preferably the ones that come a day after a hard run – with a cross-training activity.

The exercises Cycling, pool running, swimming and rowing will all give your running muscles a break and let them recover for your next hard run.

INJURY-PRONE RUNNERS

This is for runners who experience two or more running injuries per year.

The basics Surveys show two out of three runners will be injured in the course of a year. "With two to three times your body weight coming down on your legs with every stride, each step you run brings you closer to injury," says Flynn, "and if you have a biomechanical problem, the risk is greater."

This doesn't mean, though, that you can't run. Cross-training can help in two ways. First, it can keep you healthy by allowing you to stay fit without the constant pounding of running. Second, cross-training can help forestall the performance losses that come when an injury keeps you from running. Studies have shown that runners can maintain their running times for up to six weeks by cross-training alone if it is done at the proper intensity.

The programme The best cross-training programme for injury-prone runners includes two to four runs per week (depending on how much your body can tolerate) and two cross-training workouts. Both cross-training workouts should target running-specific muscles in order to increase their strength and efficiency without subjecting them to more pounding.

The extra training of these muscles through cross-training rarely produces injuries since high impact is the main injury cause, but if you're unsure, ask your doctor. Also, since many running injuries are induced by high-intensity workouts, don't run more than one of these per week.

The exercises As stated above, injury-prone runners should keep their cross-training workouts as specific to training as possible. In-line skating, stair climbing, rowing and cross-country skiing are good choices. Unfortunately, some injuries – stress fractures in particular – don't allow many cross-training options. In these cases, cross-training in the pool by swimming or deep-water running is the best alternative. These are non-weight-bearing activities that don't hurt the legs.

GENERAL-FITNESS RUNNERS

This is for low- to mid-mileage runners who are more concerned with overall fitness than racing performance.

The basics Look at any elite runner, and you'll notice that running doesn't do much for the upper body. It also neglects quadriceps in favour of the calves, hamstrings and buttocks. Furthermore, after the age of 30, all the muscles in bodies begin to lose some of their strength. Fortunately, exercise can cut the rate of losses almost in half.

The programme For total-body fitness, run twice a week and do a complementary exercise on one or two other days of the week. In addition, 20 minutes of circuit weight training twice a week will help you condition any muscles that you may have missed.

The exercises General-fitness runners need exercises that target the upper body and quadriceps. The best choices are rowing, swimming, cross-country skiing and cycling on a stationary bike that has attachments to work your upper body. ■

HARD CORE

A little gym work can lend a lot to your running

It's not just strong legs and lungs you need for running. You need core strength too – a strong mid-section to help maintain posture and running style when you tire. To keep running efficiently, you need to strengthen your lower abdominals, hamstrings, glutes, quads and rotators of the hip, in the functional movement patterns that allow the muscles of the legs and core to work together.

You should perform the exercises below two or three times a week, either on a day you are not running, or after your run. The following exercise series is recommended by corrective exercise specialist and performance running coach Chris Maund.

LOWER ABDOMINALS

To balance and strengthen the muscles that rotate the pelvis backwards, you need to strengthen your lower abdominals.

Lie on your back with your knees bent. Place one hand under the lower back and the fingers of the other hand just inside and slightly lower than the bony prominence on the front of your hip (see below). From here, gently pull your belly button inwards at about 30 per cent effort. You should feel a muscle push upwards below your fingers – this is your transversus abdominus, the primary stabiliser for your hips, pelvis and spine. You should be able to do this without moving your pelvis or flattening your back – use the hand under the lower back to monitor this. Your aim is to be able to do this while breathing through your nose only, so that your belly rises as you inhale. This is known as diaphragmatic breathing.

The next stage is to contract your pelvic floor at the same time. To do this you need to contract the muscles that you would use to stop yourself from urinating. Once you can complete three repetitions of 60 seconds with a 30-second rest period, you can add alternate leg movements, to replicate the movement of the legs in gait.

To perform this variation you should roll your pelvis backwards slightly and keep a constant pressure on your fingers, under your lower back. The knees stay at 90 degrees and you then slowly lift one leg at a time until the thigh reaches vertical and then slowly lower to the floor. You should then perform the exercise on the other side, maintaining gentle pressure on the fingers. Your aim is to be able to continue the exercise continuously for two minutes.

SWISS BALL HAMSTRING CURLS

In Maund's experience, most runners have hamstrings that are both tight and weak. This means that they need to be both stretched and strengthened to stay injury free. The best way of strengthening your hamstrings is by using a Swiss ball. This stops the lower back muscles from working excessively and pulling you into a pelvic tilt.

To start the exercise, lie on your back with your feet on the ball (which should be inflated firmly and sized so that when you sit on it your legs are at 90-100 degrees). Keep your palms facing up. From here, push upwards from the hips, keeping the glutes tight and the tummy button pulled slightly inwards. The next stage is to pull the ball towards you, keeping your hips high throughout the movement. You should aim to pull the ball up to your backside before extending back out to a bridge position and repeating. The inward and outward movements should take two seconds each. You should aim for eight to 12 repetitions, beginning at one set and gradually increasing to three sets with 45 seconds of rest between sets.

BELT SQUATS

Sit on a bench with your knees at 90 degrees. Place your feet shoulder-width apart with the toes pointed out slightly and the knees directly aligned above your second toes. Take a belt and position it around both thighs, keeping your legs in the same position. Keep the belt in this same position when you start your squats. Begin with a barbell across the front of your shoulders with the arms crossed and elbows kept high. From here, take a diaphragmatic inward breath (as described below in the lower-abdominal exercises), hold the air in your lungs and then draw the belly button inwards. This position will protect your spine through the exercise.

BALL SQUATS

This exercise should be performed with the same form as the belt squats, but using a ball between the knees instead of a belt around them. This recruits the internal rotators of the hip and maintains a balance of hip musculature. Ideally you should use a 12-inch diameter ball or a medicine ball of eight to 12 pounds. Do the exercise with your knees slightly closer together than hip-width, and your feet parallel rather than turned outward.

Perform six to eight repetitions per set. Start with one set and gradually build up to three, with at least 60 seconds between sets. ■

INSIDE KNOWLEDGE

Sometimes circumstances prevent you running outside, but that shouldn't stop you working out, inside – or even building gym sessions into your weekly schedule

Running is such a low-maintenance sport. All you need is some ground to cover, and enough time to cover it, but we're all busy and, especially in winter, those dark afternoons and mornings can make it tough to run outside. That's where the temperature-controlled, bright-as-sunlight, fully equipped gym comes in handy. Another bonus is that since you have access to both cardio and strength equipment at the gym, one visit can provide an excellent two-for-one workout that'll benefit your whole body – not just your legs. Best of all, you can do something worthwhile in as little as 20 minutes. If you have more time, all the better.

We've put together three routines designed to take 20, 40 or 60 minutes, depending on the time you have. They are simple, effective and each comes with running (Plan As) and non-running options (Plan Bs), in case you're in the mood for a little variety.

SESSION ONE – 20 MINUTES

Plan A

Do a hill pyramid on the treadmill. Warm up for three minutes, then increase the incline by two degrees at a time (for two minutes at each setting). After four increases, lower the platform in two-degree increments (stay at each level for one minute). Total time on the treadmill: 15 minutes.

Straight after, get down on the floor for 20 crunches, 20 back extensions and 20 press-ups. Or find three or four strength machines that work the upper body (chest press, biceps curl, triceps pushdown), and aim for 10-15 repetitions on each. Cool down by walking for two minutes.

Plan B

Hit the stationary bike, stepper or elliptical trainer. Start with a three-minute warm-up, then increase your intensity to 70-80 per cent of your maximum heart rate. Continue for a total of 10 minutes, then head to the rowing machine for eight minutes of high-intensity intervals (one minute at 80- to 85-per cent effort, 30 seconds of recovery). Cool down with two minutes of easy rowing.

SESSION TWO – 40 MINUTES

Plan A

Jump on the treadmill for a 35-minute hill pyramid (five-minute warm-up, 20 minutes of increasing inclines and 10 minutes of decreasing gradients). Then do one or two sets (about 10 minutes) of the following exercises:

Assisted Pull-ups

With a chair below you, grab a pull-up bar with your hands roughly shoulder-width apart, palms facing you. Slowly lower yourself until your arms are nearly straight; pause, then pull yourself back up into the starting position. Use your chair between repetitions, when needed.

Ball Crunches

Lie with your mid-to-lower back on a Swiss ball, knees at a 90-degree angle, torso parallel to the floor and fingers laced behind your head. Crunch up, pause, then slowly uncurl back down.

Ball Press-ups

Get into the press-up position with your hands on a Swiss ball. Bend your elbows and lower your chest, hold, then straighten your arms.

STAR TRAC Pro

EFX544

Wall Squats

Stand with a Swiss ball between your lower back and a wall, then squat down as if you were sitting in a chair, letting the ball roll against your back as you slide down. Stop when your thighs are parallel to the floor, then slowly straighten your legs again.

Plan B

Warm up for five minutes on a stationary bike, stepper or elliptical trainer. Then for the next 20 minutes, do 20- or 30-second bursts of high-intensity effort (alternating with 30 seconds of recovery); then cool down for five minutes. Follow that with two sets (10-15 repetitions each) of these three plyometric (explosive jumping) moves, which replicate hill running.

Bench Jumps

Stand in front of a low bench. Bend slightly forward at the waist, keeping your knees soft and your hands at your sides. Swing your arms back, lower your hips slightly, and jump up on to the bench, swinging your arms forward as you jump. Try to land as lightly as you can. Pause briefly, then step off the bench, and repeat.

Depth Jumps

Start as described above, this time on top of the bench. Now jump forwards and on to the floor. Pause briefly, then step back on to the bench, and repeat.

Jump Lunges

Stand with your feet together and hold your hands behind your head with your fingers laced and your elbows sticking straight out. Step forward with your right foot, lowering your hips and balancing your weight between your feet. Now spring up vertically, quickly "scissoring" your legs so that your left foot is in front and your right leg at the back as you land. Hold, then spring up, and reverse your legs again.

SESSION THREE – 60 MINUTES

Plan A

Spend 40 minutes on the treadmill (five-minute warm-up, 25 minutes going up the hill pyramid and 10 minutes going down). Then do three sets of 10 to 15 repetitions of the following moves, which use rubber or elastic band, a weighted ball or your body's own weight as resistance. Again, keep your movements slow and controlled, counting to two in each direction.

Side-Bends

Stand holding a weighted medicine ball over your head (as if taking a throw-in during a football match). Keeping your arms straight, bend at the waist (about 15 degrees) to the right, then straighten up, and bend to the left.

Rubber-Band

Stand with your right foot a few inches in front of your left, with a stretching band under your right toe; grab each end of the band so that it's tight. Pull your elbows up and back and squeeze your shoulder blades together; hold, then slowly lower your hands.

Standing Calf Raises

Stand on a stair or wooden block with your heels hanging off the edge. Raise up onto your toes, then slowly drop back down.

Triceps Dips Sit on the edge of a bench and grip the edge with your hands just beside your hips. Supporting yourself with your arms, slide your hips forward and off the bench, lower them slowly until your waist is level with the seat, then straighten your elbows.

Travelling Lunges

Stand with your feet together, holding a dumbbell in each hand. Step forward as far as you can with your right leg, lowering your hips as you land (don't bend your right knee any more than 90 degrees). Lift yourself forward and up into the starting position; repeat with your left leg.

Plan B

Spend 40 minutes on the bike, stepper or elliptical trainer (five-minute warm-up, 30 minutes at a steady 70 to 80 per cent effort, and five-minute cool-down). Then, for the next 20 minutes, perform one or two sets (12-15 repetitions each) of the following exercises, using either machines or free weights. Make your movements slow and controlled, counting to two in each direction.

Chest Press

Starting with your elbows bent at 90 degrees and your upper arms at shoulder level, straighten your arms and concentrate on using your chest muscles to push the weight away.

Lat Pulldown

Using an underhand grip, grab the bar's handles and extend your arms up into a "V". Lean back slightly, and pull the bar into your chest, keeping your elbows at your sides and your abdominals contracted.

Military Press

Begin as with the chest press (above), but push the weights straight up, using your deltoids (shoulder muscles).

Machine Crunches

As you pull the weight down, isolate your abdominals by trying to make your belly button touch your spine.

Leg Press

Focus on using your quadriceps to push the weight away, and engage your hamstrings to control its return.

Travelling Side-Lunges

Stand with your feet slightly wider than hip-width apart, with your toes pointing forwards, and hold a dumbbell in each of your hands. Drop your hips into a squat, keeping your quadriceps parallel with the floor. Lift your right foot and take a big step to the side, shift your weight, and bring your right leg under you. Continue for 10 steps to the right then switch directions.

Triceps Extensions

As you extend the weight, concentrate on only using your triceps (keep your other arm muscles relaxed).

Biceps Curls

Start with your palms facing in, and focus on your biceps – not your hand – as you lift. ■

NEW YORK
NEW YORK
November
ING
NEW YORK CITY
MARATHON

WHY **WEIGHT?**

Start this simple, no-frills strength programme today – and run injury-free for years to come

This simple 20-minutes-per-session programme focuses on the "core" muscles of the upper and lower back, as well as the abdominals, glutes, quadriceps and hamstrings. When any of these core muscles weakens, imbalances can occur, and that's when the stress of running shifts to vulnerable joints – the ankles, knees, shins and hips – leading to injury. "Think of this programme as system-building," says Jim Porterfield, a personal trainer with a master's degree in exercise physiology. The exercises work together to strengthen core muscles and remove any weak areas.

Two or three of these 20-minute sessions a week should help develop the strength you need. "You should feel a little muscle soreness the day after lifting," says Porterfield, "which is why you should schedule strength work-outs to be at least two days apart." There's no magic number of repetitions, but generally, you should be "feeling the burn" when you get up to between 12 and 15 reps. If you get above 15 reps with no strain, increase the weight. Remember, though, that you should stop a particular lift when you're unable to do it smoothly.

THE PROGRAMME

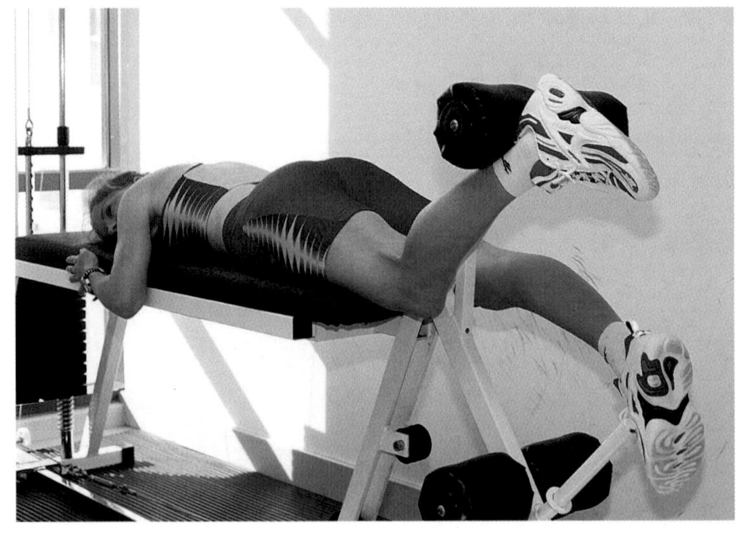

1 LEG CURLS

Benefits Leg curls strengthen the hamstrings and glutes, which in turn help to stabilise the hip and knee joints and improve forward propulsion of the body.

Description On the leg-curl machine, lie on your stomach with your knees just over the edge of the bench and your Achilles tendons pressing against the roller pads. Hold the side grips with your hands to prevent your body from sliding. One leg at a time, curl your leg upward to bring the roller pads close to your buttocks. Lower your leg back down slowly to complete the stroke. After doing reps with one leg, switch to the other. On a cautionary note, though, don't do this exercise if you've had a recent hamstring injury.

2 QUAD LIFTS

Benefits Quad lifts strengthen the quadriceps, that all-important muscle group at the top front of the leg. Strong quads stabilise the knee, cutting down on injuries to this critical joint.

Description Sit on the quad-lift machine with your feet hooked under the roller pads. Lift one leg at a time, extending the leg nearly straight out and then gently bringing it down to the starting position to finish the stroke. After doing reps with one leg, switch to the other.

3 SQUATS

Benefits This venerable exercise strengthens the glutes, quadriceps, hamstrings and lower back. When these three muscle groups are strong, you're better able to withstand the impact of each footfall, and you improve your ability to lift and drive the legs forward with each stride.

Description Stand with your legs shoulder-width apart and rest a weighted lifting bar across your shoulders behind your head. Holding the bar with both hands while keeping your back straight, slowly bend your knees. Squat down to a point where you can also stand back up, as if you were going to sit in a chair but stood up the moment you touched the seat. Keep your feet flat on the floor during the entire exercise. Squats can also be done with dumbbells in each hand (held over the shoulder), or on a squat machine.

4 LEG PRESSES

Benefits Similar to squats, leg presses strengthen the quads, glutes and hamstrings (though not the lower back). Again, strengthening these critical muscle groups will steel you against the impact that running causes, and they'll improve your push-off power.

Description Position yourself comfortably, with your feet shoulder-width apart and your back firmly against the pad. Release the lever holding the weight in place and push upwards, straightening both legs. Once your legs are straight, allow the weight to come back down, bending your knees to a point where you can comfortably push the weight upwards again. Push the weight back up to complete the stroke.

5 BACK EXTENSIONS

Benefits Back extensions strengthen the muscles of the back. Strong back muscles ensure an upright, efficient posture and limit unnecessary rocking of the torso.

Description Either on a back-extension machine or a bench, lie face-down with your hips over the support pad of the machine or over the end of the bench and, with your arms folded across your chest, slowly lift your torso above horizontal (so your back arches slightly), then lower your torso to well below horizontal. With this strength exercise, you can do 15-20 reps initially, and work up to 30 or more reps as your back strength improves.

6 CRUNCHES

Benefits Like their ancestor, the sit-up, crunches work the abdominals. Strong abdominals stabilise your trunk during running, so you're less likely to experience excessive and inefficient torso twisting.

Description This exercise isn't weight lifting per se, but it's an important one for building core strength. Lie on your back on the floor, with your knees bent at a 45-degree angle. Cross your arms over your chest and raise your shoulder blades an inch or two off the floor. Keep your torso straight as you rise off the floor; don't curl upward toward the knees. Move slowly and deliberately. Return to the starting position to complete the stroke. As with the back extensions, you should work up to at least 30 reps of this exercise. Advanced crunches can be done on an incline board.

7 LAT PULL DOWNS

Benefits These strengthen the latissimus dorsi muscles (the large muscles of the upper back), ensuring an efficient forward-and-back (as opposed to an across-the-chest) arm swing. Proper arm carriage makes your overall running stride smoother and more economical.

Description Most runners who use lat machines in the gym pull the weight down behind the head. A better way to target the lats is to pull the bar in front of your head to your chest. This puts less stress on the neck and shoulders. Straighten your arms slowly to complete the stroke.

CORE ISSUES

Six exercises to get right to the core of your training and work those oft-neglected back, stomach and hip muscles

As runners, we tend to focus on building a stronger heart (cardiovascular system) and stronger legs, but too often we neglect the areas in between. That's a mistake. A mechanical structure is only as good as its weakest link, and weak core muscles can lead to injuries and below-par race efforts. Not to mention less-than-iron abs.

In recent years, core strength training, which develops the muscles of the stomach, back and hips, has become one of the hottest areas in the fitness field. Increasing numbers of athletes in all sports have come to realise core training gives you more than just gorgeous, washboard abs – it also improves your performance and reduces injuries.

Take your pelvic area, for example. "When your pelvis is not aligned properly while you run, you become prone to injury," says Mark Fidel, director of Sports Medicine Institute International, and designer of many of the following exercises. "You can get hamstring pulls, Achilles problems and lower-back pain," he adds. Which is why you need strong core muscles to keep your pelvis right where it's supposed to be.

A well-balanced core also helps to improve your running economy. "The stronger your core is, the more solid you are as you hit the ground," explains exercise physiologist Jack Daniels. "This reduces your need for unnecessary stabilisation, and allows you to be a more economical runner," he adds.

Each of the following exercises is designed to help you develop that strength and stability. Fidel suggests doing the exercises in the order shown, and resting for 15 seconds before moving to the next exercise. After completing all six, take a three- to five-minute break, and repeat the entire series. Try to complete this routine three times a week.

While doing each exercise, move slowly and aim for total control. If you get tired and lose form, stop for the day. It's more important to maintain quality than quantity. ■

1B

1 Step Downs

(A) Lie on your back with one hand under your lower back. Lift your legs so your thighs are at a 90-degree angle to the floor, and bend both knees to a 90-degree angle. **(B)** Tighten your lower back so it doesn't move up or down, and slowly lower your right foot to within one inch of the floor. Keep your right knee bent at a 90-degree angle, and maintain the position of your left leg. Hold your right foot one inch off the floor for two seconds, then return it to the start position and repeat the action with the left foot. Do the full sequence three to five times.

2A

2B

2 Prone Stabiliser

(A) Start on your stomach, and raise yourself into a modified press-up position with all your weight balanced on your forearms and toes. Keep your back as straight as possible.

(B) Slowly raise your left leg until it is in line with your back. Hold this position for four seconds, then lower the left leg and repeat for four seconds with the right leg. Run through this left-right sequence three to five times.

3A

4

3 Bridge

(A) Lie on your back with your arms behind your head, and your feet planted on the floor directly below the knees. Press down on your feet, and lift your torso and thighs until they form a straight line. **(B)** With your weight on your shoulders and your feet, slowly extend the right leg by straightening the knee. (Be sure to keep your back straight.) Hold for four seconds, then repeat with the left leg. Repeat three to five times for each leg.

3B

4 Side Stabiliser

Lie on your right side with your right elbow under your shoulder, and your left foot resting on your right foot. Press down with your forearm and foot until you lift your body off the ground. Keep your body as straight as possible; don't allow your hips to sag. Hold this position in a controlled fashion for 30 seconds. Repeat on your left side.

5A SIDE VIEW

5B SIDE VIEW

5 Fire Hydrant

(A) Start on your hands and knees. **(B)** Maintaining the 90-degree angle of your left knee, lift your left leg until the thigh is parallel with your upper body. Hold for four seconds, then lower.

(C) Repeat the same motion, but this time continue it by forcing the knee and thigh as far to the left as possible. Hold for four seconds. Do the same with the right leg. Repeat both sequences three to five times.

5B TOP VIEW   **5C** TOP VIEW

6A

6 Supine Stabiliser

(A) Lie on your back with your legs fully extended. With your elbows under your shoulders, lift your entire body onto your forearms and heels. Keep your legs, hips and back as straight as possible. **(B)** While maintaining this position, lift your left leg four inches off the floor. Hold for four seconds, then repeat with your right leg. Do both sequences three to five times.

6B

CHAPTER 8

Women's Running

It was once said that men are from Mars and women are from Venus but when it comes to running we are all from the same planet: what applies to the male, applies to ladies too. There are some considerations that men don't have to make, though. From the physical and biological to the emotional and social, women can face barriers to their training that can seem insurmountable, but there's no problem you have that another woman hasn't already overcome. Here's how they do it.

THE **BALANCING** ACT

What with all of life's other demands, running can seem like just another chore – but that shouldn't, and needn't, be the case

There's a name for women who pursue a career, family, exercise and social life – they're called superwomen, but by that measure, what busy woman isn't a superwoman? Today, increasing and myriad demands on time mean every day is a balancing act of priorities. Although on some days you might juggle it all with aplomb, at other times your tugging requirements can cause life's fabric to fray at the edges, and when life's fabric frays stress is never far away.

Running presents both a solution to this problem and a contribution to it. Finding the time to run adds another task to the to-do list in an already overbooked day. Yet for so many women, running is their salvation, their key to health and sanity; certainly more necessity than luxury.

TAKING THE TIME

"Exercise is not a selfish thing," says Susan Kalish, executive director of the American Running Association. "You become a better person, and that ultimately helps your family, your work, and everything else. Exercise keeps you young. It helps keep you who you want to be over the years." Kalish, a mother of two, says she never feels guilty about making time for running. Aside from the health benefits, running makes her a more confident and optimistic person. "I'd rather give my family an energetic mum who's going to be around a long time than not take the time to run," she says.

Research has shown that a programme of regular running or walking reduces anxiety, stress, and depression and increases feelings of well-being and self-esteem. Those things in turn translate into a healthy lifestyle that fosters more energy, better relationships, and a better outlook on life. Being fit makes you a positive role model for children. It creates a foundation of self-respect that permeates your other relationships, and it inspires confidence in all of life's exploits. "When you are a strong person, you will be treated as a strong person," Kalish says.

CONDESCENDING OBJECTORS

Unfortunately, not all boyfriends and husbands are as thrilled by your running as you are. Reactions in partners can range from the rather silly (he's embarrassed because it turns out you're faster than he is) to the frightening (he's threatened by your new-found confidence and discourages you from continuing).

If your partner is less than supportive of your running, try to determine the reason. If he's a non-runner, he might be jealous of your time away from him or of your improving fitness. In this case, encourage him to join in on the act. Otherwise, as you grow more serious about your running, the gap between you and your partner in terms of fitness, lifestyle, and time commitment will only grow wider, maybe irrevocably so. If he already is a runner and still disapproves, he's probably uncomfortable with the idea that you can keep up with him – or beat him – on the road. Sadly, some men hold on to the archaic and chauvanistic belief they should be able to beat any woman at any athletic pursuit.

If you happen to be with such a man, you can sidestep this affront to his masculinity by isolating your running from his, but perhaps better for the long term (and for womankind in general) is to let him come to grips with it on his own terms – and be sure to inform him that the best women runners can beat virtually any man, so he's not in bad company. Women whose partners never come to accept their running might have a problem that's much larger than disagreement over your running predilection. Although a husband might complain about the amount of time spent running, the real issue could be one of control.

RUNNING COMMITMENTS

Even if you're already convinced your health – and your running – is a priority, scheduling your runs on busy days can still be a struggle. So...

Do it first It sounds crazy, but many women run as early as four or five in the morning, when interruptions and excuses are least likely. If you have trouble overcoming the temptation to sleep another hour, set your shoes and clothes by your bedside so they serve as a reminder of your commitment come morning.

Do it immediately after work A run can help shake-out job stress and serve as a relaxing end to the day, but beware of motivation sappers, such as the couch and the television. Instead of stopping at home first, go straight from work to your running location.

Use creative scheduling at work Arrive earlier in the day or work later at night in order to take a midday break. Make your runs more than just exercise. Instead of meeting friends for lunch or dinner, suggest a group run.

CHILD-CARE ISSUES

If you have an infant or toddler, you may have plenty of time on your hands – time stuck in the house making sure your little darling doesn't create any mischief. Several of the following options will help you combine your workout time with family time, which works especially well for multi-taskers with busy schedules.

Strollers These days, it's easy to run with a baby (or even two) in a stroller. Choose a stroller that is specifically designed for running so it can handle wear and tear from the road.

Treadmills Investing in a treadmill is an instant child-care solution that will last for years. You can run at home and maintain a close watch over your child. (A bonus: you'll be happy to have the machine on hand when the weather turns ugly.)

Pool running You can take your child along while you run in the deep end of a public pool. Pool running is accomplished with the help of a special flotation belt available at sports shops. They can also be borrowed or rented at many public pools.

Babysitting co-ops Find or start a group of women runners who have young children. Each woman can take turns watching the little ones on one day while the others run.

Tracks and parks When children are old enough to play on their own, you can bring them with you to a track, park, or other area of limited size.

Family fitness Have young ones ride a bike alongside as you run.

FUN RUNNING FOREVER

To strike a balance, try to find a place for running not only during your day or week but also within your life. The role of running in your life inevitably changes over time. Your fitness goals may fall by the wayside when life intervenes in the form of work, children, marriage, or anything else that puts demands on your time and energy.

›› 30 THINGS EVERY WOMAN SHOULD KNOW ABOUT RUNNING

Knowledge is power, in running as in any other pursuit. The more you know about training, nutrition and health, the better you'll be at maximising your running, whether that means fitness, weight loss, great race performances or just plain fun. In this section, you'll find loads of useful information to help you reach your goals. These facts and tips cover health, psychology, weight loss, pregnancy and motherhood, training, racing and more. Some apply to all runners, but most address the specific needs of women. You may find things you already know, but we're sure you'll discover new ideas that can help you become the runner you want to be.

1 Running is a state of mind The only thing that determines your success, or lack of success, is the way you think about your running. If it works for you – if it relieves stress, burns calories, gives you time to yourself, enhances your self-esteem – then it doesn't matter what anyone or any stopwatch says about your running.

2 Anaerobic results For female runners, controlled anaerobic training – intervals, hills, fartlek training – may lead to gains in strength and speed similar to those produced by steroids, but without the noxious side effects. Why? High-intensity anaerobic running is one of the most potent stimulators of natural human growth hormones – those that contribute to stronger muscles and, ultimately, enhanced performance.

3 Dire straits Running with headphones outdoors is a safety hazard in more ways than one. You won't be able to hear cars, cyclists or someone approaching who intends to do you

harm. Attackers will always pick a victim who looks vulnerable. When you have headphones on, that means you.

4 Weight loss Fast running burns more calories than slow running, but slow running burns more calories than just about any other activity In short, nothing will help you lose weight, and then keep it off, like running does.

5 Running with child Doctors consider moderate exercise during a normal pregnancy is completely safe for the baby. Running should cause no problems in the first trimester and it should be fine for most people in the second trimester. Few women would run in their final three months, however. The most important precaution is to avoid becoming overheated; a core body temperature above 101°F could increase the risk of birth defects. So make sure you're staying cool enough, and if in doubt, take your temperature after a run. If it's over 101°F, you're probably overdoing it. Also, skip that post-run soak in a hot bath.

6 Running races Races are not just for competitive types. You'll find lots of racers aren't overly competitive. They're out there because it's fun and social, and it motivates them to keep on running.

7 Shoe selection Women generally have narrower feet than men, so when buying running shoes, you're best off going for a pair designed specifically for women, but everyone's different – if your feet are wide, you may feel more comfortable in shoes designed for men. The bottom line: buy the shoe that's best for you. If

If you have become more serious about running, and especially if you are competitive, it can be hard to accept these changes. "You have to roll with the punches," says Kalish. "You do what you can, and you set priorities, but then you must be willing to give yourself a break." For Kalish, it was children who rearranged her priorities. "Work didn't do it; marriage didn't do it; but children certainly did it." She had been competing seriously before the birth of her first child and thought she'd quickly pick up where she left off. "If you'd asked me before, I'd never have said that I would let that affect my training, but then, four months after giving birth, I realised my expectations had to change."

It was years before Kalish was able to resolve the anger and frustration of not being able to resume her running career at the same high level. "I finally realised that I was at a different segment of my life but that I could still have fun with running. My focus now is on building a fit family.

"You just never know which category you'll fall into, whether it will be a piece of cake to run with kids or a job, or whether it will be impossible, and it can change from one experience to the next for the same woman. If you live long enough, you eventually will find balance," Kalish says.

Many women echo her frustration when they are forced to ease their training. They miss the feeling of being at peak fitness and the confidence that comes from pushing limits. They don't like the way their less-fit bodies feel – or look. At times like these, it's helpful to focus on positives. Running can still be a stress reliever, a social outlet, a healthy pastime, and a reason to head outdoors. For all these reasons, any running is still better than no running. Sometimes it can take months or years to adjust, but all those good aspects are still there without the competitive aspects of the sport.

When things aren't going as planned, perspective can be lost, but running itself teaches the importance of patience, endurance, and a long-term outlook. "Occasionally, I have let running control my life," says Betty Roberts, who has been a runner for almost 20 years. "At those times, it ceases to be fun and it becomes the source of my stress rather than the release, but now I realise that even that has helped me to grow. I've learned to recognise when it is happening – not to take the bait of every challenge – and to have fun with my running. That's the key, since I know it's a thread that will weave its way through my entire life." ■

---

there's any question – or if you suffer blisters or injuries because of ill-fitting shoes – consult a podiatrist who specialises in treating runners.

8 Reduce cancer rates An American study found running women produce a less potent form of oestrogen than their sedentary counterparts As a result, female runners cut by half their risks of developing breast and uterine cancer, and by two thirds their risk of contracting the form of diabetes most common in women.

9 Sisters united Having another woman or a group of women to run with regularly will help keep you motivated and ensure your safety. It's also a lot more fun than running alone. Women runners become more than training partners; they're confidantes, counsellors and coaches, too.

10 Keep it real Women who run for weight control may lose perspective on what is an appropriate body size. A recent survey of thousands of women found while 44 per cent of respondents were medically overweight, 73 per cent thought they were.

11 Wee oui Men are in and out of public toilets in a flash, while women stand in long, slow queues. When it comes to running, men enjoy the ultimate convenience, but a female runner needn't be a prisoner of her anatomy. Simply find a private place behind a tree or dense shrubbery, squat and pull the lining of your shorts to one side. Just beware of using unfamiliar leaves as toilet paper.

12 Calcium and iron The two minerals women runners need to pay the most attention

WOMEN'S **HEALTH**

Apart from the sort of injuries that can plague all runners – shin splints, black toenails, tendinitis – there are some health issues that are more prevalent in women runners, and some that are exclusively female.

ACNE

Women runners can be plagued by skin breakouts on their face, hairline, upper back, chest, upper arms and buttocks. Sweat production combined with hair follicles or friction from rubbing clothes is a formula for acne. Increased temperature and humidity exacerbate the problem, as do products such as sun screen and make-up, which sweat off on to the skin and clog pores.

To fend off acne, follow these steps:

- Minimise the use of make-up and hair-care products before running. The best make-up for running is no make-up at all. If time allows, wash your face before running, and again after you run before re-applying make-up.
- Use a sunscreen specifically formulated for the face on your face and neck. Choose a gel or lotion for the rest of your body, rather than a cream.
- Wipe acne-prone areas with an astringent pad or towelette immediately after running. (Once your body's natural oils cool, they harden, leading to plugged pores.)
- Change out of sweaty exercise clothes straight after running, and shower as soon as possible.
- Cleanse acne-prone areas thoroughly. Gentle exfoliation can help, but don't scrub to the point of aggravating your skin.
- If you are prone to acne, consult a dermatologist about the use of prescription medication.

"THE PILL"

Researchers disagree about the impact of the pill on athletic performance. Though most studies have shown the pill has no effect on performance, some research indicates it may cause a slight reduction in aerobic capacity.

On the other hand, some runners feel the pill helps performance by reducing menstrual

---

to are calcium and iron (iron is especially important for menstruating women.) Good sources of calcium are dairy products, dark leafy vegetables, broccoli, canned sardines and salmon, while foods high in iron include liver, fortified dry cereals, beef and spinach.

13 Iron Women who train intensively, have been pregnant in the past two years or consume fewer than 2,500 calories a day should conduct more than routine blood tests for iron status, since these test only for anaemia, the final stage of iron deficiency. Instead, ask for more revealing tests, including those for serum ferritin, transferrin saturation and total iron-building capacity.

14 A woman's best friend Running with a dog gives you the best of both worlds – you can run alone, but with a friend. A dog is both a faithful companion who will go anywhere, any time, and a loyal guardian who'll discourage anyone from harming you. The optimal running dog is medium-sized, with a bloodline bred for endurance. An easy rule of thumb: hunting breeds make the best runners.

15 Period gains There's no need to miss a run or a race just because you're having your period. If you're suffering from cramps, running will often alleviate the pain, thanks to the release during exercise of pain-relieving chemicals called endorphins. Speedwork and hill sessions can be especially effective. To guard against leakage, try using a tampon and a towel for extra protection.

16 Skin wins Running helps produce healthy skin. According to dermatologists, running stimulates circulation, transports nutrients and

symptoms. These runners prefer taking the pill so they can control their cycle and don't have to race when they are having their period. Although it is safe to manipulate the timing of your period, experts generally agree this practice should be reserved for major competitions and done only a few times a year. Ultimately, you need to decide for yourself whether taking the pill makes sense for you. For every runner who swears by it, there is another who insists she feels and performs better without it. If you run recreationally, you probably don't have to worry about any athletic impact of the pill. On the other hand, if you race competitively and don't want to risk sacrificing aerobic capacity, you might want to consider using another method of contraception.

INCONTINENCE

Women are more prone to stress incontinence because of their anatomy. It's estimated that one in two women experience some level of urine leakage and it is annoying and disconcerting.

Although running does not cause incontinence, the activity – as well as that of other exercises and sports – can induce urine leakage in women who are already prone to it.

---

flushes out waste products. All of this leads to a reduction in subcutaneous fat, making skin clearer and facial features more distinct.

17 Ignore taunting It may not be much consolation, but men are sometimes verbally harassed and occasionally threatened while running, just as women are. Be sensible when you run, but don't let insignificant taunting limit your freedom.

18 Don't overdo it If you run so much your periods become light or non-existent, you may be endangering your bones. Amenorrhoea (lack of a monthly period) means that little or no oestrogen, essential for the replacement of bone minerals, is circulating in your body. Amenhorroeic women can stop, but not reverse, the damage by taking oestrogen and ensuring they have plenty of calcium. If your periods are infrequent or absent, consult a gynaecologist, preferably one sensitive to the needs of runners.

19 Stronger babies If you were a regular runner before you became pregnant, you might have a bigger baby – good news, since, up to a certain point, larger infants tend to be stronger and weather physical adversity better. Researchers in the US found women who burned up to 1,000kcal per week through exercise gave birth to babies weighing five per cent more than the offspring of inactive mums. Those who burned 2,000kcal per week delivered babies weighing 10 per cent more.

20 In the interest of your own safety Women who run alone should take precautions. Leave a note at home stating when you left,

where you'll be running and when you expect to return. Carry a personal attack alarm. Stick to well-populated areas, and don't always run the same predictable route. Avoid running at night and don't wear jewellery. Pay attention to your surroundings and recurring faces. Carry identification, but include only your name and an emergency phone number.

21 Chest support No matter what your size, it's a good idea to wear a sports bra when you run. By controlling breast motion, it'll make you feel more comfortable. Look for one that stretches horizontally but not vertically. Most importantly, try before you buy. A sports bra should fit snugly, yet not feel too constrictive. Run or jump on the spot to see if it gives you the support you need.

22 Late pregnancy and birth If you ran early in your pregnancy, you might want to try switching to a lower-impact exercise during the latter stages and after delivery. Because of the release of the hormone relaxin during pregnancy, some ligaments and tendons might soften. This will make you more vulnerable to injury, especially around your pelvis. Walking, swimming, stationary cycling and aquarunning (you'll be even more buoyant than usual) are good choices.

23 Run well, eat well Trying to lose fat by eating less and less and running more and more doesn't work The more you exercise and the less you eat, the more likely your body is to "hibernate". That is, you'll conserve calories and thwart your efforts to lose fat. The better bet is to exercise reasonably and increase your food

Many women find relief by strengthening the muscles in the pelvic area with Kegel exercises. To do these, contract your pelvic muscles as if you are attempting to stop a flow of urine. Hold for a few seconds, and then release, and repeat for up to five minutes. For greater effectiveness, do this exercise in a variety of positions: sitting, standing, lying down. There are also several devices that can be bought over the counter or with a prescription that help control leakage. Talk to your GP about what might work best for you.

MENSTRUAL PROBLEMS

Although some women complain of discomfort during their periods, it is generally accepted menstruation has limited impact on exercise performance. Women have run well, set records and won championships at all phases of the menstrual cycle. Clinical studies have shown no change in heart-rate, strength or endurance during the cycle. Exercise can improve your feelings of well-being before and during your period. Some doctors even prescribe exercise for women who suffer discomfort at this time of the month. Research has shown moderate exercise can alleviate physical pre-menstrual syndromes, including breast tenderness and fluid retention. Working out regularly is also thought to relieve the mood disturbances characteristic of premenstrual syndrome.

A potential problem for runners is the cessation of menstruation. Women who run strenuously may be at higher risk of having "athletic amenorrhoea", or irregular or absent periods. Training stress, performance pressure, low body fat and inadequate nutrition are all possible contributing factors. These elements create an equation of energy balance, and when it tips towards the negative – whether from running itself or from associated stress – some women will suffer menstrual irregularities. Young runners, those who train at intense levels and those with a history of menstrual irregularities are most likely to suffer from these problems.

One of the most serious consequences of amenorrhoea is osteoporosis, which happens because female hormones, which protect calcium in bone, are in short supply. An early onset of osteoporosis can lead to a greatly increased risk of stress fractures and acute fractures, and since decreased bone density is not easily reversed, it might last for the rest of your life.

An additional concern is lack of ovulation.

---

intake early in the day to fuel your training. Eat breakfast, lunch and an afternoon snack. Then eat lightly at dinner and afterwards.

24 Morning has broken Morning is the best time for women to run, for lots of reasons. First, it's the safest time; statistics show women are more likely to be attacked late in the day. Second, studies have shown that morning exercisers are more likely to stick with it, because what you do first thing stays done. Third, it saves you a round of dressing, undressing and showering at lunchtime or later. Fourth, it gives you a feeling of accomplishment, which is a great mental and physical start to the day.

25 Competitive kudos Exploring your competitive side can offer benefits beyond running. Racing can help you tap into a goal-setting, assertive and self-disciplined side of your personality. Channelled correctly, these attributes can boost your success in other parts of your life, such as in the workplace.

26 Monthly moments "That time of the month" (or even the few days preceding it) is not the time when women run their worst. The hardest time for women to run fast is about a week before menstruation begins (a week after ovulation). That's when levels of the key hormone progesterone peak, inducing a much-higher-than-normal breathing rate during physical activity. The excess ventilation tends to make running feel more difficult.

27 Making time Just because you're married and have young children and a job doesn't mean you don't have time to run. Running is time-efficient and the best stress-reducer on the

Because women can menstruate even when not ovulating, the presence of a period does not guarantee a healthy menstrual cycle. A lack of ovulation can signal insufficient levels of progesterone, which can lead to over-stimulation of the uterine lining, putting you at risk of endometrial cancer.

If you suspect you are not ovulating, track your temperature as if you were trying to conceive. A woman's body temperature is generally lower at the beginning of her monthly cycle and higher for the last two weeks. The increase in temperature occurs at the time of ovulation. To track this cycle, take your temperature first thing in the morning, before you wake. If your results don't follow the pattern, the chances are you aren't ovulating. A complete lack of pre-menstrual symptoms is another clue. If your conditions point towards any sort of irregularity, consult your doctor.

OSTEOPOROSIS

Weight-bearing exercise, such as running, can help build and maintain bone density levels in women, but women who have abnormal menstrual cycles, that can arise from the combined physical and mental stresses of over-training and disordered eating, may not gain these benefits.

Several studies have shown women who have disrupted menstrual cycles suffer more stress fractures than their counterparts with normal cycles. These women typically exhibit lower levels of bone mineral density. Although it's generally accepted that hormonal disruptions and premature loss of bone density are linked in female athletes, the cause and effect relationship is not clear. For example, some researchers think the kind of woman drawn to intense exercise is more likely to exhibit stress in all areas of life, which could affect hormone levels even without exercise.

Experts agree women must act to protect themselves from early-onset osteoporosis. It's particularly important as once she is past her mid-thirties, a woman can no longer build bone mass, but only maintain her reserves. You should take every precaution to ensure you are not losing bone mass. That means eating a properly balanced diet – in addition to all the important nutrients, and calcium in particular, you should make sure you are consuming enough fat and calories overall to sustain your level of exercise. Monitor your menstrual cycle, and if there are any irregularities consult your doctor. A bone test might be in order. ■

---

market. You need this time. Taking it for yourself (by letting your husband baby-sit while you run, for instance) will benefit the whole family.

28 Breastfeeding Some studies have suggested that babies dislike the taste of post-exercise breast milk, because it is high in lactic acid and may impart a sour flavour. One study found that nursing mums who logged 35 minutes on the treadmill had to cope with grimacing, reluctant infants if they nursed too soon afterwards. These studies are not conclusive (see page 234) but you may like to either express milk for later feeding, or breast-feed before running.

29 Women sweat less than men However, contrary to popular belief, women dissipate heat as well as men. The reason: women are smaller and have a higher body-surface-to-volume ratio, which means that although their evaporative cooling is less efficient, they need less of it to achieve the same result. Nonetheless, be sure to drink plenty of water (you know you've had enough when your urine runs clear) to offset the effects of sweating and prevent dehydration.

30 Made for marathoning While no one has ever proved the old theory that women are better marathoners than men (because they have more body fat to burn), you never hear anyone argue the opposite. Men tend to use their strength to push ahead in short races, but this can backfire in a marathon. Women seem perfectly content to find a comfort zone and stay there. This makes them ideally suited for the marathon – the ultimate keep-your-cool and keep-your-pace distance. So why not be bold and set your sights on a marathon?

LADIES' **WEAR**

There was a time when women's kit wasn't up to much. Thankfully that time has passed. Tailor-made "sisters'" equipment now abounds

In her book, *The Complete Book of Women's Running*, Dagny Scott recalls trying to find appropriate shoes first as a youngster, and then as an adult runner, in what she calls "the stone age of the sport" – the 1970s. She'd simply buy the smallest men's shoes she could find, and stuff the toes with paper towels.

Eventually, manufacturers started making women's shoes that were more than simply small, cutesy-coloured versions of their regular shoes. The same now goes for all running gear: you don't have to make do with ill-fitting men's clothes and footwear. So be specific in your demands, and remember that investing in quality kit will potentially save you from injury, and will certainly save you from discomfort.

And while function takes precedence over form for this section of your wardrobe, manufacturers know looking good is inextricably linked to feeling good, so you'll find flatteringly cut running kit that makes you want to head out and run.

SHOES

Many women have narrower feet than men of the same shoe size – if you are one of them, try brands such as New Balance or Asics, who do a range of width fittings. Alternatively, Nike's PEG system and adidas' miadidas system allows you to custom-build your own shoe.

Remember, your feet need plenty of room when you're running, so don't let vanity convince you to chose a pair smaller than you really need. Most runners wear trainers at least one size bigger than their normal shoes – if they are too small, you'll end of with sore feet, black toenails, or no toenails at all. There's a full run down of trainer-technology on pages 43-50.

SPORTS BRAS

Along with good shoes, a sports bra is the most important piece of kit you need. The benefits they offer are not dissimilar to a proper pair of trainers: comfort and support are the priorities. There's no one right bra for any particular size or shape, and you'll probably try several before you find one that works for you. Perceptions of acceptable comfort and bounce are individual — you might love a bra that a friend simply can't abide, so trust your own judgment.

There are two different styles of sports bras: the traditional, encapsulating sort that "divide and conquer", and compression bras, that "squash" everything into place. If you have wide shoulders then compression bras may be more tricky to put on and take off.

It is important to replace your sports bra once it has worn out. Watch out for elastic that sags, or fabric that piles or loses its shape. Some women find their shape changes so much during their menstrual cycle that they need bras in two different sizes to stay comfortable. So re-measure yourself if your weight changes, you start or stop taking the pill or go through the menopause – you may well have changed size.

If you have had children and breastfed them, the structure of your breasts will be altered permanently. A bra with a higher front will be more supportive and comfortable. Traditional-style bras are best for new mums who are breast-feeding.

Avoid bras with a deep, elasticated band around the ribs if you want to wear a heart-rate monitor. If a bra has catches or seams that rub, try using a natural, oil-based lubricant. Whatever you use, remember it is likely to discolour a white bra.

For advice, check out a women's sports specialist such as www.girlsruntoo.co.uk, www.lessbounce.com or www.boobydoo.co.uk

WATCHES AND HEART-RATE MONITORS

When RUNNER'S WORLD readers were asked to list their essential kit last year, heart-rate monitors came out on top. Unfortunately for the female runner, using a heart-rate monitor can be an uncomfortable experience, requiring 10 minutes before your run to make an extra hole in the strap of the huge wrist monitor and then another 10 minutes to fit the chest strap under your sports bra in a way that won't inhibit your breathing.

Realising the potential in this market, more HRM manufacturers are producing models for women, and some come with sports-bras specifically designed to accommodate the chest strap without impinging on the performance of either the bra or the sensor.

If you are choosing a watch, go for a female-specific model only if it has all the functions you want. Ask to see the specifications for both male/female versions of the watch you are interested in – unfortunately, there are some manufacturers who think that a runner who wants a watch with a baby-blue strap won't also want a 50-lap stopwatch and multiple-countdown function.

SAFETY

The chances of a woman being attacked while out running are very, very small. But don't take unnecessary risks: be aware of your surroundings, don't wear a personal stereo; if you need more peace of mind, consider carrying a personal alarm and/or your mobile phone. Then if you turn an ankle you can call for a lift, rather than face a long limp home.

A more pressing hazard is being knocked down by a car or a cyclist. Wear bright, reflective clothing for high visibility when running after dark; don't assume a driver has seen you and is going to slow down to let you cross. ■

TWO FOR THE ROAD

Becoming pregnant needn't mean your running has to fall by the wayside. It can benefit you both

It was a beautiful winter day – snowy but sunny – and I felt great running on snow-packed roads. I was as pregnant as possible – that evening, I gave birth. I had gone out for a five-miler, but I felt I could have run forever. No matter how much time passes, I can still mentally put myself on that road. A perfect run on a perfect day." (From Joan Samuelson's bible *Running for Women*.) Okay, so you're not an Olympic champion like Joan Benoit Samuelson – fair enough – but if you're a pregnant runner who wants to maintain her fitness, then your running doesn't have to suffer. While adhering to certain fundamental principles to ensure your health and that of your baby, as an expectant mum you can enjoy running much the same as in your

non-expectant condition, and – who knows – maybe you too will reach Samuelson's state of bliss even before your baby is born.

First and foremost, it's crucial to listen to your doctor's advice. Complications during pregnancy are rare, but if they do arise they may prevent you from carrying on with your training, no matter how committed and motivated you are to running. A frank and open discussion with your obstetrician – particularly about your exercise programme – is essential.

A supportive doctor who recognises the benefits of an exercise programme will not only listen to your concerns, but should also address your individual needs, although you shouldn't hesitate to seek a second opinion if you're uncomfortable with your doctor's diagnosis. Your well-being and peace of mind, as well as the livelihood of your baby, are at stake, so don't be afraid to speak up.

If you've been given the green light to run, then proceed with cautious enthusiasm, says Dr Rod Jaques, medical advisor to the British Triathlon Team at the British Olympic Medical Centre. The health benefits to women who exercise while pregnant have been well-documented. They include: less lower-back pain; reduced amounts of analgesic at delivery; fewer instances of operative deliveries; and fewer cases of post-natal depression. What's more, women who exercise during pregnancy gain less weight, have improved mood and sleep patterns and lose weight more rapidly after giving birth. Although now is not the time to begin a running programme, if you're already an experienced runner then there's no reason to stop – just modify.

HOW INTENSE IS TOO INTENSE?

Dr Jaques notes concrete answers to the questions of "how much and at what intensity?" will never be found on the research block, since scientists will be hard-pressed to find a woman willing to subject her pregnancy to such experiments.

The best evidence doctors can come up with is based on animal testing. "Although we can't make that leap into the human world based on the animal experiments, we can try to extrapolate the effects of high-intensity exercise during pregnancy, interpret the data and apply the results to human beings," he says.

Dr Jaques advises women to keep their heart rate at or below 140 beats per minute (bpm) while exercising. Experiments on pregnant dogs suggest that running at an intensity greater than 70 per cent VO2max (the point of maximum oxygen capacity) for two hours or more is potentially damaging to a litter of puppies: dogs forced to run at such an intensity and duration gave birth to a high proportion of runts and had a greater number of abnormalities in the litter. "Big babies do better, smaller babies do worse," notes Dr Jaques. "If the dog studies are anything to go on, then high-intensity exercise must be avoided to ensure the health of the baby. Use 140bpm as a ceiling."

Furthermore, recent studies conducted on sheep – in which they were made to exercise at 70 per cent of their VO2max – revealed the animals experienced a significant rise in their intrauterine temperature (the temperature within the womb).

Although the human implications are admittedly frightening, the doctor additionally noted that both the sheep and their offspring were perfectly fine at delivery. "Researchers have determined that a rise in intrauterine temperature would have to be fairly prolonged to produce damage," Dr Jaques says.

CHILL OUT AND RELAX

Some research shows an internal body temperature above 101°F may cause birth defects in the developing foetus; yet other studies fail to confirm these findings. Given such conflicting reports, however, most experts agree that a pregnant woman must keep her core body temperature at a recognised safe level (below 101°F) to protect her unborn baby from potential birth defects, particularly to the foetus's central nervous system.

What can an expectant mother do to stay cool? In addition to keeping your heart rate at or below 140bpm, experts advise you to train outdoors, rather than indoors on a treadmill where the wind's cooling effect is eliminated. If you are inside, be sure the area is well-ventilated; keep the windows open and consider investing in a fan or two. Avoid running in very warm and hot conditions. Pregnant women should never run to the point of breathlessness or exhaustion – it's important to work to a comfortable level and not overdo it. You should additionally ensure you remain very well hydrated before, during and after a run. Dr Jaques advises pregnant athletes to drink 100ml of water every 15 minutes during a run, and to keep pumping the fluids afterwards.

During pregnancy, a woman's body produces the hormone relaxin, which relaxes joints and ligaments. Loose joints and ligaments can make you more susceptible to injury, and the gradual widening of your hips will change your biomechanics and make your feet more likely to over-pronate. Easing gently into a run and stretching properly afterwards will help prevent injuries, as will choosing shoes with increased stability and cushioning.

According to the National Childbirth Trust, during the first trimester of pregnancy you may experience increased tiredness, nausea, breast tenderness, pressure on your bladder and constipation. Many of the side effects of pregnancy are due to the sudden rush of hormones in your body. Yet many women surveyed by Dr Jaques report having "a wonderful time" when running during their first trimester. Be sure to map out toilet stops along your route, wear a supportive bra and stop running if you feel too tired at this stage. Weeks 0-14 are crucial as far as your baby's development goes.

At week five the foundations of the brain and the spinal cord are growing, and at week six the head begins to form, followed by the chest and the abdomen. By the 10th week the heart will be pumping blood to all parts of the body and the internal organs will be functioning. Your "little runner" is now completely formed, and just needs to grow.

From weeks 14-28 your pregnancy begins to show, and your breasts grow as milk-producing cells develop. Your pregnancy is now fully-established and your baby is well-formed; you should be feeling more energetic, and any sickness will lessen. Many women experience lower-back pain at this time due to the increased pressure on their pelvis; this may contribute to other unexpected pain, such as knee strain. With the added weight, your running gait may change, so be alert to terrain and traffic while running.

›› TOP TIPS

Here are the golden rules for any expectant runner:

Talk to your doctor or midwife Find out their attitude towards combining exercise with pregnancy.

Train, don't strain Forget about speedwork and long endurance runs. Pay attention to your level of exertion, and mind your heart rate and temperature.

Don't overheat Run in the most temperate part of the day. Drink plenty of fluids before, during and after a run, even if you have to visit the loo more.

Know when to say when Stop running if you begin cramping, gasping for air or feel dizzy. If you experience pain or bleeding or your water breaks, get medical attention immediately.

Consider your options If running is becoming uncomfortable, try walking or swimming – activities that don't introduce new stress to your body.

Dress for success Wear appropriate clothing to avoid overheating. Don't wear tight-fitting clothes.

Eat well Be sure you're getting enough iron, calcium, folic acid and other essential nutrients.

Go easy Running to the point of exhaustion doesn't do you or your baby any good.

Properly formed, your baby now looks like a real human being – and behaves like one: moving limbs in response to stimulation from the brain and exercising his or her muscles. At any time between 18 and 22 weeks you may start to feel the baby moving.

During the last lap of pregnancy your weight-gain – finally – will begin to slow down. You may experience a shortness of breath and your feet may swell, making running taxing. Dr Jaques notes: "It would take a heroic woman who would consider running during this stage of pregnancy. Physically, it's extremely challenging." Concentrated weight gain at the bottom of the sternum and pubic bone makes it difficult, biomechanically, to run.

Add to that the increased back pain, and running begins to seem a rather uncomfortable and painful – though not impossible – proposition. At this point it may be time to consider alternatives to running, such as swimming, cycling, low-impact aerobics or walking. At 28 weeks your baby will be about 14 inches long and will weigh about two pounds; he or she will be gaining weight rapidly, and from week 36 will put on around an ounce a day.

GETTING BACK TO YOUR OLD ROUTINE

Returning to your pre-pregnancy running form largely depends upon two things: the type of birth you experience and your fitness level. In a normal birth – if too much blood wasn't lost at delivery – a woman can most likely begin exercising again when she feels no pain. It's advised to wait at least two days before beginning any aerobic exercise. According to Joan Samuelson's *Running for Women*, exercise begun any sooner may increase bleeding and delay a full recovery.

If you have a Caesarean section, consult your obstetrician. Doctors say you should give yourself at least a week before any light exercise, and at least three weeks for intense exercise. Residual scarring and bleeding may interfere with your ability to return to proper form as soon as you may like. Remember to take it nice and slow. Low-impact exercises, such as walking and swimming, are good choices to ease you back into shape.

Dr Jaques explains that a woman may begin vigorous training from six weeks to three months following delivery – three months is more likely if there were any complications, but since everyone is different it's important to listen to your own body and not to push it if you aren't fully healed.

After pregnancy, the increased plasma volume in your bloodstream may spur recovery. After being mentally starved of running, you may have an increased appetite for it. With less time on your hands now that your little one has arrived, concentrate on quality sessions, which lead to an improved running performance.

MILKING THE SYSTEM

If you've decided to breastfeed your baby, then here's some good news: it seems exercise does not affect the quality or quantity of a mother's milk. Although an American study reported that many babies refuse post-exercise milk because of high levels of lactic acid, it has been suggested that the study may be flawed, since the milk samples were given by bottle, and many breastfed babies simply won't take a bottle if they're not used to it.

It's been widely reported that breastfed babies are less likely to suffer from gastrointestinal problems, diarrhoea, respiratory problems, ear infections, pneumonia and food allergies, than formula-fed babies.

Here are three key tips to bear in mind for those women who run and choose to breastfeed their babies:

- Breastfeed your baby before going out for a run
- Keep note of your weight loss. If you're losing more than one pound a week then add nutritious snacks to your diet in between meals
- Eat healthy, well-balanced meals and stay properly hydrated

For more information on breastfeeding, contact the La Leche League (www.laleche.org.uk), an international support group for mothers who breastfeed their infants. ■

LIFE AFTER **BIRTH**

Sonia O'Sullivan achieved a 5K personal best eight months after having her second baby. Norwegian marathon runner Ingrid Kristiansen was out there winning races just four months after giving birth. In fact, last year's Olympic Games were awash with women athletes achieving lifetime bests, despite having recently had children. So what about us lesser mortals? Can we expect to see our running performances improve after nine months of pregnancy? We spoke to three ordinary women whose fitness gains after pregnancy seem to suggest they can.

VICKI SMITH
Age 38
Children One
PBs before children 5 miles 34:59; 10K 43:49; half-marathon 1:40:50
PBs after children: 5 miles 34:46; 10K 43:00; half-marathon 1:40:12

"Difficult breathing was probably the most noticeable 'symptom' throughout my pregnancy. Even the most simple tasks made me short of breath. However, I carried on running for seven months. My legs were fine and I took it easy, averaging about five miles on each run. I gained about two stones, but it was all out the front. My fellow club runners were very supportive, as were the doctors and midwives. They all encouraged me to carry on as long as I felt okay.

"It's a good job I was so strong and fit when I went into labour because the whole thing was very fast but very difficult. My son's heart kept stopping so they prepared me for a Caesarean, but I did finally manage to push him out. My mother, who used to work on the maternity ward, said my fitness and endurance were absolutely vital in helping me to avoid an operation.

"Joe was born on October 1, and I went out for my first run/walk at the beginning of December. I did my usual five-mile loop in 65 minutes. Everything felt really strange, my insides were all moving about and my pelvic floor didn't seem to exist. After about three weeks I was able to do the same route in less than 45 minutes. Since then, I've gone on to break my five-mile, 10K and half-marathon PBs. I can't say why: I haven't increased my training. In fact, I'm doing less. I run twice a week with the buggy, which I suppose counts as resistance work."

EMMA LITTERICK
Age 34
Children Two
PBs before children 5K 20:42; 10K 44:10; half-marathon 1:35:25; marathon 3:39
PBs after children 5K 20:10; 10K 43:40; half-marathon 1:34:12; marathon 3:33

"After having my first baby, I was determined to get back to pre-pregnancy fitness. I hated carrying all that extra weight and refused to wait the statutory six weeks before heading out for a run. The first few weeks were very painful. I experienced a continual stitch-like feeling across my abdomen as my muscles strengthened and realigned, but everything else felt great. The mental satisfaction from being out there outdid any physical discomfort.

"Within three months, I was back up to my pre-pregnancy times and training load, and I was ready for my first race. I'd just had a baby, so it didn't matter if things didn't go to plan, but they did. I came fourth out of 2,000 runners in a personal best of 20:10. It's difficult to explain this improvement. My training and weight was the same as before my daughter was born but I had more confidence."

HELEN WAGSTAFF
Age 34
Children Two
PBs before children N/A
PBs after children 10K 1:00; half-marathon 2:11

"When I had my first daughter, I no longer had time for the gym, so I tried running. I plodded around the local park three or four times a week. This gave me a great sense of well-being and it helped with the weight loss.

I became pregnant again in September 2001, and didn't get back to running for six months. Again, I built up gradually, starting with a gentle run/walk programme. Soon I was getting up at 5:30am to fit in my sessions before my husband went to work. It has helped me maintain my sanity. This time, the weight loss has been more dramatic. I'm now between a size 8/10, and I'm stronger and a lot more muscular than before and have more self-confidence.

My first race was a local 10K. I structured my training and completed the race without having to walk any of it. Four months later, I entered a half-marathon. I did it in 2:11, and could have run even further. I just felt fantastic when I came over the line."

CHAPTER 9
The Running Environment

For most of us, running in our immediate environment means pounding along on the unforgiving roads and pavements near our homes and offices. Crashing down on the concrete isn't ideal – though we'll tell you how to make the best of it – so why not head out into the countryside and hit the trails or just take a detour into your local park, defy the park-keeper and take to the grass? Better still, head to sunnier climbs and run on the beach for a sandy speed session. Just make sure that you heed our advice on training in the heat.

SURFACE WITH A MILE

Not all running surfaces are created equal, so we've rated seven of them – from asphalt to woodland – giving you the pros and cons of each

One of the beauties of running is that you can run on just about any surface, anywhere in the world, but not all surfaces are created equal. Vary your location and you'll vary your session because of the different impact involved. (Scores are out of 10.)

1 GRASS

At its best, the grassland of parks, golf courses and football pitches provides the most natural surface for running. Areas where sheep graze are often home to fine, close-cropped turf.

Pros While grass is soft and easy on the legs in terms of impact, it actually makes your muscles work hard. This builds strength and means you'll notice the difference when you return to the road. When it's flat, it provides an excellent speedwork surface (spikes may be necessary in wetter conditions).

Cons Most grassland is uneven and can be dangerous for runners with unstable ankles. It can be slippery when wet, aggravate allergies, tire legs surprisingly quickly. Finally, while the very best grass for running is often found on bowling greens and golf courses, the owners are not always happy to find you on them.

Conclusion If you can find a flat, even surface, grass is the best training surface for most runners, especially as you get older.

Rating 9.5

2 WOODLAND TRAILS

For a run that mixes constantly changing surroundings with near-ideal running surfaces, head for your local woodland. Soft peat is God's gift to runners, trails are usually quite level, and in some forests they can go on for miles. They can sometimes be rather muddy, though.

Pros Usually easy on the legs and located in scenic areas that make you keen to return.

Cons Unless you're lucky enough to find wood chips or well-drained peat, woodland trails can be muddy and slippery. Tree roots can be a hazard.

Conclusion Woodland trails can be a mixed bag in terms of quality, though the odds are usually in your favour. A wood-chip trail through a huge forest is the ultimate runner's treat.

Rating 9

3 EARTH

This covers a wide spectrum of trails, from worn-out routes across playing fields to winding tracks heading out into the back of beyond. There's a point at which an ideal trail becomes too muddy or too hard-baked to be of much benefit, but in practical terms, you can't go far wrong.

Pros The medium to soft surfaces decrease the risk of overuse injuries and reduce impact on downhills. Bare earth trails are often in inspirational settings with shade in the summer.

Cons Wet, slippery mud is very hard to run on and increases your risk of injury – especially to calves and Achilles tendons. Also, as you get further away from civilisation, the surfaces are likely to become less even, making twisted ankles more likely.

Conclusion One of the best surfaces to run on, though difficult for the city-based runner to find.

Rating 8

4 SYNTHETIC TRACK

Nowadays, almost all British tracks are made of modern synthetic materials. While most people think of them purely as fast surfaces for fast runners, they're more versatile than that.

Pros Synthetic tracks provide a reasonably forgiving surface and, being exactly 400 metres around, make

measuring distances and timing sessions easy.
Cons With two long curves on every lap, ankles, knees and hips are put under more stress than usual. Longer runs also become very tedious.
Conclusion Tracks are ideal for speedwork, but you have to be dedicated to use them for anything else.
Rating 7

5 TREADMILL

When the weather's bad, a treadmill is the best indoor running option. Most treadmills have monitors that display incline, pace, heart rate, and calories burned. The hardness of the running surface varies between machines.
Pros The smooth surface is easy on the legs and hitting a desired pace is simply a matter of adjusting the machine. You don't have to worry about external factors such as dogs and bad weather. The precise level of control makes it ideal for speedwork
Cons Effectively running on the spot isn't very exciting and if you don't concentrate on keeping up your pace, you could be unceremoniously dumped behind the machine. Without the benefit of a natural breeze, treadmill runners tend to sweat profusely. The machines are too expensive for most individual runners and gym membership may be uneconomical if you just go there to run.
Conclusion Fine if you live in an area with few trails, little grass and freezing weather. Also good for runners who find it hard to keep up a steady pace.
Rating 6.5

6 ASPHALT

Asphalt is the mixture of gravel, tar and crushed rock that makes up 95 per cent of Britain's roads.
Pros As all road-runners know, asphalt is one of the fastest surfaces you can find, it's easy to measure distances on it, and it's simple to keep up a steady rhythm. While it's rather solid, it's a predictable, even surface that puts less strain on the Achilles tendon than softer or uneven terrains.
Cons You face cambers, pot-holes, traffic and an unforgiving surface that puts a strain on the body.
Conclusion Though it's a hard surface to run on, it's also one that's hard to stay away from. If you intend to race on it, some training on it is advisable.
Rating 6

7 CONCRETE

Concrete is primarily made up of cement (crushed rock) and it's what most pavements and five per cent of roads are formed from. It delivers the most shock of any surface to a runner's legs.
Pros Concrete surfaces tend to be very flat, and if you stick to pavements, you can avoid traffic.
Cons The combination of a hard surface, kerbs, and the need to sidestep pedestrians, can lead to injury.
Conclusion City dwellers have little choice but to do most of their running on concrete. If you get the opportunity, though, look for softer surfaces.
Rating 2.5 ■

HEAT SEEKER

Summer is the season to celebrate running, but be careful – sizzling heat could cook your best efforts

It's hard to beat summer running. As the air warms, leg muscles lose their winter tightness, energy levels increase, longer days lend themselves to quality training, and almost every weekend holds the promise of a dream run with a friend or a new PB.

But summer also presents a range of physiological challenges.

BODY HEAT

Your body produces about 10 times more heat when you run than when you're at rest. On cool days, the excess heat is carried by the blood to the skin, where it is lost through sweating. During sultry weather, however, when the sun bakes your body like bread in an oven and high humidity seals your sweat glands, your body can turn into a raging inferno. Runners' body temperatures have been measured at 106°F after races as short as 5K, and 109°F after 10Ks. Such upswings in temperature are more than unpleasant – they can be life-threatening.

The main problem with running in hot weather is that it starts an argument between your skin and leg muscles. The leg muscles, the culprits creating all the heat in the first place, cry out for more blood, which contains what they need – oxygen and fuel. Meanwhile, your skin is also asking your heart to send more blood in

its direction. Unless your blood brings most of the muscle-generated heat to the surface of your body, you'll overheat like a clogged car radiator in Death Valley. So your poor heart increases its rate of beating in an effort to keep both parties happy; that's why your heart rate always seems so high when you run in hot weather.

Your ticker might be up to the task of satisfying your muscles and skin if it wasn't for one additional problem: so much water can be lost through your sweat glands that the total amount of blood in your arteries and veins may actually fall. The heart then has less blood to work with, so something has to give. If less blood is shunted to your legs, you'll slow to a plod; if less goes to your skin, your body will heat up dramatically. The first situation is merely unpleasant and disappointing. The second can endanger your health.

Fortunately, your body can change the way it functions so your chances of slowing or dying are lessened. There are two aspects of this process: your kidneys lower your output of urine, which increases your blood volume and lessens the severity of the skin/muscle conflict, and your sweat glands learn to sweat more quickly and profusely when you run, which keeps you cooler. Your sweat glands also put less sodium into your sweat. This retained sodium then "pulls" more of the water inside your body into your blood, which again helps to resolve the skin/muscle antagonism. Without this pull, the water might simply lurk inside cells or in tissue spaces, where it wouldn't boost blood volume.

A QUESTION OF ACCLIMATISATION

But how can you ensure your kidneys and sweat glands are ready to keep your blood from boiling over? Lingering in a sauna or sitting outside in the afternoon sun won't work; you actually have to exercise in the heat to become acclimatised. In the past, scientists have recommended two strategies:

1 Running slowly in the heat, for about an hour a day, for a week.

2. Running vigorously (at about 85% of maximum heart rate) for about 30 minutes a day for a week.

The main problem with these techniques is that many runners simply aren't ready to run for an hour – or at a high heart rate – when temperatures climb.

You could try to avoid the problem by running early in the morning or late at night, when temperatures are lower. The only trouble is that many races start at 10am, when the sun is ready to make your skin look like the outer layer of a fried chicken. Or you could simply continue with your normal training and hope you adapt.

However, here's a safer, more efficient way to prepare yourself for the heat. On your first training day in warm weather, simply jog at a comfortable pace for 15-20 minutes. On each subsequent day, increase your amount of moderately paced

running by 5-10 minutes until you can run comfortably for 45-50 minutes. Then try to run for 30 minutes at about 85 per cent of your maximum heart rate (roughly marathon pace, or 35 seconds per mile slower than 10K pace), stopping if you feel uncomfortable. After several days of this you should be pretty well adapted to the heat.

TAKE IT EASY

Once you've become acclimatised, there are a few other things you need to do on warm days. Firstly, start your training runs more slowly than usual, and start your races at a little slower than your average race pace. If you don't, your heart rate may go through the roof, and lactate production (which increases in the heat) may end your run prematurely, or slow you to a near-standstill in the final mile of your race.

Also, eat a little salty food after a run. The salt will help you retain the fluid you ingest and will restore your blood volume more quickly; pretzels and crisps are a popular choice (NB: if your doctor has placed you on a sodium-restricted diet, you should ignore this advice).

And don't forget the old warm-weather standbys: drink 8-10 big glasses of water a day, and take 3-4 swallows of fluid every 10 minutes as you run. (Plain water is fine if your effort lasts less than 50 minutes; use a sports drink for longer sessions.) Drink an electrolyte-replacement beverage or tomato juice – not plain water – after a run, and don't hesitate to use the salt shaker at meal times.

Finally, if you ever feel dizzy or light-headed while running, stop immediately. Remember you've only adapted to the conditions you've trained in; if the weather becomes hotter or more humid, take it easy on your training runs and avoid racing. You can always set your PB on a cooler day.

SUN DOWNS

We've dealt with the effects of running in the hot weather. But what about the source of the heat: the sun. Make no mistake, the sun can be a dangerous foe, causing heat stroke, dehydration, sunburn, melanomas... not to mention minor irritations such as heat rashes. But that doesn't mean you have to pack your running shoes away until November. With a little common sense and a few sensible precautions there's no reason why you should have to stop.

Some of these precautions, such as drinking regularly, avoiding the sun between 11am and 3pm and applying petroleum jelly to areas susceptible to chafing should already be as much a part of your training as long Sunday runs. Others, such as using the correct sunscreen, may not be.

STAY COOL

When you lace up your shoes on a hot, humid, August day, there are basically two problems you have to deal with: the heat of the sun, and its rays. Of the two, heat is easier to deal with, as you're more aware of its effects. What's more, your body will automatically try to cope with the heat by increasing the rate at which you sweat, as we've seen.

Although the amount you sweat is genetically determined (it can be anything from two to six pints an hour), you can train your body to sweat more efficiently, which keeps you cooler and this helps to sustain your performance. That is

» HOLIDAYS IN THE SUN

During the summer, runners often encounter a dilemma: while you're on holiday with the family, your training time may be severely limited, but on certain days there may actually be extra time to run. So what are the best training sessions to carry out when time is short – or when there's enough time to do almost anything?

If time is short, try this 30-minute session. Warm up by jogging easily for 10 minutes, and then alternative four-minute surges at what feels like 10K pace with one-minute jog recoveries until you have completed three surges (14 minutes in total). Jog easily for six minutes to cool down.

If time is endless, and you're capable of running for long periods of time, find a pleasant area and amble along for an hour or so, concentrating on feeling free and letting your hips, legs and ankles work in a loose, relaxed manner. Then burst along at 10K pace for a minute at a time, alternating the bursts with 2-3 minutes of very easy jogging. This improves the aerobic capacity of your fast-twitch muscle fibres. When you begin to feel tired, stop "bursting" and jog easily for 10 minutes to cool down.

best achieved by improving your fitness, which increases the size of your sweat glands. Actually running in the heat will also help. As your body acclimatises, the volume of blood flowing around your body increases, and with it the sweat rate.

Your role in this battle is not to interfere with your body's sweat glands. That means wearing clothing that helps to shift sweat away from your body, rather than blocking its passage to evaporation. Basic comfort should dictate this, but there are materials which take the process a step further. Coolmax is probably the best known and the most widely available, although there are several other microfibre materials which also wick sweat away from the skin's surface.

Unfortunately, the desire to keep your body cool usually leads to a fairly minimalist approach to summer kit, making you more susceptible to the sun's rays and clothes less capable of playing a protective role. However, as Coolmax T-shirts are now available, there's no reason why you should have to bear your shoulders.

The other weapon you might consider in the war against heat is a body cooler. These accessories, which are worn around the neck or head, work by keeping an area of your body constantly damp. However, as with tipping a cup of water over your head in the latter stages of a race, the benefit may be more psychological than physical. According to research carried out at the University of Wisconsin, skin wetting doesn't actually keep you cooler. A study conducted on two groups of runners in humid conditions found spraying one group with water every 10 minutes had no impact on body temperature, heart rate or perceived effort.

Given the choice, you should certainly be drinking water rather than tipping it over your head. Dehydration as a result of increased sweating is far more likely than overheating. In fact, most of the problems you are likely to encounter in the heat can be overcome by replacing the fluid you lose through sweat. This is rule number one of running in the heat, and should become second nature if it isn't already.

There are no short cuts: you should drink both before and after training, and during longer runs. Unlike food, you can't stock up on water; the fluid in your body is carefully balanced, so that drinking too much forces you to urinate more. Although there is some evidence to suggest glycerol added to a carbohydrate supplement will aid your water retention, and hence your performance, the reported side effects (nausea and headaches) suggest overall impact needs further evaluation.

RAYS OF LIGHT

While heat is likely to affect your performance, the sun's rays can be a major threat to your health. The problem is that the most serious damage, to your eyes and skin, is gradual, long-term and

» BURNING ISSUES

Sun-protection lotions were once a rarity, only to be found in holiday suitcases or medical bags. Fortunately, they are now commonplace, although a Which? report suggests many people misunderstand their use.

The idea of a lotion that aids your tan persists. Some people only start to apply it when they begin to burn, which is too late. There is no such thing as a healthy tan. A tan is an indication your lotion isn't working.

So forget the idea of a suntan lotion and starting thinking about sunblock or sunscreen. A lotion's effectiveness against UVB is indicated by its SPF – sun protection factor – rating. An SPF of 10 means you can stay out in the sun 10 times longer than if you had no lotion on at all. In general, the higher the number, the greater the protection, though the effect tends to level off after SPF15, which cuts out 93 per cent of UVB.

The amount of UVA protection is indicated by a star rating on the reverse of the container, ranging from one to four. But, as the UVA protection is relative to the UVB, a higher SPF is still a better guide to the overall protection offered.

Although there are a number of sweat-proof lotions available, they usually aren't wipe-proof, so beware – if you tend to rub sweat away from your face when running, you could also be wiping away your protection.

Lastly, don't treat the lotion as a pass to stay out in the sun all day. Even with an SPF of 15-25, you are still likely to burn a little.

largely imperceptible until it's too late.

Fortunately, it's relatively easy to protect yourself. The danger comes from two types of ultraviolet (UV) rays: UVA which causes your skin to age, and UVB, which causes it to burn. Although UVB is a more pressing concern – you can feel its effects almost immediately – you need to block both. You can do this by covering up: avoid running bare-chested or, if your hair is thinning, bare-headed, and use a sunscreen or sunblock on exposed skin. The most susceptible areas are the tops of the ears, the nose, the shoulders, and the lips. As for clothing, tightly-woven fabrics are more protective than those with a looser weave, which gives synthetics an advantage over natural fibres. Darker colours also absorb more UV, although the protection provided by fabrics is lower when they are stretched and wet.

Keeping the UV away from your eyes is also a smart move; as it can penetrate clouds and reflect off light surfaces you probably won't notice the damage being done. The matter is made more pressing by the depletion of the ozone layer, nature's own barrier to UV, which isn't doing a great job these days. To do it yourself, you should either use a shade which covers your eyes, or a pair of sports sunglasses designed specifically for the task. Look for a pair that has a UV shield and a grey, green or brown tint to cut down on glare, and that fits securely to your head and doesn't move while you're running.

Going into battle against the sun is a serious challenge, and runners are more at risk than most people. Take a long term view: the real danger is not what will happen today or tomorrow, but the damage you could be storing up for years to come. So be smart, follow these simple guidelines, and you'll be able to think of the sun as something to enjoy, rather than endure. ■

» TOP TIPS

- Drink regularly before, during and after running
- Dress for the heat
- Use petroleum jelly on areas of the body which may rub and chafe
- Use an SPF 15 sunscreen on all exposed areas of skin
- Wear a visor or sunglasses with a UV protective shield, even on overcast days
- Avoid the midday sun (between 11am and 2pm), when the path from the UV to the Earth is at its shortest, and hence its most dangerous

CHAPTER 10
Training for Racing

Once you're running fit, the next step is to try a race. Here's how

MILE IN A **MONTH**

The magic of the mile has enchanted runners from Roger Bannister to Steve Cram, and it's a classic test of speed you should try, too

Training for the mile is something you have probably never dreamt of doing, but the change of focus, albeit for a short time period, and the variety can be surprisingly enjoyable and may also reap benefits when you return to training for longer distance. Racing a mile – there a variety of open events to try up and down the country – is also about as close as most of us will come to feeling like an elite athlete. These are a few key points to consider before you start your mile training.

1 QUALITY SESSIONS

Being of a shorter duration and a higher intensity, miling requires a greater amount of anaerobic work than races of 10K or longer. This means you need to train your body to cope with the rapid onset of fatigue, which results from faster anaerobic work. The best way to do this is to run interval sessions – preferably on the grass, which is more forgiving than the track. The duration of the repetitions should be short, because you will be running at a speed equal to or faster than your mile time. Your session should be preceded by a good warm up and some stretching exercises (it's preferable to stretch before an interval session rather than afterwards) and followed by a cool down. It's best to build up to the pace at which you run the reps

in successive sessions, rather than increasing the volume, because you are, after all, training your body to run faster.

2 FLEXIBILITY

Running speed is dictated by two factors: stride length and stride rate. Developing flexibility of the correct muscles will help you to increase your stride length without overtraining. Concentrate on stretching the muscles in the hamstrings, gluteals, calves, groin and quadriceps areas. Hold stretches for at least 30 seconds. Do the stretches before and after a session because the increased intensity of the exercise will lead to muscle tightening and stiffness. Self-massage will also help to counter this tightening.

3 DOWNHILL RUNNING

Increasing your stride rate will also help to boost your running speed. The most effective way to increase your stride rate is to do some downhill running, where you are almost forced to move your legs quicker. It is important that you do this in a safe manner to avoid the obvious injury problems. Find a suitable location that consists of a stretch of grass with a very gentle down slope. It makes sense to do this sort of workout when you are relatively fresh and warmed up; so following a 20-30 minute run will be better than after your longer Sunday effort. A good way to structure the run is to stretch, and then to do six to eight strides at a fast pace with a walk-back recovery. The emphasis should be on a fast pick-up of the legs.

4 STRENGTHENING

There is a strong association between muscle strength and speed, which is partly why most sprinters are bulky creatures and marathon runners are often frail waifs. Improving your strength will help to improve your miling but you need to work on the right muscles. As you will be on your toes more in the mile than in a long-distance race, it will help to strengthen the calves with a series of calf raises. You will also need driving quads, and half squats will strengthen those. Initially your body weight alone will provide sufficient resistance, but you may start holding weights when you want to progress.

5 THINK LIKE A MILER

Running or indeed racing on the track may be a completely different experience for you, but you have to think in a positive way and attack the track rather than being scared of it. It might be a refreshing change to have a bash at the mile, but your attitude must change to meet the new demand. Things happened very quickly – whatever the standard – in a race over this distance. You have to think about what you are doing. Decide in advance what pace you want to run at and calculate your desired 400m splits. Don't get carried away at the start if everyone else goes off a fast pace, be disciplined and run at the pace that suits you. That said, if you feel good with a lap to go, don't be afraid to take a risk and make a bold strike for home. ■

›› MILE PREDICTOR

The table below will give you a basic idea of what mile time you should be capable of on the basis of your best 10K performance. It presumes that you are really more of a distance runner, but that you have reasonable basic speed. If you run much quicker than the predicted time, forget about the marathon, you may have talent for miling!

10K Best	Mile Prediction
34:00	4:41
36:00	4:57
38:00	5:13
40:00	5:31
42:00	5:49
44:00	6:07
46:00	6:25
48:00	6:42
50:00	7:01
52:00	7:19
54:00	7:37
56:00	7:55
58:00	8:12
60:00	8:30

THE ULTIMATE 5K PLAN

Whatever the racing aim, one thing we could all do with a little more of is speed – and preparing for a 5K is a sure-fire way of quickening up

The 5K is a great distance for every level of runner. It's a fail-safe, achievable distance for first-timers; there's one almost every weekend for PB-chasing intermediates; and it's the ideal fast time trial, tough tempo run or 10K-to-marathon tune-up for more experienced competitors. On the following pages, you'll find six-week schedules for each of the three groups. You'll also see our "Four Training Universals" (page 253). Look at these before starting your schedule, as these principles apply to everyone. First things first, though, have a look at the three training levels overleaf to determine which best describes you, and therefore which schedule you should follow.

» WHO AM I?

BEGINNER You're running recreationally two to three times a week for a total of six to eight miles or more, and you've done a few fun runs. But now you want to enter a real race – and finish. Earn that first medal and boast about it around the office.

INTERMEDIATE You've been running consistently for at least a year and have run in a few races, but mainly for the experience. You've dabbled in some modest interval training or other speedwork. Now you want to think seriously about your finishing time and how to lower it: to race, not just participate.

ADVANCED You have several years of serious running behind you, follow a year-round schedule, have run in many races at various distances, do regular speedwork, want to discover your own performance limits and are willing to push hard in training.

BEGINNER

At this stage, you just run. A little more this week than the week before, and more again the following week. No interval training, no flirting with injuries, no serious discomfort. It's just running.

"For runners without a competitive past, the first training goal is to raise mileage by adding easy volume," says Jon Sinclair, a former elite athlete who has moved on to a career as a successful coach. "First of all, it develops increased aerobic conditioning, which by itself yields faster times. Secondly, it produces the physical strength on which later, harder training can be built.

"At this level, interval training is not a good idea," says Sinclair. "Adding any intensity in the form of fartlek or hills to a person's programme can be dangerous and counterproductive. At this stage in a runner's development the first rule should be, 'Do no harm'. If they just run more, they will, in a few months' time, run faster."

Remember that every run in this six-week schedule should be a steady run, done at an effort that has you breathing "comfortably hard", but well short of squinty-eyed wheezing. Enjoy each run, feel yourself getting stronger and leaner, be proud of what you're doing.

Race-day rules "For a beginner, expending energy in a race can be frightening and a potential barrier," says RW coaching adviser, Bud Baldaro, "but if you've run at least that long in training many times, and run negative splits – the first half slower than the second – in the race, you'll enjoy the experience and finish feeling good."

Have an energy bar for breakfast with some fluids, then arrive early so you can pick up your race number and avoid the drain of long queues. Do a little warm-up walking and jogging, sip some water, stretch a bit, and generally relax and stay stress-free until the start. Remind yourself that your goal is to finish, to run the whole way, to finish feeling tired – but not completely exhausted.

WEEK	M	T	W	T	F	S	S	TOTAL
1	Rest	2 miles	Rest	2 miles	Rest	2 miles	Rest	6 miles
2	Rest	2.5 miles	Rest	2.5 miles	Rest	2.5 miles	Rest	7.5 miles
3	Rest	3 miles	Rest	3 miles	Rest	2.5 miles	2 miles	10.5 miles
4	Rest	3.5 miles	Rest	3.5 miles	Rest	3 miles	2 miles	12 miles
5	Rest	4 miles	2 miles	3.5 miles	Rest	3.5 miles	2 miles	15 miles
TAPER	Rest	4 miles	2 miles	Rest	2 miles	Rest	5K Race	

» FOUR TRAINING UNIVERSALS

Rest

No running at all. Walk, bike or swim if you want to – just not very hard. Don't regard rest days as "nothing" days, but rather a different kind of training that allows your body to recover while it absorbs and consolidates the strength gains your hard runs produce.

Easy Runs

Totally comfortable. Breathing hard enough to know that you're running, but still able to hold up your end of an on-the-run chat. If you can't, it's too hard. On the other hand, if you can sing every verse of "Bohemian Rhapsody" en route, it's too easy.

Long Runs

Anything longer than race distance the purpose of which is to build endurance, specifically the ability to run for longer and longer periods of time without falling apart.

Speedwork

Shorter than race distance repetitions at or below your goal race pace. Can be hard to very hard to nearly flat out. Produces leg speed, elevated lactic threshold, stamina, biomechanical efficiency and the ability to tolerate the discomfort that's essential to racing fitness.

INTERMEDIATE

To move from finisher to racer, you'll need to add more weekly miles, but also, more importantly, intensity in the form of timed intervals both at (pace intervals) and below (speed intervals) your 5K goal pace, along with a crucial weekly hill-training session.

"Running hills once a week at a fairly hard effort for up to three minutes at a time is an ideal way to become stronger," says Baldaro. That's because hill training greatly improves leg and gluteal strength while increasing aerobic capacity and stride length, along with ankle flexion, which enables you to spring off the ground more quickly.

How hard is "fairly hard"? A classic study from years ago found that running up even a slight hill at a steady pace raises your heart rate up to 26 beats higher than the same effort on the flat. So 5K effort (not pace) is what you should aim for.

Again, regarding intensity as opposed to mileage, a recent study in the journal *Peak Performance* found that you'll run your best races from 5K upwards not when you've run the most miles, but when you hit a reasonable mileage level and then turn up your intensity.

To enjoy the fullest benefit of the intermediate programme, there are a few specific types of training you'll need to use:

Pace Intervals (PI) For a 5K goal of nine to 10-min/mile pace (28-31 minutes finishing time), run intervals between 1:07 and 1:15 (for 200 metres), 2:15 to 2:30 (400m) and 4:30 to 5:00 (800m).
For 8:00 min/mile pace (24:50), it's 1:00 (200m), 2:00 (400m), 4:00 (800m).
For 7:00 min/mile pace (21:44), it's 0:53 (200m), 1:45 (400m), 3:30 (800m).

Speed Intervals (SI) For nine to 10:00 min/mile pace, run 1:04 to 1:11 (for 200 metres), 2:08 to 2:22 (400m) and 4:15 to 4:44 (800m).
For 8:00 min/mile pace, it's 0:56 (200m), 1:53 (400m), 3:45 (800m).
For 7:00 min/mile pace, it's 0:49 (200m), 1:38 (400m), 3:15 (800m).

Recovery time For pace intervals, slowly jog half the distance of the repetition (ie 200m jog after

400m repetitions). For speed intervals, jog equal distance (ie 400m jog after 400m repetitions).

Hills and easy runs For 9:00 min/mile pace, use the lower number in the schedule; those running at 7:00 min/mile pace, move towards the higher.

Interval and hill days Jog two miles, then run 4 x 100m strides to get ready before the session. Jog two miles to cool down, then stretch.

Race day rules "It's all about negative splits," says Bud Baldaro. "Always." Which means you run the first half of the race slower than the second half. Tough to do when you're pumped up, but you must. Hold back in the first mile, Baldaro advises, then "seek out other runners to pass in the second mile, but don't push beyond a comfortably hard effort." Increase gradually to discomfort in the last mile, and over the final 400 metres, try to pick it up.

	M	T	W	T	F	S	S	TOTAL
1	Rest	6 x 400m PI	2–5 miles, easy	Hills, 5–8 min	Rest	2–5 miles, easy	4–6 miles, easy	18-26 miles
2	Rest	2 x 800m PI, 2 x 400m PI, 2 x 200m PI	2–5 miles, easy	Hills, 5–8 min	Rest	2–5 miles, easy	4–6 miles, easy	18-26 miles
3	Rest	2 x 800m PI, 2 x 400m SI, 4 x 200m SI	2–5 miles, easy	Hills, 6–9 min	Rest	2–5 miles, easy	5–7 miles, easy	19–28 miles
4	Rest	2 x 800m PI, 1 x 800m SI, 2 x 400m SI, 2 x 200m SI	2–5 miles, easy	Hills, 6–9 min	Rest	2–5 miles, easy	5–8 miles, easy	19–30 miles
5	Rest	2 x 800m SI, 4 x 400m SI, 4 x 200m SI	2–5 miles, easy	Hills, 7–10 min	Rest	2–5 miles, easy	6–9 miles, easy	20–31 miles
TAPER	Rest	4 x 400m SI, 4x 200m SI	2–5 miles, easy	Rest	3 x 200m SI, 3 x 150m SI, 6 x 100m SI	Rest	5K Race	

ADVANCED

Two words define the training goal at this stage of your running life: "race feel". To reach your 5K ceiling, you must replicate in training how it feels to run that far that fast. Which means timed repetitions both at (pace) and faster than (speed) your 5K goal pace – but with short recovery. Uncomfortably short. Because in a race, of course, there is no recovery. So the more intimate you become with the sensations of the race itself on a twice-weekly basis, the more you'll be able to handle the 5K's physical and mental combination punches on race day.

Frank Horwill, a leading coach and founder of the British Milers Club, found that when athletes were stuck at a certain 5K time – sometimes for years – and could not break through, they were almost always running lots of repetitions significantly faster than 5K race pace with 400-metre jogs. When Horwill pointed out that they would not get 400-

WEEK	M	T	W	T	F	S	S	TOTAL
1	Rest	2 x 1,200m PI, 2 x 800m PI, 4 x 100m S	4–6 miles, easy	2 x 800m SI, 2 x 400m SI, 4 x 200m SI	Rest	4–6 miles, easy	7–9 miles, easy	28–34 miles
2	Rest	10 x 300m PI, 4 x 100m S	4–6 miles, easy	2 x 1200m SI, 1 x 800m SI, 2 x 400m SI, 4 x 200m SI	Rest	4–6 miles, easy	7–9 miles, easy	28–34 miles
3	Rest	2 x 1,200m PI, 2 x 800m PI, 2 x 400m PI, 4 x 400m S	4–6 miles, easy	2 x 800m SI, 4 x 400m SI, 4 x 200m SI	Rest	4–6 miles, easy	8–10 miles, easy	29–35 miles
4	Rest	3 x 800m SI, 4 x 100m S	4–6 miles, easy	3 x 800m SI, 3 x 400m SI, 3 x 200m SI, 2 x 100m S	Rest	4–6 miles, easy	8–10 miles, easy	30–36 miles
5	Rest	2 x 1,200m PI, 2 x 800m PI, 2 x 400m PI, 2 x 200m PI	4–6 miles, easy	4 x 400m SI, 4 x 300m SI, 4 x 200m SI, 4 x 100m S	Rest	4–6 miles, easy	8–10 miles, easy	31–37 miles
TAPER	Rest	2 x 400m SI, 2 x 300m SI, 2 x 200m SI, 6 x 100m S	3 miles, easy	4 x 200m SI, 4 x 100m S	Rest	2 miles, easy	5K Race	

metre recovery periods in a race, the usual reply was, "But I'm running so much faster than race pace." Sorry, Horwill said, it doesn't work that way.

Invariably, when he had his runners do the repetitions slightly faster than the projected 5K pace, with recovery jogs as short as 50 metres (about 20 seconds), their times dropped. "They needed to get the feel of what it was like to run a tough 5K race," Horwill explained. "The recovery time after repetitions at 5K pace is a crucial factor." Aim to jog a quarter to half of the distance of the repetition.

To enjoy the fullest benefit of the advanced programme, there are a few specific types of training you'll need to use:

Pace Intervals (PI)

If your 5K goal is 8:00 min/mile pace (24:50 finishing time), run pace intervals at 1:00 (for 200 metres), 1:30 (300m), 2:00 (400m), 4:00 (800m), 6:00 (1200m).

For 6:00 min/mile pace (18:38), run 0:45 (200m), 1:07 (300m), 1:30 (400m), 3:00 (800m), 4:30 (1200m).

Speed Intervals (SI)

For 8:00 min/mile pace, it's 0:56 (200m), 1:19 (300m), 1:52 (400m), 3:44 (800m), 5:38 (1200m)
For 6:00 min/mile pace, run 0:41 (200m), 1:01 (300m), 1:22 (400m), 2:44 (800m), 4:08 (1200m).

Strides (S) Gradually pick up your speed to 90 per cent effort, hold that for 20 yards, then decelerate. Do four to six repetitions of 80-100m after your Wednesday and/or Saturday runs.

Recovery time For pace intervals, slowly jog half the distance of the repetition (ie 200m jog after 400m repetitions). For speed intervals, jog equal distance (ie 400m jog after 400m repetitions).

Interval and hill days Jog two miles, then run 4 x 100m strides to get ready before the session. Jog two miles to cool down, then stretch.

THE ULTIMATE **10K** PLAN

It's the nation's favourite distance, long enough to test your endurance, short enough for you to switch on the afterburners. Here's how to perfect your 10K

You'll be glad to hear that 10K training forms the ideal foundation of almost all types of running performance. That's because it includes ample amounts of the three core components of distance training: strength, stamina and speed. Obviously, you can use it to train for your goal 10K, but with certain adjustments you can also use it to prepare for everything from the 5K to the marathon. This is the classic distance, made famous by Viren, Bedford and the transcendent Gebrselassie. So read through the runner profiles below, and decide which of our six-week plans is best for you, but remember that these are not one-size-fits-all plans. If you can't complete a given session, you don't have to, and if you need to rearrange training days to fit your schedule, do so.

» WHO AM I

BEGINNER You're a notch above novice. You've been running at least six months, and may have done a 5K or two. You run three to five miles, three or four days a week; have done a little fast running when you felt like it; and now you want to enter – and finish – what you consider to be a real distance race.

INTERMEDIATE You've been running a year or more, have done some 5Ks and maybe even a 10K, but you've always finished feeling as if you could or should have gone faster. You consider yourself mainly a recreational runner, but you still want to make a commitment, and see how fast you can go.

ADVANCED You've been a serious runner for several years, have run many races – perhaps even a marathon. You're familiar with fartlek and intervals, and can run comfortably for an hour or more. Now you want to make a significant improvement to your personal best, and you're willing to put in a rigorous six weeks to achieve it.

BEGINNER

If you are a beginner, your 10K goal should be less about achieving a personal best (PB) than an LDF (longest distance finished). You want to run the whole 6.2 miles, so your main aim is endurance, because it's likely to take you an hour to get there. "Basic aerobic strength is every runner's first need," says RW coaching advisor Bud Baldaro, so you should doaim to most of your running at a steady, moderate pace.

However, we're also going to add a dash of pseudo-speedwork into your endurance stew for flavour. This will put some added spring into your step, give you a brief taste of what it feels like to run a little faster, and hasten your progression to the Intermediate level. So, every week, in addition to your steady running, you're going to do two extra things:

Aerobic Intervals (AI) In these, you push the pace on a bit – until you breathe just a little harder than usual – followed by slow jogging until you feel rested enough to resume your regular speed, and you always, always stay well short of going anaerobic (simply stated that means squinty-eyed and gasping for breath). Treat these runs like play. When you do them, try to recreate that feeling you had as a child when you ran to the park and couldn't wait to get there.

Gentle Pick-ups (GP) With pick-ups, you gradually increase your pace over 100 metres to about 90 per cent of all-out, hold it there for 10-20m then gradually decelerate. Walk to full recovery before you start the next one. Nothing big, nothing really stressful – just enough to let your body go. (After a few AI/GP weeks, your normal pace will begin to feel more comfortable, and you'll get race-fit more quickly this way.)

Race-Day Rules Have something to drink and an energy bar or bagel two hours to 90 minutes before the race, and arrive early enough to make your way to the start without great stress. Walk around for about 10 minutes before the start; maybe even do a few minutes of slow jogging. Start off at a slower pace than you think you should, and work gradually into a comfortable and controlled pace. Let the race come to you. If there is a water station, stop to drink and relax for 10 seconds.

WEEK	M	T	W	T	F	S	S	TOTAL
1	Rest	2 miles, 4 x 1 min AI, 2 miles	3 miles or rest	4 miles + 3 GP	Rest	5 miles	Rest	16-20 miles
2	Rest	2 miles	3 miles or rest	4 miles + 3 GP	Rest	5.5 miles	3.5 miles	18-21 miles
3	Rest	2 miles, 4 x 90 secs AI, 2 miles	3 miles or rest	4.5 miles + 3 GP	Rest	6 miles	4 miles	18.5-22 miles
4	Rest	2 miles, 6 x 90 secs AI, 2 miles	3 miles or rest	4.5 miles + 6 GP	Rest	6.5 miles	4.5 miles	20-24 miles
5	Rest	2 miles, 4 x 2 mins AI, 2 miles	3 miles or rest	5 miles + 6 GP	Rest	7 miles	5 miles	21.5-26 miles
TAPER	Rest	2 miles, 3 mins, 2 mins, 1 min AI, 2 miles	2 miles	Rest	2 miles + 2 GP	Rest	10K Race	

INTERMEDIATE

Here's the two-pronged approach that will move you from recreational runner to the cusp of competitive athlete. First, you'll be adding miles to your endurance-building long run until it makes up 30 per cent of your weekly mileage. Second, you'll now be doing a substantial amount of tempo running aimed at elevating your anaerobic threshold, the speed above which blood lactate starts to accumulate in the system. You can avoid this unpleasantness with regular sustained sessions at just below 10K pace; that is, tempo-run pace. This will significantly improve your endurance and running efficiency in just six weeks.

So your training will include weekly 10-10 sessions as tempo work (PI), along with a mix of intervals and uphill running, all of which strengthen your running muscles, heart and related aerobic systems.

Oh, one more thing. Running fast requires effort and some discomfort. Even so, be conservative. If you can't maintain the same pace throughout a given session, or if your body really starts to complain, call it a day and think about adjusting your pace next time.

Pace Intervals (PI) Run at target 10K pace to improve your efficiency and stamina, and to give you the feel of your race pace. For 10-minute/mile pace (a 1:02:06 10K), run 2:30 (for 400m), 5:00 (800m), 7:30 (1,200m). For nine-minute/mile pace (55:53), run 2:15 (400m), 4:30 (800m), 6:45 (1,200m). For eight-minute/mile pace (49:40), run 2:00 (400m), 4:00 (800m), 6:00 (1,200m). With pace and speed intervals (below), jog half the interval distance to recover.

Speed Intervals (SI) Run these at 30 seconds-

WEEK	M	T	W	T	F	S	S	TOTAL
1	Rest	2 miles, 1-2 x 10-10, 2 miles	4 miles	400m, 800m, 1,200m, 800m , 400m PI	Rest	4 miles + 4 x 100m S	6-7 miles	24 miles
2	Rest	6 miles inc 6 mins TUT	4 miles	1,200m, 2 x 800m, 4 x 200m PI + 4 x 200m SI + 4 x 100m S	Rest	4.5 miles + 5 x 100m S	7-8 miles	26 miles
3	Rest	2 miles, 2-3 x 10-10, 2 miles	4 miles	800m, 1,200m, 800m PI + 2 x 400m, 4 x 100m S	Rest	5 miles + 6 x 100m S	7-8 miles	27.5 miles
4	Rest	6-7 miles inc 8 minutes TUT	4 miles	1,200m, 800m, 2 x 400m, 2 x 200m SI + 4 x 100m S	Rest	5 miles + 6 x 100m S	8-9 miles	29 miles
5	Rest	2 miles, 3-4 x 10-10, 2 miles	4 miles	800m, 4 x 400m, 4 x 200m, 800m SI, + 4 x 100m S	Rest	6 miles + 6 x 100m S	8-9 miles	31 miles
TAPER	Rest	800m, 2 x 200m, 400m, 2 x 200m SI + 6 x 100m S	4 miles	4 x 200m SI + 4 x 100m S	Rest	3 miles easy + 3 x 100m S	10K Race	

per-mile faster than race pace. For 10-minute/mile pace, run 2:22 (for 400m), 4:44 (800m), 7:06 (1,200m).
For nine-minute/mile pace, 2:08 (400m), 4:16 (800m), 6:24 (1,200m).
For eight-minute/mile pace, 1:53 (400m), 3:45 (800m), 5:38 (1,200m).
10-10 10-minute tempo repetitions at 30 seconds per mile slower than 10K goal pace, with three- to five-minute slow jogs after each.

Total Uphill Time (TUT) Run repetitions up the same hill, or work the uphill sections of a road or off-road course.

Strides (S) Over 100 metres, gradually accelerate to about 90 per cent of all-out, hold it there for five seconds, then smoothly decelerate. Walk to full recovery after each.

Race-Day Rules "Many intermediate runners run too fast in the first half of the race," says Baldaro. "That's almost a guaranteed way of running a mediocre time. Even pace is best, which means the first half of the race should feel really easy." Divide the race into three two-mile sections: in-control pace for the first two, push a bit the middle two, then go hard the last two and sprint when you see the line.

ADVANCED

The cornerstone of 10K training has long been the tempo run. Great for stamina-seeking intermediates working their way up the racing-fitness food chain, but not for you. That's because a recent study found that short intervals at – not below – 5K and 10K race pace (roughly our speed and pace intervals) produced huge improvements when compared with tempo runs. (Tempo running did produce improvements, but faster running did better still.)

The study, as reported in the journal *Peak Performance*, found that "those doing intervals trained faster than the tempo runners and therefore developed better economy, co-ordination and comfort while running fast." This, in turn, translated into faster 10K running. Moreover, the interval group spent just 31 minutes during two sessions per week running their repetitions, while the tempo runners required 58 minutes for their two sessions. That's why this programme puts you on a six-week diet of quick stuff: medium-long on Tuesdays, short and swift on Thursdays. That said, we're still going to make sure you maintain your vital aerobic base, by doing some solid mileage as well. Even experienced runners often don't do enough of the mileage to support their harder work.

Pace Intervals (PI) For eight-minute/mile pace (49:40), run 2:00 (400m), 4:00 (800m), 6:00 (1,200m). For seven-minute/mile pace (43:28), run 0:53 (200m), 1:45 (400m), 3:30 (800m), 5:15 (1,200m). For six-minute/mile pace (37:15), run 0:45 (200m), 1:30 (400m), 4:30 (1,200m). Recover with a one-minute jog after 400m efforts, two minutes after 800s, and three after 1,200m. (Note: For both pace and speed intervals, run two miles easy and four 100m strides before each session, and two miles easy after.)

Speed Intervals (SI) For eight-minute/mile pace, run 1:53 (for 400m), 3:45 (800m) 5:38 (1,200m). For seven-minute/mile pace, do 0:49 (for 200m), 1:38 (400m), 4:53 (1,200m). For six-minute/mile pace, it's 0:41 (200m), 1:22 (400m), 2:44 (800m), 4:08 (1,200m). Jog half the interval distance to recover (ie, 400m jog after each 800m).

Lactate Sessions (LS) LS training involves running as fast as you can for one minute, followed by two minutes of slow jogging.

Strides (S) Over 100 metres, gradually accelerate to 90 per cent of all-out, hold that for five seconds then smoothly decelerate. Recover completely after each stride: they aren't meant to tire you out, just add zip to your legs.

Race-Day Rules

Make sure you know the course. "If you know how the hills and turns go," says Baldaro, "you can much more easily match your efforts to the course. Also, study the last mile. In fact, if possible, run the last mile as a warm-up. Look for markers a certain distance from the finish so you can expend your final energy at the right time."

WEEK	M	T	W	T	F	S	S	TOTAL
1	Rest	2 x 1200m, 2 x 800m, 4 x 400m PI + 6 x 100m S	4-6 miles	2 x 800m, 4 x 400m, 4 x 200m SI + 4 x 100m S	Rest or 3-4 miles easy	4-6 miles + 6 x 100m S	8-10 miles	32-37 miles
2	Rest	2 x 1200m, 800m, 400m, 200m SI + 6 x 100m S	4-6 miles	4 x 200m SI + 4 LS + 4 x 100m S	Rest or 3-4 miles easy	5-7 miles + 6 x 100m S	8-10 miles	33-38 miles
3	Rest	2 x 1 mile PI, 1,200m, 800m, 400m SI + 6 x 100m S	4-6 miles	4 x 200m SI + 4 LS + 4 x 200m SI + 4 x 100m S	Rest or 3-4 miles easy	5-7 miles	9-11 miles	34-39 miles
4	Rest	2 x 1,200m, 800m, 400m, 200m 800m SI + 6 x 100 S	4-6 miles	5-7 LS + 6 x 100m S	Rest or 3-4 miles easy	5-7 miles + 6 x 100m S	9-11 miles	35-39 miles
5	Rest	2 x 400m, 800m, 200m, 800m SI + 6 x 100m S	4-6 miles	6-8 miles	Rest or 3-4 miles easy	5-7 miles+ 6 x 100m S	10-12 miles	36-40 miles
TAPER	Rest	1,200m, 800m, 2 x 400m SI + 4 x 100m S	Rest	4 x 200m SI + 4 x 100m S + 4 x 200m SI + 4 x 100m S	Rest or 3-4 miles easy	3 miles easy + 3 x 100m S	10K Race	

THE ULTIMATE HALF-MARATHON PLAN

As a goal in its own right or as a stepping stone on the way to a marathon, a quick half can be very satisfying indeed

For many runners, the half-marathon is the ideal racing middle ground. Newer racers, who've probably finished a couple of 5 or 10Ks, can get to grips with a worthy, yet doable, challenge, but without the training and racing grind of the marathon. For more experienced athletes, training for a half bolsters stamina for shorter, faster races, plus it boosts endurance for a full 26.2-mile challenge at a later stage. Unlike a marathon, which can leave your tank drained for a month or more, you can bounce back from a hard half in as little as a week. Here are three can't-fail nine-week schedules to get you primed and ready to put in the performance of your life at your next race.

» WHO AM I?

BEGINNERS You've run for at least a year, but you're still a racing neophyte. You can run five miles at a time without distress, average 15 to 20 miles a week, and have finished a 5K, perhaps even a 10K. Now you want to go longer, though not yet to a marathon, and your race time is less important to you than finishing

INTERMEDIATE You have a solid aerobic base. You have been running consistently for several years, tried various kinds of speed training, average 25-30 miles a week, and may even have finished a half-marathon, but now you want to race a half. That is, you have a specific finishing time in mind, and you're willing to train hard to achieve it.

ADVANCED You've run and raced for many years. You've finished just about every distance – half-marathon and perhaps full marathon included – and have averaged 35 or more miles a week for at least the last six months. Now you want to push yourself without putting in the major mileage a marathon demands. And you're willing, even eager, to increase the intensity of your speedwork.

BEGINNER

First, gradually increase your weekly mileage and long run, to give you more endurance, which you'll need to run for more than two hours. Second, you'll do some longer runs at a faster pace to build stamina and keep you strong over the last third of the race.

"It doesn't matter how new you are to running, two of your training days a week should be challenging," says leading coach Bud Baldaro. To this end, if you can handle it, make uphill running a part of your Thursday routine.

To enjoy the fullest benefit of the beginner programme, there are a few specific types of training you'll need to use:

Aerobic Intervals (AI) Push the pace a little. Find a tempo that feels somewhere between comfortable and a bit of an effort. Don't run this too hard. Trying to add too much intensity while increasing mileage courts injury. When you finish the timed AI, jog very slowly until your breathing returns to normal, then either do the next timed AI or run at your regular pace as per the schedule (below). On all other days, just run your assigned miles as you feel.

Gentle Pickups (GP) At the end of a run, walk for few minutes, then slowly increase your leg turnover on a flat stretch for 100m until you start to breathe hard. Continue for 10 to 20m, then gradually slow down. Walk to full recovery before you start the next one. The purpose of both AI and GP is to improve your stamina, leg speed and running efficiency, and to make your normal pace feel more comfortable.

Race-Day Rules Start towards the back of the pack, and run more slowly than you think you should for the first few miles. Stay comfortable. Work your way into a controlled rhythm as the race proceeds, and stop at every aid station. Don't just slow down, stop. Drink plenty, eat something, rest a bit. Then get going again. With a well-rested body from your taper week – that's the week before race day – and thanks to race-day adrenaline and the energy of the field, you'll get through the last three miles fine, you might, perhaps, even enjoy them.

WEEK	M	T	W	T	F	S	S	TOTAL
1 & 2	Rest	2 miles, 5–7 x 1 min AI, 2 miles	Rest	4 miles, 4 GP	Rest	3-4 miles	Week 1: 5 miles. Week 2: 7 miles	19-21 miles
3	Rest	2 miles, 2 x (1 min, 90 secs, 2 mins) AI, 2 miles	Rest	4 miles, including 4 x 1 min AI, 5-6 GP	Rest	5K race	4-5 miles	22-24 miles
4 & 5	Rest	3 miles, 3 x (2 mins, 2 mins 30 secs) AI, 2 miles	Rest	5-6 miles, including 4 x 90 secs AI, 6 GP	Rest	3-4 miles	7-8 miles	24-26 miles
6	Rest	3 miles, 2 x 2 mins AI, 2 x 2 mins 30 secs AI, 1 x 3 mins AI, 6 GP, 2 miles	Rest	5-6 miles, 4 GP	Rest	10K race	4 miles	27-30 miles
7 & 8	Rest	3 miles, 2 x (2 mins, 3 mins, 4 mins) AI, 2 miles	Rest	6 miles, including 4 x 2 mins AI, 6 GP	Rest	5-6 miles	10 miles	32-34 miles
TAPER	Rest	2 miles, 4 x 1 min AI	Rest	2 miles easy, 4 x GP	Rest	Rest	Half-Marathon Race	

INTERMEDIATE

"Intermediate runners have enough experience and strength to support some faster running – but within the context of increased weekly mileage and an adequate long run, which remains the key to improvement at this level," says coach Jon Sinclair. "So be careful when you add speed, because what we're after here is greater endurance – the ability to run longer at race pace." To that end, Sinclair also suggests "adding some tempo to at least some of the long runs when you're maybe going just a bit faster over the final 10 to 15 minutes." That's a bit faster, not eyeballs-out straining.

"I would also include some interval miles at faster than projected race pace," Sinclair adds. "Interval tempo here should be challenging, but not too challenging. And the recovery should be enough to support the effort – down to a 120 heart rate, 400m jog, whatever it takes. If the rest isn't long enough, you can't maintain the quality."

To enjoy the fullest benefit of the intermediate programme, there are a few specific types of training you'll need to use:

Pace Intervals (PI) Relatively lengthy repetitions

WEEK	M	T	W	T	F	S	S	TOTAL
1 & 2	Rest	1 x 1,200m PI (400m), 2 x 800m CI (200m), 4 x 200m SI (200m)	3-4 miles,or Rest	2 x 2 miles PI (800m), 4 x100m S	Rest	4 miles, 4 x 100m S	8-9 miles (Week 2, Include 4 mins TUT)	26–30 miles
3	Rest	2 x [1,200m CI (600m), 800m CI (400m), 400m SI (200m)]	2 miles	3 miles, 4 x 100m S	Rest	5K race	6 miles	24 miles
4 & 5	Rest	2 x 1 mile CI (800m), 6 x 200m SI (200m)	3-4 miles, or Rest	4 miles PI (800m), 1 mile CI, 6 x 100m S	Rest	5 miles, 6 x 100m S	Week 4: 10 miles (Including 6 mins TUT). Week 5: 11 miles	28–32 miles
6	Rest	2 x [800m SI (400m), 400m SI (200m), 200m SI (200m) 1,200m PI]	Rest	4 miles (including 6 x 1 min SI), 4 x 100m S	Rest	10K race	8 miles	30 miles +
7 & 8	Rest	2 x 1,200m CI (600m), 4 x 400m SI (200m), 4 x 200m SI (100m)	3-4 miles, or Rest	4 miles PI (800m), 1 x 800m CI (400m) 2 miles PI	Rest	6 miles, 6 x 100m S	Week 7: 11-12 miles (including 8 mins TUT). Week 8: 6 miles	32–36 miles
TAPER	Rest	4 x 400m CI (200m), 2 x 200m SI (100m)	2 miles PI, 4 x 100m S	2 x 400m CI (200m), 1 x 200m SI	Rest	Rest	Half-Marathon Race	

at your goal half-marathon pace to build endurance and develop pace judgment. Note: All numbers in parentheses in the schedule (above) denote distance of recovery jog.

Cruise Intervals (CI) Run at 10K race pace for stamina and to stay strong when tired. For 10-minute/mile half-marathon pace (2:11:06), run 7:07 for 1,200m and 4:45 for 800m. For nine-minute/mile half-marathon pace (1:57:59), run 6:24 (1,200m) and 4:16 (800m). For eight-minute/mile half-marathon pace (1:44:52), run 5:42 (1,200m) and 3:48 (800m).

Speed Intervals (SI) Run at 5K race pace to promote relaxed speed and a sense of comfort at your considerably slower half-marathon pace. For 10-minute/mile half-marathon pace, run 4:30 for 800m, 2:15 for 400m and 1:07 for 200m. For nine-minute/mile half-marathon pace, run 4:04 (800m), 2:02 (400m) and 1:01 (200m). For eight-minute/mile half-marathon pace, run 3:37 (800m), 1:48 (400m) and 0:54 (200m).

Strides (S) Over 100m, gradually accelerate to 90 per cent of all-out pace, hold it for five seconds, then decelerate. Walk to full recovery after each.

Total Uphill Time (TUT) Work the uphill sections during your run, at something near a strong 10K effort.

Race-Day Rules To warm up, jog just 800m, then do a few fast strides. That's it. Keep your glycogen (the carbohydrate stored as fuel in your muscles) tanks topped up and your legs fresh. Divide your race like this: 10-mile run, 5K race. Run the first mile just slower than goal pace, then work into a rhythm and run just below your lactate threshold level so you don't implode halfway round, and draft off other runners to conserve energy. Do all these things, and you'll be fine.

ADVANCED

"A primary goal at the advanced level is increased weekly mileage, but make sure it includes an adequate long run," advises Sinclair. "Everyone understands the need to do a long run for a marathon, but too many fail to see the need for it in training for a half. Don't do a ton of them, but doing one or two really helps."

And there's another thing: "long run" doesn't mean just more time on your feet. It means greater intensity. Focusing less on adding length and more on adding quality is vital to a good racing effort over a long distance like the half. We have a few patterns for you to play with, such as LRS and LRFF (see opposite). We also have you doing increasingly longer runs at your half-marathon pace to teach your body what it feels like.

Lastly, to run a half-marathon personal best, you must be able – and willing – to maintain a fast pace in the face of increasing fatigue. So you need to train to run goal pace after having already done enough running to tire yourself. This is the purpose of our Fatigue Fighter Intervals (see opposite) – short, sub-race-pace intervals followed by an extended run at your half-marathon goal speed to simulate the demands of the race itself.

Pace Intervals (PI) See the Intermediate schedule above. All numbers in parentheses in the schedule (opposite) denote distance of recovery jog.

Cruise Intervals (CI) For what and why and for eight-minute/mile half-marathon pace, see the Intermediate schedule. For seven-minute/mile half-marathon pace (1:31:46), run 6:40 for a mile, 5:00 for 1,200m and 3:20 for 800m. For six-minute/mile half-marathon pace (1:18:39), run 5:34 (mile), 4:10 (1,200m) and 2:47 (800m).

Speed Intervals (SI) For what and why, see the Intermediate schedule. For eight-minute/mile half-

WEEK	M	T	W	T	F	S	S	TOTAL
1 & 2	Rest	4 x 1 mile PI (400m), 6 x 200m SI (100m)	4 miles, or Rest	3 miles PI, 2 x 800m CI (200m), 4 x 100m S	4 miles, or Rest	6 miles, 4 x 100m S	Week 1: 13 miles LR. Week 2: 14 miles LRFF	40-45 Miles
3	Rest	FFI 2 x [400m SI (100m), 1,200m CI (300m), 2,000m PI]	4 miles, 6 x 100m fast S	4 miles PI	Rest	5K race	10 miles LR	35 miles
4 & 5	Rest	Week 4: 3 x 1.5 mile CI (400m). Week 5: FFI 2 x [400m SI (100m), 1,200m CI (200m) 2,400m PI]	4 miles or Rest	6 miles alternating 2-3 mins CI with 1 min jogs	3 miles easy, or Rest	6 miles, 6 x 100m S	Week 4: 15 miles LRS. Week 5: 16 miles LRF.	42-47 miles
6	Rest	4 x 1,200m CI (200m), 6 x 200m SI (100m)	4 miles, or Rest	2 x [400m SI (100m), 800m SI (200m), 400m SI]	Rest	10K race	12 miles LR	38 Miles
7 & 8	Rest	Week 7: FFI 2 x [400m SI (100m), 1,200m CI (200m), 3,200m PI]. Week 8: 2 x 1,200m SI (400m), 6 x 200m SI (55m) 2 x 1,200m SI (400m)	3 miles PI	Week 7: 5-6 miles PI. Week 8: 6-7 miles PI	Rest	6 miles, 6 x 100m fast S	Week 7: 17 miles LRS. Week 8: 10 miles LR	44-50 miles
TAPER	Rest	6 x 400m CI (100m)	3 miles PI	2 x 400m CI (200m), 2 x 200m (100m)	Rest	Rest	Half-Marathon Race	

marathon pace (1:44:52), run 3:37 for 800m, 1:48 for 400m and 0:54 for 200m. For seven-minute/mile pace, run 3:09 (800m), 1:35 (400m) and 0:48 (200m). For six-minute/mile half-marathon pace, run 2:42 (800m), 1:22 (400m) and 0:41 (200m).

Strides (S) See Intermediate schedule.

Fatigue Fighter Intervals (FFI) These combine SI and PI nearly back-to-back-to-back (very short recoveries) to work on pace and staying relaxed as you gradually tire. Yes, they're challenging. Jog five to seven minutes easy between sets.

Long Run (LR) A moderate pace (roughly 60 to 75 seconds slower per mile than your half-marathon goal pace). Long Run Stamina (LRS) means to run three to six miles at half-marathon goal pace in the middle third of the run. Long Run Fartlek (LRF) means to alternate one minute at 10K pace with one-minute jogs in the middle third of the run. Long Run Fast Finish (LRFF) means to run the final 15 minutes at 10K pace.

Race-Day Rules Jog just 800m, then do a few fast strides. Keep your glycogen tanks topped up and your legs fresh. Divide your race thus: 10-mile run, 5K race. Run the first mile just slower than goal pace, then find a rhythm and run just below your lactate threshold level so you don't implode halfway round. Draft off other runners to conserve energy..

MARATHONING FOR MORTALS

With a little commitment and training canniness, there's scant chance your first marathon will also be your last

If you've applied for a place in a big city marathon such as London or New York, you'll know four months before the event whether you've been successful. You have ample training time in the period between starting your training schedules, around three months before the race and the big day itself – but you'll benefit from doing some initial preparation early on. You'll find training schedules in RUNNER'S WORLD magazine and at www.runnersworld.co.uk.

How you prepare largely depends on how much training you're doing already – if you're starting from scratch, for instance, your approach will be different from that of a hardened club runner. But even before you start honing your training, there are some key questions all prospective marathon runners should ask themselves.

CAN YOU AFFORD THE TIME?

Training for a marathon is a big commitment. It's not just physically demanding – it can also place a strain on your family life and your social life. Even a schedule to get you round in five hours requires you build up to training five times a week, with long runs of two to three hours on three weekends out of four. The good news

Which time target should you aim for? Here's a rough guide, based on your current race form. (If you have no idea of your race form and you haven't been running three times a week or more in the last six months, you should follow a Get You Round schedule.)

	10K	10 Miles	Half-Marathon
Get You Round	60 mins+	1:38+	2:11+
Sub-4:00	44-50 mins	1:13-1:22	1:40-1:54
Sub-3:30	38-43 mins	1:02-1:12	1:25-1:39

The 'Get You Round' Schedule

A beginner's programme, mixing some walking with running, over 4-5 days a week.

The idea here is to have you fit enough to make it round the course, regardless of speed, so there'll be very little fast work. You need to build up endurance and this kind of schedule will help you to cut down on body weight. The first target is simply getting used to running regularly. Pace isn't important, in fact it's a good idea to go out with the slowest group of friends or clubmates you can find.

The only serious training is the long weekend "ramble". Walk briskly most of the way and put in the occasional trot. You shouldn't become too sweaty or short of breath, but you'll be spending long enough on your feet to build your endurance.

You may find that, after the initial burst of enthusiasm, regular training starts to feel tedious, and you may be tempted to miss a day or two. Try to resist this, because these schedules rely very much on continuity. If you're forced to miss most of a week for some reason, don't proceed to the next week, but repeat the one you should have done. It may mean you have to miss half or all of a two-week module, but at least you'll have built up to the "plateau of fitness" in the right way.

The Intermediate And Advanced Schedules

Intermediate For runners aiming to finish inside 4:00, with training over 5-6 days, and running from 32 to 48 miles a week. This type of schedule is more demanding and, since you are looking for a particular time, combines the first elements of speedwork with the weekly long run. This is a good programme for someone with a good base of fitness from another sport or natural athleticism.

Advanced For runners aiming for sub-3:15-3:30, with training over 6-7 days, and from 44 to 60 miles a week.

This type of schedule contains a mixture of repetition running, hill sessions and pace runs, for improving running speed, plus long runs for endurance. Advanced runners need to put as great an emphasis on the quality mid-week sessions as on the longer runs – they ultimately determine how quickly you will be able to cover the marathon distance. The highest weekly mileage typically reaches a plateau of 55-60 miles a week, but there's no reason why you shouldn't do more than that. Usually these plans are based on one session a day, but you could easily add 15-20 miles a week by putting in an extra daily session of three or four miles before breakfast or lunch. However, it is training hard and training long that counts – the rest makes little difference.

is that once you've accepted the idea of all the hard work, you'll stick with it and put in a performance to be proud of. If you're not sure you'll have the time or dedication at this stage, it would be better to focus on a shorter race distance this time, and postpone your marathon goal for a year.

DO YOU HAVE PEOPLE TO TRAIN WITH?

Your preparations will be easier if you can find a partner, or better still, a small group to go out with. The added motivation is invaluable, especially on long runs. (The forums on runnersworld.co.uk are a great way to find out about clubs and training partners near you.)

DO YOU HAVE THE RIGHT SHOES?

Don't leave it until six weeks into your training schedule to discover your shoes have been progressively injuring you. If you know the sort of shoes you should wear, make sure yours are in good condition. If you don't know, head to a proper running shop, where you'll receive expert advice. Alternating two pairs during training is a good idea, and if you want a lighter pair to race in, now may be the time to shop for ones you feel comfortable in.

SHAPING UP

Once you're kitted out, partnered up and committed to solid training, you can focus on getting into the best shape possible before you launch into the schedules – that should be three months before the day of your race.

THE BEGINNER

If you've never run before, your priority is being able to jog for 20-30 minutes non-stop. So, four months before the race, start by doing 10 minutes of walking and jogging three times a week, plus a five-mile walk at the weekend. Build up week by week, but don't overdo it.

THE FIT CROSS-TRAINER

Even if you do other sports such as cycling, canoeing or football, marathon running is different because you will be supporting your own bodyweight and hitting the road 8000 times an hour for hours on end. Your feet, ankles, knees and hips need to adjust to this gradually. Holding yourself back at first is frustrating, but it pays dividends by keeping you injury-free. A good rule for any runner is to aim to do half your training off-road, to minimise the impact on your joints and muscles.

» TOP TIPS

- ◆ Marathon training is a big commitment. Make sure you can afford the time. If not, try a shorter race
- ◆ Find people to train with. There's no better motivator than others in the same boat as yourself
- ◆ Purchase a good pair of running shoes
- ◆ Find a programme in line with your goals and stick to it

THE REGULAR RUNNER

If you're running regularly, use the pre-schedule month to build up your base mileage if necessary. If you're aiming for a marathon time of under four hours, put in a few weeks of regular, steady running at around 20-25 miles a week. Don't worry about speed in the early stages; just accustom yourself to regular running, so you feel you're building up your stamina gradually. If you're aiming for a sub-3:30 time, you should be running 30-35 miles a week.

You may already be comfortably running at your target. If so, don't increase your mileage yet. Fifteen weeks is plenty of time to train for a marathon from a solid running base, so boosting your training volume before January is only likely to make you stale. Instead, use this time to concentrate on your speed and strength. Cross-country racing is classic preparation, as are hillwork and speed sessions of varying lengths. If you don't do at least two weekly quality sessions like these already, getting into the habit of it now will make your chosen marathon schedule less of a shock when you begin in earnest. Similarly, running often will help: five times a week for the sub-4:00 schedule, or six times a week for sub-3:30. ■

MAIDEN MARATHONS

It's a moment you'll always remember and forever cherish – crossing the finish line at the end of your very first marathon. Here four first-timers recount their experiences

CHRISTOPHER CLAXTON
Residence London
Occupation General manager of the International Express newspaper
Debut marathon Flora London Marathon at age of 60
Having never seriously run before, and being recently divorced after a 30-year marriage, I began walking to get fit and to throw off my deep sadness. Weekend walks of 30 miles became common. I even walked 90 miles in four days – almost a marathon a day for four days!

Fitter and healthier, I began running in October, six months before my intended marathon. I started running a few hundred yards at a time, gradually building to miles, and then multiples of miles.

Business travel forced me to be creative with my training routes. With just a couple of months to go I found myself running up through mud, around huge boulders and down steep slopes on Zomba Mountain in my boyhood country of Malawi. The inevitable happened afterwards – twisted limbs and torn muscles.

The injuries put a stop to my training programme. With less than a month to go before the race, and still hoping to run, I consulted a top-notch osteopath who clicked my dislocated pelvis back into place.

Come race day I felt well rested and ready to go. Soon after the gun at the start of the race, the huge mass of runners moved off slowly, like an unfolding snail along the course. The streets were lined with half a million cheering and waving wonderful Londoners. The pubs were open, the bands were playing, and children were high-fiving.

The first refreshment station had run out of water when I arrived, but the second had plenty. I began to feel tired, my muscles aching at the halfway mark, but I pressed on across Tower Bridge. A supportive family and the cheering crowd kept me going. Along the Embankment was when I began to feel I was really a part of it.

Finally, the long-awaited sight of Buckingham Palace – the Mall stretching in front of it where I'd trained months ago – came into sight. Masses of people were cheering the runners on and the loudspeakers were blaring away. I turned the final corner and made it to the finishing line. I thought to myself, "It's all over! I've done it."

ANDREW JOHNSON
Residence London
Occupation Chartered surveyor for Fraser Trust
Debut marathon Flora London Marathon at age of 34
I was working on a short-term contract and growing increasingly frustrated with my tedious and thus far unsuccessful job hunt when I started training. I needed something new to focus on and a positive outlet for the extra time on my hands

– and feet. That's why I decided to run the Flora London Marathon.

Although I kept reasonably fit, I had never run long distances. I began running with a friend in Hyde Park, and ran home after work, saving commuting time and building my mileage. During the weekends I would loop Richmond Park twice, running nearly 15 miles.

I secured my place in the London Marathon through Whizz-Kidz, and attribute much of my running success to its friendly and helpful staff. While job hunting I also enjoyed working in its offices for a few days. At the charity's thank-you parties I had the opportunity not only to meet the children whom I was helping, but also the parents whose lives are dramatically changed for the better as a result of the charity's work. Identifying with the individuals I was running for made all the difference.

By running on behalf of this charity I was helping people who can't walk. I found I had a more positive mental attitude when doing something for other people. I was overwhelmed by the generosity of my family and friends, who liberally contributed to my fundraising campaign.

A week before the race my growing excitement was somewhat tempered by increasing nervousness. Every time someone mentioned the marathon I was absolutely petrified. I kept saying to myself, "Do I really want to do this? I must be mad." The night before the race I relaxed and enjoyed a drink with a friend (only two pints though). I felt relatively prepared for the morning ahead.

On the day of the marathon itself I was overwhelmed by the supportive crowd. I wrote my name on my vest and remember total strangers calling me by name, urging me on to the finish. The renowned Whizz-Kidz caps helped my sisters to spot me as I ran along the Embankment, drenched by the pouring rain. The noise was deafening and people were cheering all around. This is what helped to keep me going to the finish, where, along with complete exhaustion, I

experienced mixed emotions of pride and elation; I had a serious lump in my throat.

I was stiff and sore in the days following the marathon; walking down stairs proved particularly painful. I think after the next race I'll go for a full-body massage!

Now I'm in full-time employment and have begun a romance with another runner who I met during one of the long training runs. I've helped to organise several training runs for the charity, and I'm proud of my affiliation to the organisation, and of its outstanding work on behalf of children and their families.

HELEN STOKES
Residence Wiltshire
Occupation Mother and part-time English and drama teacher
Debut marathon Flora London Marathon at age 40

If you're a runner it helps to be in contact with others like yourself to swap training tips and discuss your progress. If you're thinking about running a marathon, it's even more beneficial – and fortunate – to be good friends with Bruce and Sue Tulloh.

I started running in 1994 with the thought that it would be a wonderful thing to run a marathon some day. I had participated in a number of 10K races and a triathlon, and felt mentally and physically ready to tackle the challenge.

Many times during my training, rain-drenched with freezing hands or aching legs, I would ask myself, "Why am I doing this?" Nevertheless, I pushed onward and was determined to continue with my programme. For me there was a sense of starting out on something new – and something I hoped I could do. There was a goal to achieve, and this is what motivated me.

As my training progressed I grew more determined, but still felt uncertain the closer it got to marathon day. I was filled with apprehension and excitement. Even before the race began I was in awe of the hoo-ha surrounding the event; the build-up before the race was hugely exciting. I visited the runners' exhibition beforehand and found the degree of sports commercialism and marketing simply daunting. Some competitors strolled very confidently around the expo, while others seemed less sure of themselves and held back a little. I found that attending the marathon church service on the Saturday was a helpful and uplifting experience.

I was becoming more nervous about the race, and worried about whether I was doing the right thing. As a mother you have a huge responsibility. What if something were to go wrong? What would I do? What would my children do? How would my family cope?

Running a marathon is like having a baby: until you experience it first-hand, you just don't know what it will be like. You can be told by any number of people, but it's not the same. You know there will be pain and, hopefully, elation at the end. In a sense you're waiting for the rest of your life to start.

On race day I had no idea how many people would participate in the event – both as runners and spectators. I wrote my name on the front of my shirt and the crowd cheered me on by name. It felt terrific. I put all of my physical and mental energies into repeatedly putting one foot in front of the other.

I was filled with an enormous sense of satisfaction and joy after the finish, which lingered on into the following week, and still remains with me in the present.

ROB WALKER

Residence Cornwall

Occupation Postgraduate student in broadcast journalism at Falmouth College of Arts

Debut marathon Flora London Marathon at age 21

No matter what distance you run, watching the London Marathon is totally inspirational. I ran the Flora London Marathon as part of the British University Sports Association (BUSA) British Student Marathon Championships. Yet that was only part of my motivation – I really wanted to be a part of the event.

I've run for clubs since 1986, and more recently for Exeter University. Although a middle-distance runner since childhood, I gradually built up my weekly mileage and began to focus increasingly on longer distances.

As a full-time student having a really hectic term, I felt these demands impact on my training programme. My running became quite erratic. I indulged in regular student sessions at the pub – perhaps more than I should have, and in hindsight I wish I'd trained a little smarter.

So to train for this marathon I made a concerted effort to resist the pub's temptations. I also pledged not to repeat a disastrous mistake I made in the previous year – the scheduling of my longest run. I ran a 22-miler too close to marathon day. I could still feel the effects in my legs during the marathon. You have to allow your body sufficient time to recover and rest following a long run, which I'd failed to do.

The week before the marathon I loaded up on pasta, bread and jacket potatoes; I remember driving to certain destinations I ordinarily would have walked to – all to conserve energy for the big day. The race dominates your thoughts more than you think it will in the weeks before the event. You know it's going to hurt, but not how much. You wonder how you'll feel at the finish. So many thoughts rush through your mind.

On race day I drank water at every station, and took full advantage of the run-through showers. They were great. There were gaps along the course where spectators were scarce. It's a tremendous help to prearrange a point along the route where family and friends will be waiting for you. You have to run on the right side of the road to enable them to catch your eye; it makes a massive difference. It's also really encouraging to hear the crowd cheering you on if you write your name on your shirt.

Feeling tired, somewhat proud, and most definitely relieved, I finally got to the finish. Running engenders such an amazing feeling, and nothing surpasses the elation you feel at the end of a marathon. What an accomplishment! ■

THE ULTIMATE MARATHON PLAN

There's no greater challenge most runners will face than finishing a marathon, and that means there's no greater sense of achievement either... if you get the preparation right

No two marathons are the same and you learn a great deal about yourself when you take up the 26.2 challenge. It requires commitment, sacrifice and, most of all, planning. However, the reward and sense of achievement when you cross the finish line will make all this effort worthwhile.

The following marathon schedules are divided into key phases with each phase having a slightly different emphasis. You will also find a description of how each session should be carried out, the right effort level for the best results and what effect the training will have.

Rather than giving a specific schedule for your time goal, there are only three schedules: beginners, improvers and achievers. In the panels *Is This Schedule Right For You?,* on pages 281, 283 and 285, you'll find a description of the kind of runner each schedule is intended for. Find which best applies to you, then match yourself to the right plan.

LONDON

Phase	Weeks	Emphasis for this phase
1	1-4	Building endurance
2	5	Recovery and adaptation
3	6-8	Building running economy
4	9	Recovery and adaptation
5	10-12	Final marathon pace practice/ start taper
6	13-14	Taper to race day

The schedules are flexible because we realise that the rest of your life has a tendency to get in the way of marathon training. To help you at the times when you would love to run but simply cannot we have underlined the "must-do sessions". If you can't fit any other runs into your week, at least complete these.

Training for a marathon is not an exact science but an effective and efficient training programme does require a number of essential elements. Here are the ones that underpin our schedules:

Rest There's no doubt about it: you're going to be putting your body through a lot over the next three months. To help your body cope with this added workload, rest is going to be as important a part of your training schedule as the running. Listen to your body and take heed of any warning signs. If you feel fatigued even before you've run a step, find yourself thinking up excuses not to run, or start suffering a series of minor injuries, you probably need more time off. Taking enough rest allows physical and mental recovery and gives your body the time to adapt to your workload. Remember: on rest days that's what you should be doing. Active rest is oxymoronic.

Recovery Runs Training for a marathon requires your body to work harder than it has ever done. To see improvement without breaking down, you'll need some recovery runs. These should be nice and easy and you should feel relaxed. Enjoy the scenery. You should be breathing easily and capable of holding a conversation throughout the run. This will mean that you are running

in the 60-65 per cent range of your Working Heart Rate (WHR) and should be no more than 45 minutes in duration (to work out your WHR, turn to page 59). This allows your body to adapt to the training workload and therefore improve. It also helps with the removal of the waste products, which accumulate in your muscles after harder efforts.

Threshold (Tempo) Runs After the long endurance runs, tempo runs are probably your most valuable workouts. You will find them

slightly uncomfortable and they'll require concentration, but they are well worth the effort. As they're run at a controlled brisk pace, about 80-85 per cent of your WHR, you'll only be capable of uttering a couple of words to your training partners. Tempo runs improve your lactate threshold (the speed above which your body struggles to cope with the lactic acid created by burning energy without oxygen), your running efficiency and aerobic capacity (your body's ability to utilise oxygen). All this helps to improve your marathon performance.

Long Runs Long runs are vital. After all, a marathon is a very long run. At first concentrate on increasing the time on your feet rather than worrying about distance. Start off by heading out for at least an hour and run at 65 per cent of WHR (conversational pace). Gradually, towards the end of the schedule, this will build to 75 per cent of WHR as you start to practise periods of marathon pace (MP) running. These runs improve your muscular endurance and condition your body to burn fat as its primary fuel source. They also prepare you physically and mentally for the task ahead.

Kenyan Hills Hill running develops strength in your muscles and tendons without putting them under the type of stress they are exposed to during faster running. Run up a 10 per cent gradient for 90 seconds to two minutes at a steady pace. Turn immediately at the top and jog down the hill at a relaxed pace, then turn and repeat the effort with no recovery. This type of session is used extensively by elite Kenyan athletes, who know a bit about distance running – so we'll call them Kenyan Hills. They are used as one of their main conditioning sessions. Like a tempo run, a hill session isn't a time for witty social intercourse, as you should be working at about 80-85 per cent of WHR and able to utter just a word or two.

Fartlek This is a Swedish term that literally means "speed play". It involves a number of bursts of effort over a variety of distances with a variable recovery. Originally the length of effort was based on the terrain: for example, pushing harder every time you came to a climb, no matter how long it was, but you can adapt it for your needs.

Interval Training Runners following the *Improvers* and *Achievers* schedules will use interval training to boost their speed. Intervals involve running timed efforts with a controlled recovery. The effort level is about 90-100 per cent of WHR.

Marathon Pace Practice Understanding the pace you are able to run your marathon is very important. Pace judgement is crucial to running your best marathon. Marathon Pace Practice, at about 75 per cent of WHR, allows your body and mind to get used to what will be required on the big day.

Warming Up When you are going to do any faster running such as Hills, Threshold Runs, Intervals or a race, it is important to warm up gradually. A 10-15 minute jog lets your muscles warm up and improve their range of movement. It also allows your cardiovascular system to prepare.

Cooling Down Gentle jogging and light stretching allow your body to adjust back to a steady state. Cooling down stops blood pooling in your legs, and helps remove waste products, such as lactic acid, from the muscle cells, which helps to avoid undue muscle soreness.

Cross-Training If you are new to running, you should think about balancing your training schedule with some non-impact activities such as swimming or cycling, otherwise you are more likely to pick up an annoying injury that will set back your training. More experienced runners should also add cross-training to their regime. The marathon, especially the last six miles, requires whole body-conditioning. To achieve this you should aim to work a variety of muscle groups and not just your legs. Remember, though, that you are a runner, so just be careful not to make the cross-training, whether it is lifting weights, using an elliptical trainer or practising Pilates, so intense that you are left too tired for your running. (See Chapter Seven.) ■

BEGINNERS MARATHON SCHEDULE							
WEEK	M	T	W	T	F	S	S
1	Rest	Recovery Run 25 mins	Cross-Training 30 mins	Threshold Run 3 x 5 mins effort with 2 mins recovery jog between	Rest	Bike ride 60 mins	Long Run (run/walk if necessary) 60 mins
2	Stretch session 30 mins or yoga class	Rest	Cross-Training 30 mins	Hill Run 30 mins working harder on uphills	Rest	Brisk walk 90 mins	Long Run 75 mins
3	Rest	Cross-Training 2 x 20 mins	Recovery Run 30 mins	Threshold Run 2 x 10 mins effort with 5 mins recovery jog between	Rest	Bike ride 90 mins	Long Run 90 mins
4	Cross-Training 30 mins	Rest	Recovery Run 30 mins	Kenyan Hills 15 mins effort	Rest	Recovery Run 30 mins	Long Run 105 mins
5	Rest	Recovery Run 25 mins	Rest or Swim	Recovery Run 25 mins	Rest	Bike ride 120 mins	Easy Run 45 mins
6	Rest	Recovery Run 25 mins	Threshold Run 15 mins effort	Rest	Cross-Training 2 x 20 mins	Hill Run 40 mins working harder on the uphills	Long Run 120 mins
7	Rest	Recovery Run 30 mins	Cross-Training 2 x 20 mins	Kenyan Hills 20 mins effort	Rest	Rest or Swim	10 mins walk, Long Run 150 mins
8	Rest	Cross-Training 3 x 20 mins	Threshold Run 2 x 12 mins effort with 3 mins recovery jog between	Rest	Recovery run 25 mins	Bike ride 60 mins	10 mins walk, Long Run 135 mins, 10 mins walk

BEGINNERS MARATHON SCHEDULE							
WEEK	M	T	W	T	F	S	S
9	Rest	Cross-Training 30 mins	Threshold Run 2 x 10 mins effort with 3 mins recovery jog between	Rest	Recovery Run 20 mins	Rest	Race a half-marathon
10	Rest	Cross-Training 3 x 20 mins	Recovery Run 20 mins	Threshold Run 2 x 10 mins effort with 3 mins recovery jog between	Rest	Recovery Run 20 mins	Marathon Pace Practice Long Run 120 mins
11	Rest	Cross-Training 3 x 20 mins	Kenyan Hills 20 mins effort	Recovery Run 20 mins	Rest	Brisk walk 90 mins	Long Run 165 mins
12	Rest	Cross-Training 2 x 20 mins	Rest	Threshold Run 2 x 10 mins effort with 3 mins recovery jog between	Rest	Recovery Run 30 mins	Long Run 120 mins
13	Rest	Recovery Run 25 mins	Threshold Run 3 x 5 mins effort with 3 mins recovery jog between	Rest	Recovery Run 25 mins	Rest	Long Run 60 mins
14	Rest	Recovery Run 20 mins	Rest	Recovery Run 15 mins	Rest	Recovery Run 10 mins	The Marathon

IS THIS SCHEDULE RIGHT FOR YOU?

Beginners

You've run between 10 and 20 miles a week for at least three months and completed a 5K or 10K. You can now run between five and six miles without collapsing afterwards and you want to gradually become a stronger runner. Your goal is to finish your first marathon feeling good about it and excited to run another in six months. You're less concerned by time than improvers are, though you'd prefer to run the whole distance without having to stop to walk.

Target time 5:30-4:30

IMPROVERS MARATHON SCHEDULE							
WEEK	M	T	W	T	F	S	S
1	Rest	Recovery Run 25 mins	Threshold Run 2 x 10 mins effort with 2 mins recovery jog between	30 mins Cross-Training and 30 mins Recovery Run	Rest	Kenyan Hills 15 mins effort	Long Run 75 mins
2	Stretch session 30 mins or yoga class	Recovery Run 25 mins	Hill Run 30 mins working harder on uphills	Cross-Training 2 x 20 mins	Rest	Interval Training 4 x 6 mins at 10K pace with 5 mins jog between	Long Run 90 mins
3	Rest	Recovery Run 30 mins	Threshold Run 2 x 15 mins effort with 5 mins recovery jog between	Recovery Run 20 mins and 2 x 20 mins Cross-Training	Rest	Kenyan Hills 20 mins effort	Long Run 115 mins
4	Rest	Recovery Run 40 mins	Kenyan Hills 25 mins effort	Recovery Run 40 mins	Rest	Fartlek on hilly route 20 mins pushing up hills	Long Run 120 mins
5	Rest	Recovery Run 30 mins	Rest	Recovery Run 30 mins	Rest	Recovery Run 20 mins and 30 mins stretching	Easy Long Run 60 mins
6	Rest	Recovery Run 25 mins	Threshold Run 25 mins effort	Recovery Run 20 mins plus Cross-Training 2 x 20 mins	Rest	Intervals 4 x 6 mins at 10K pace with 3 mins recovery jog between	Long Run 140 mins
7	Rest	Recovery Run 30 mins	Threshold Run 30 mins effort	Cross-Training 3 x 20 mins	Rest	Intervals 4 x 5 mins at 10K pace with 2 mins recovery jog between	Long Run 150 mins
8	Rest	Cross-Training 3 x 20 mins	Threshold Run 2 x 15 mins effort with 3 mins recovery jog between	Recovery Run 25 mins	Rest	Fartlek hilly route 30 mins pushing harder up hills	Long Run 150 mins
9	Rest	Cross-Training 30 mins	Threshold Run 2 x 10 mins effort with 3 mins recovery jog between	Rest	Recovery Run 40 mins	Rest	Race a half-marathon

IMPROVERS MARATHON SCHEDULE							
WEEK	**M**	**T**	**W**	**T**	**F**	**S**	**S**
10	Rest	Cross-Training 3 x 20 mins	Recovery Run 40 mins	Threshold Run 2 x 20 mins effort with 3 mins recovery jog between	Rest	Recovery Run 20 mins	Marathon Pace Practice – Long Run 110 mins
11	Rest	Cross-Training 3 x 20 mins	Medium Run 60 mins at marathon pace	Recovery Run 30 mins	Rest	Threshold Run 30 mins	Long Run 170 mins last 30 mins at marathon pace
12	Rest	Cross-Training 3 x 20 mins	Threshold Run 2 x 15 mins effort with 3 mins recovery jog between	Recovery Run 30 mins	Rest	30 mins run at marathon pace	Long Run easy 120 mins
13	Rest	Recovery Run 30 mins	Threshold Run 2 x 10 mins effort with 3 mins recovery jog between	Rest	25 mins run at marathon pace	Rest and 30 mins stretching session	Long Run easy 60 mins
14	Rest	Recovery Run 25 mins	Rest	Recovery Run 20 mins include 5 x 30 second pick-ups	Rest	15 mins jog	The Marathon

IS THIS SCHEDULE RIGHT FOR YOU?

Improvers

You regularly run between 20 and 35 miles a week and have done so for a year or more. You already do a weekly long run of between eight and 10 miles and have some experience with threshold runs or intervals. You've run 10K races, probably finished a few half-marathons and quite probably a marathon as well. Now you have a specific marathon goal in mind and you're prepared to do the training to make it a reality.

Target time 4:30-3:30

ACHIEVERS MARATHON SCHEDULE							
WEEK	M	T	W	T	F	S	S
1	Recovery Run 30 mins	Threshold Run 20 mins	Recovery Run 20 mins and Cross-Training 2 x 20 mins	Steady Run 30 mins	Rest	Kenyan Hills 20 mins	Long Run 90 mins
2	Recovery Run 40 mins Cross-Training 3 x 20 mins	Kenyan Hills 30 mins	Recovery Run 30 mins	Steady Run 40 mins	Rest	Kenyan Hills 25 mins plus 20 mins stretching	Long Run 110 mins
3	Rest	Kenyan Hills 30 mins	Recovery Run 20 mins plus 3 x 20 mins Cross-Training	Fartlek 40 mins 2 mins hard 2 mins easy, repeat	Rest	Recovery Run 30 mins	Long Run 120 mins
4	Recovery Run 30 mins plus Cross-Training 3 x 20 mins	Threshold Run 30 mins	Recovery Run 30 mins plus Cross-Training 3 x 20 mins	Rest	Steady Run 40 mins	Kenyan Hills 35 mins	Long Run 130 mins
5	Cross-Training 3 x 20 mins	Recovery Run 40 mins	Cross-Training 3 x 20 mins	Easy Run 60 mins	Rest	Cross-Training 3 x 20 mins plus 30 mins stretching	Easy Run 75 mins
6	Rest	Threshold Run 40 mins	Recovery Run 30 mins	Intervals 3 x 10 mins at 10K pace with 5 mins jog recovery between	Rest	40 mins Steady Run	Long Run 120 mins
7	Rest	Threshold Run 45 mins	Recovery Run 30 mins	75 mins run include 15 mins at half-marathon pace	Rest	Intervals 5 x 5 mins at 10K pace with 3 mins recovery jog between	Long Run 135 mins
8	Rest	Recovery Run 30 mins Cross-Training 3 x 20 mins	90 mins run including 20 mins at half-marathon pace	3 x 20 mins Cross-Training	Rest	3 x 10 mins at 10K pace with 5 mins recovery jog	Long Run 150 mins

ACHIEVERS MARATHON SCHEDULE

WEEK	M	T	W	T	F	S	S
9	Rest	Recovery Run 30 mins Cross-Training 2 x 20 mins	Intervals 4 x 5 mins at 10K pace with 2 mins recovery jog between	Recovery Run 30 mins	Rest	15 mins Recovery Run	Race a half-marathon
10	Rest	Recovery Run 25 mins	Recovery Run 35 mins	Intervals 2 x 10 mins at 10K pace with 5 mins recovery jog between	Rest	20 mins Recovery Run	Marathon Pace Practice – Long Run 100 mins
11	Rest	Recovery Run 40 mins	Threshold Run 40 mins	Recovery Run 20 mins plus Cross-Training 2 x 20 mins	Rest	Recovery Run 30 mins plus 30 mins stretching	Long Run 170 mins last 45 mins at Marathon Pace
12	Rest	Recovery Run 40 mins	Threshold Run 30 mins	Cross-Training 3 x 20 mins	Rest	Intervals 3 x 10 mins at 10K pace with 5 mins recovery jog between	Long Run 90 mins with last 30 mins at Marathon Pace
13	Rest	Recovery Run 30 mins	Recovery Run 30 mins plus Cross-Training 2 x 15 mins	Threshold 2 x 10 mins with 3 mins recovery jog between	Rest	Intervals 3 x 5 mins at 10K pace with 2 mins recovery jog between	Long Run 60 mins very easy
14	Rest	Recovery Run 30 mins	Rest	Recovery Run 20 mins	Rest	Recovery Run 15 mins include 5 x 30 second pick-ups	The Marathon

IS THIS SCHEDULE RIGHT FOR YOU?

Achievers

You're a running veteran, someone who's been a regular participant for at least three or four years and regularly logs 35-40 miles a week. You've regularly, if cyclically, included serious interval training in your regime. You've raced all distances from 5K to the full marathon and now want to run the fastest 26.2 miles you're capable of.

Target time 3:30-2:45

MARATHON RUNNING IN **26.2 TIPS**

The advice you'll be offered when you start marathon training will be endless. Here's some from someone worth listening to

Good marathon running is about learning from experience, so take some tips from a man with plenty. Doug Kurtis looks like an ordinary guy. He's not particularly big, not particularly strong, and he's an ordinary guy in other ways too – wife, children, mortgage, full-time job. That's until he steps on to the start line. Then he becomes the Marathon Man. Mr Consistency. Mr Sub-2:20 – he ran a dozen of them in 1989 alone. Very nice, you say, but what's in it for me? Lots. Because Doug Kurtis is also Mr Nice Guy. He's willing to share his marathon secrets, all 26.2 of them, with you. Best of all, you don't have to catch up with him between training runs.

Doug Kurtis strides smoothly beneath shady trees and past emerald lawns through the streets of his home town. He is on his lunch hour, running his usual eight-mile route near the car company where he works as a systems analyst.

Accompanying Kurtis are two friends, both sweating heavily on a humid day, though Kurtis seems barely damp. Later, after work, he will run another eight-mile route from his home – just part of his regular training week.

Kurtis is between marathons. Two weeks earlier, he ran one and finished in 2:19:32. Three weeks after this workout, he will run another, and finish sixth in 2:17:59. They are his 117th and 118th marathons respectively. "Doug breaks every rule," explains Dennis Quenneville, who trains

FLORA
49195
adidas
FLORA
28402
adidas

with Kurtis. "You're not supposed to be able to run marathons back-to-back. He does. You're supposed to rest for a week afterwards. He doesn't."

Kurtis smiles at Quenneville's comments. Though he may break a few of the accepted rules of smart marathon running, Kurtis abides by, and indeed has invented, several. Otherwise, he couldn't race as often and as well as he does. "Everybody has to learn to what works for them," says Kurtis. "I couldn't run a dozen marathons a year if I hadn't established my own rules."

So here they are:

1 Consistency At 1.70m (5'7") and 60kg (9st 4lb) I'm built to run marathons, but the key factor in my success is my consistency. I run the same mileage (105) week after week – no down time, no up time, no breaks. I recover well and rarely get injured. I could probably run more, but I would have a harder time avoiding injuries. When you're consistent with your training, you have a much lower chance of entering a race under-trained or over-trained – two reasons why people get hurt or run poorly.

2 Mileage I have a strong incentive to train twice daily because my high mileage permits me to run sub-2:20 marathons, but everybody has a mileage level that's best for them. Each person has to decide what's important in life and use that as a guide to dictate training levels.

3 Intensity Many people believe that they have to train hard all the time. They feel they're not getting anything out of a workout unless they're running at race pace, but I often run two minutes per mile slower than my marathon race pace – even three minutes per mile slower at the beginning of a workout. If I ran any harder, I would burn out and get injured.

4 Speedwork If you expect to run fast, you need to do some speedwork. My favourite is a workout that I read about in RUNNER'S WORLD and adapted for myself: 8 x 800m with 200m jogs in between (for more information see page 74). I average 2:24 for the 800s, faster on a good day, slower if it's hot or windy. Another favourite workout is mile repeats – four of them at about the same pace as the 800s. Sometimes, if someone runs with me, I'll do their workout, often 400s. Usually, I prefer to train at a track where something is going on, even if it's only a football practice and nobody's watching me. I always feel more comfortable with people around.

5 Diet With my high mileage and twice-daily workouts, I burn an extra 1,500kcal a day. To maintain my energy levels, I need to pay close attention to my nutritional needs. I eat at last three good meals a day, plus snacks in between. I'll start with a good breakfast: a mix of several cereals with fruit, toast with peanut butter and a large glass of orange juice. I'll have a solid lunch and a dinner that varies from Italian to Mexican to good old meat and potatoes. I drink plenty of fluids. I never pass a water cooler at work without stopping.

6 Rest I'm not afraid to take days off. Usually I average 15-20 rest days a year. I don't plan them in advance but take them when something comes up – travel or illness or a family outing. Rest days are good for me, and I should probably take them more often.

7 Training routes I don't train just to race. I run because I enjoy it. I do my first workout in my lunch hour, picking scenic routes near my office. In the evening, I often run from home through a park. I like to find pleasant places to run and to see the sights. I enjoy being out there day after day.

8 Goals I go into marathons very relaxed. People worry about the weather or about their competition, but I worry only about myself. I'm fortunate to have a goal of running more sub-2:20 races than anyone else, catching Kjell-Erik Stahl. I can be placed 10th or 15th, it doesn't bother me as it's the time I'm after. If race circumstances prevent a faster time, I don't worry because there's another marathon three to five weeks later.

Marathon runners also need short-term goals, which can mean other races leading up to the marathon. I'm amazed when I meet people whose first race is a marathon. It's hard to keep up your enthusiasm for a marathon that's two to three months away. Focusing two to three weeks ahead on a 10K can help to keep you motivated.

9 Travel I usually run my local marathon every year because I've won it six times and it's held in my home town. It's obviously a very convenient race for me to run, but I recommend that you use marathons as an excuse to travel. Why not plan a holiday around your race and make it a festive occasion? You could spend a long weekend or a week. Take the family. Do some sight-seeing. See the museums. Take in a show. Relax and make yourself comfortable. I love walking around the expos, looking at the equipment, and seeing and talking to other runners. It's good to hear everyone else's stories.

10 Tapering The hardest thing for me to do is to taper for a marathon. I have a tendency to over-train just before a marathon, and not back off early enough. Often, when I run marathons back-to-back, I run the second marathon better. Part of that is because I taper for two weeks: one week before the first marathon and a week of rest between the first and second. I enjoy running so much that I find it difficult to eliminate any of my workouts before a race.

11 Confidence You can talk to runners before a marathon and know whether or not they're going to have a good race based on their confidence in their training. If I've invested a lot of time in training, I go into the race with more confidence because I know I'm ready. The same rule also applies if I have performed well in short races leading up to the marathon. Inevitably, a high level of training builds a high level of confidence and leads to success.

12 Equipment After a blister problem almost forced me out of my first marathon, it took me a long time before I found shoes that were the right fit. I now tell people that the time to experiment is not during the race, yet I still see runners turn up at the start line with new shoes. I won't even try new socks. I break everything in: socks, shorts, vest, shoes. I do track workouts in my racing flats to make absolutely certain that they're comfortable at racing speeds. Sometimes I only put in a few miles, but I know those shoes work for me. One good way to work out the bugs and test your equipment is to enter shorter races before the marathon.

13 Fate Things sometimes happen that you have no way of controlling. For example,

early this year en route to a marathon in Arizona, I got snowed in at Chicago airport, and I didn't get as much sleep as I would have liked to on Friday night. On top of that, it was a warm day for the marathon, yet I came eighth in 2:24:31.

How do you cope with the misfortunes that come along that you can't deal with? You adjust your goals. You try to think positively. Many people tend to dwell on the negative rather than the positive. Inevitably, these people end up beating themselves.

14 **Pre-race meals** Usually, I eat my last meal the night before the marathon. I

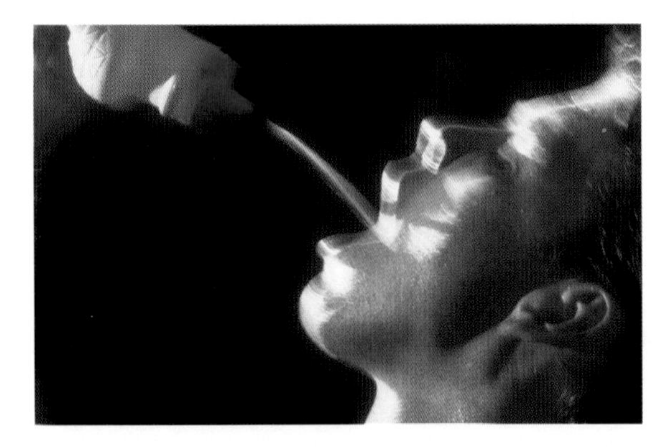

rarely eat anything the morning of a race, unless it begins late, such as at noon. I'd rather lie in bed an extra hour than get up just to eat. Some runners can eat and be ready to run an hour later. I find that I need three to four hours to digest my food before I feel comfortable running. I've experimented with eating two to three hours before a race, but it didn't work. Again, it comes back to what you feel comfortable doing.

15 Pre-race sleep The general rule is the most important hours of sleep are those that you get two nights before the race, not the night before. I find that to be true. If I have a good night's sleep on Friday night before a Sunday race, the amount I sleep on Saturday night makes little difference. Before most races, I have no problems sleeping, unless I'm nervous or have to get up early to go to the start. For example, one marathon I run begins at 5:30am, so you know that you're going to come up short on sleep unless you go to bed right after dinner, but everybody seems to survive. As long as I'm in bed relaxing, I don't worry whether or not I'm actually asleep.

16 Pre-race fluids Once in a while, before I run a cool-weather race, I'll have a cup of tea to introduce some caffeine into my system, but when I've tried that before a hot-weather race, I just felt nauseous. Most of the time, I drink only water in the last few hours before a race. I drink whenever I'm thirsty.

17 Warm-up I like to be at the start line at least an hour before the race. That way, I don't worry about little things going wrong, such as being caught in traffic or not finding a toilet. Usually I find a quiet, cool place to sit and relax. Half an hour before the race, I start walking briskly. Then I'll jog. I used to think I needed four miles of warm-up, but I do fewer now; two, maybe three if it's cold. I mix that with walking. I do a little bit of stretching but not much. Then I wait for the starting gun.

18 Race start You need to run intelligently. When I see the early leaders go out hard, my first reaction is to want to go with them, but I always start slow. It's hard to hold back and be patient. But experience has taught me that this is my best strategy.

19 Race pace I don't pay much attention to splits. I think of the course and the weather conditions. If it's hot, you don't want to overheat early. If the course is hilly, you can't run fast. A lot of runners go out too hard and fall apart later. I pass many runners in the last four to five miles.

20 Focus During a marathon, I do my best to concentrate on the race: how I feel, the weather, how my competitors look. I try to stay as comfortable as I can. Sometimes you have to push it, but not for the whole race.

I find my mind wanders at times. I like to look around and take in the scenery, but not for too long. On out-and-back courses people usually wave at me coming back. I'd like to be friendly and wave back at them, but I can't. When I run my local marathon, I appreciate the cheers I get as a local runner, but I need to think about what I'm doing. I particularly try to focus late in the race, especially when I know a sub-2:20 is on the cards.

21 Race fluids During the race, I drink only water. Sometimes I find that I drink too much, so I don't always stop if there are water stations every mile. Once in a while, late in the race, if I feel tired and think sugar will give me a boost, I'll take one of the replacement drinks. But if you have never tried replacement drinks, don't start at mile three of the marathon. Experiment on a few training runs first.

22 Bad patches Often in the middle of the marathon, I'll go through a bad patch where I don't run well. I lose the rhythm for a couple of miles. It happens to every runner, no matter how well trained or how experienced. Unless you ran too hard at the beginning of a race, you can usually work through a bad patch.

I've learnt to sometimes simply back off a bit. If I'm running with somebody, I let them go and hope to catch them later. I try to avoid negative thoughts and think positively instead. I focus on relaxation. I adjust my stride. I check my breathing.

23 Rehydration After I cross the line, I usually want something other than water to drink. It helps me bounce back more quickly. I prefer soft drinks to beer, which is a diuretic. Diet drinks don't work as well for recovery, because they don't contain sugar. I'll drink as many as 10 cups of fluid, if not more, right after a marathon. I find the only problem with drinking a lot is that you begin to lose your appetite and may not eat as well.

24 Refuelling I start with bananas and oranges, but after I get back to the hotel and shower, I'm ready to eat something more substantial. The stress from a marathon often causes me to lose my appetite temporarily, but once I see food in front of me I'm hungry again. I watch what I eat, but I'm not fussy. One year after a marathon, I craved beef burgers, chips and a milkshake.

25 Recovery I bounce back very quickly from marathons, usually by the next day. Some people say you should have a week off, and that's probably a good idea if you have really sore muscles, but, because I train so consistently, I start running straight away. Also, if I have travelled a long way to a marathon, I need to walk or jog to loosen up my muscles after the journey. Usually, I can limp through a five-mile run on the first day. By the second day, I start to feel OK. By day three, I can go out and do 15 miles without a problem. That's the one advantage of high-mileage training. You don't necessarily run that much faster, but you do recover more quickly.

26 Learning I tell all my training partners that they have to find out what works best for them. They look to me for advice, but I still make mistakes. With all my experience of running marathons, I've simply learned to minimise the mistakes. I come back to certain races year after year and know what to expect, but you have to take each marathon as a whole new race each time you run it. What worked one year may not work the next. I've finished more than 100 marathons, and I'm still learning.

26.2 Fun At the Barcelona Marathon one year, I went out too hard on a hot day and faded to eighth. Afterwards, the winner from Denmark asked me, "Was that one fun?" I had to admit it wasn't, but if I didn't think running marathons was fun, I wouldn't run a dozen a year. Often the enjoyment is the training beforehand and the memory afterwards. ■

OFF THE **WALL**

Every marathon runner dreads hitting the wall, but it doesn't have to happen – with the right preparation, you can run right through it

You won't find it on any course map, but from just over half-way of every marathon there's a big brick wall. For 364 days of the year it doesn't exist, but as soon as the race organiser has finished marking out the route, the devil's bricklayers work overtime to construct a monster for those running 26.2 miles.

For the unlucky ones, it might appear as early as the 16-mile mark, and although the most probable location is closer to 22 miles, you might come across it anywhere between there and the finish. No matter how strong you feel at 20 miles, there's a good chance that you could be reduced to a shuffling zombie just a few miles down the road.

It is made worse by the fact that when you reach the 20-mile point, there's only 10K left to run, but it is over that last stretch that you have to exert the most effort. Your legs start to feel heavy, the body runs out of muscle glycogen fuel and you have that awful sickening feeling generally known as "hitting the wall".

The good news is that it can be avoided – if you train correctly, start well rested, take on the correct fuel and fluids, use the right mental strategies and, above all, race sensibly, then you can break through that wall unscathed.

TRAINING

Training is the most important weapon in your battle against the wall. So you should have prepared diligently and at least loosely have followed one of our training schedules, incorporating plenty of long steady runs.

Ideally you should do your last long run of 165-170 minutes three weeks prior to the race. Rest and eat sensibly beforehand, and as you run take on plenty of fluids and top up your depleted reserves as soon as you can afterwards.

If you have missed any training, don't try to make up for it during the final two weeks – it is more important to save energy and taper your training ready for the big event.

RACING

You are almost guaranteed to hit the wall in spectacular fashion if you start too fast, so however good you feel, ignore your competitive urges if you see a rival up ahead in the first few miles. Many experts suggest approaching the race in the same way you did your training, with a gradual build-up. Treat the first 10 miles as a social run and enjoy the occasion. It is far better to begin a little slower than your goal pace than to start too quickly.

In big city marathons, you will undoubtedly lose time at the start. Don't try to make it up in the first few miles, and don't worry if you are behind time as you pass the 10K mark. It is difficult to concentrate fully on every mile of the marathon, so wait until you reach the 10-mile transition point, then try to focus fully, ready for those final miles.

During the last 10K, you will have to run as if you are taking part in a 10K race (albeit at a slower pace). Concentrate hard and, if you've trained diligently and started sensibly, you should be able to withstand the discomfort of those last miles.

FUELLING

Optimising your fuel intake can stop the wheels falling off in a marathon. Here are the three main nutrition mistakes that can lead to a spectacular crash in the final stages:

1 Low blood sugar

Solution Keep up your carbohydrate intake during the last few days before the race and have a light, easily-digestible breakfast (eg toast or cereal) together with plenty of water on the day. Ideally, an hour before the race take in about 300kcal, such as a banana and an energy bar, or have a carbohydrate drink. This should raise your blood sugar level, enabling you to focus on the battle ahead – but do practise this in training first to make sure it has no adverse effects.

2 Dehydration

Solution Drink 450ml (just under a pint) of water or sports drink two hours before the race and a further 180ml 10 minutes before the start. During the run, take five or six gulps of drink every 15-20 minutes (as a guide, alternate mile markers will probably suffice). This will keep dehydration at bay and allow your blood to move easily to your leg muscles. Apart from giving them much-needed oxygen, it will keep the sweat flowing, cooling you and preventing cramp. If you find it

hard to swallow on the run, stop to drink. Also, don't wait until you're thirsty – by then you're already dehydrated.

3 Depleted muscle glycogen

Solution Take in fuel during the race. Nutritionists recommend 200kcal per hour of running, which translates to about four cups of sports drink. Alternatively, you could try an energy bar or gel, or even your favourite sugary sweets – but never try anything that you haven't already successfully tested in training. Taking in fuel should ward off both glycogen depletion and light-headedness.

THINKING

Try to treat the last miles as a 10K race. This distance will take some runners over an hour, so you may need a few mental tricks to make it through.

"Don't be obsessed by the outcome," advises sports psychologist Jerry Lynch. "Focus on running one mile at a time." Another strategy is to use imagery. For example, at 20 miles visualise yourself on top of a wall, looking out at the finish line which you see as a welcoming blaze of light at the end of a tunnel.

Alternatively, you could try disassociating and thinking about anything but that last 10K. You could do sums (work out your finish time from your last mile), sing (but not too loudly) or fantasise (imagine running along a beach to a waiting Angelina Jolie or George Clooney with a delicious cold drink, or plan what you would do if you won the lottery). ■

COUNTDOWN TO THE **BIG RACE**

It's easy to become lost in an amorphous mass of "tapering" in the weeks immediately preceding your marathon, but while you can't do much to improve your fitness, you can harm it if you are not careful. So here's a detailed look at the final two weeks of preparation

Preparing for a marathon is both simple and complex. The simple part being the training. Follow any reasonable schedule for several months and you'll almost certainly find yourself in shape for the distance. More than likely, you'll have a great race

Putting all the other pieces in place, on the other hand, often amounts to a considerable challenge. You have to eat right, sleep enough, avoid injuries and colds, pick a good marathon, maybe travel to a strange city, and then negotiate all the ins and outs of number pick-up, meals, arriving at the start on time and so on. Marathon morning, by itself, is often a graduate-level course in logistics and deployment. With all this to consider, it helps to have a plan and a checklist.

Even so, attempting a marathon is a gamble. Anything can happen over the vast distances and time it demands in training as well as on race day itself. And you can't control the weather or the course (of course). So the object of the game is to focus on the things you can control – and we're not just talking about long runs and whole-wheat pasta. The well-prepared marathon runner looks after every detail of proper physical and mental training, nutrition, hydration, clothing and equipment.

In the last two weeks before your marathon, you should focus on these matters even more as you fine tune your training and your diet and put all the last-minute details of your race in order. In general, you shouldn't introduce new elements into your training or – if possible – into your life during these crucial final weeks.

To help you in your final preparation for the marathon, here's a daily checklist to guide you through the final 15 days prior to your race. Grab a calendar and a pencil and ready yourself for your most meticulously planned marathon ever.

If you've done the training and can tick off every item listed here (or most of them), you're on your way to a highly successful marathon day. You've taken control of everything you can; the rest is up to fate. With reasonably good weather and a decent course, you may have the race of your life.

DAY 15, SATURDAY

Training This is the day before your last long run, so you want to run lightly. Either take a day off or jog for 30 to 45 minutes easy. Make sure you stretch in the evening.

Mental preparation Mentally prepare yourself for your last long run. Remind yourself the hard work is nearly over, but that you want this final long training effort to

count. Do something relaxing and inspiring, such as listening to your favourite music.
Diet Eat a high-carbohydrate dinner to top off your stores of glycogen (a complex carbohydrate that your body uses for quick energy) and drink plenty of non-alcoholic beverages without caffeine.

DAY 14, SUNDAY

Training This last long run should *not* be your longest. (Most running sages suggest doing that no later than three to four weeks before your race.) Run at a comfortable pace, saving your best effort for the race. Include surges only if you have done so previously in training. A good last long run will give you a tremendous mental boost. But don't let a sub-standard effort discourage you. Remember the race is what counts.
Mental prep Plan some visualisation exercises for the next two weeks to help you relax and build your confidence. Find a quiet place, close your eyes and relax. Imagine yourself running well at various points in the race.
Diet Weigh yourself before and after your long run and drink enough to make up for any lost pounds. Or drink until your urine is plentiful and clear. Also, you should replace carbohydrates within two hours of your run, when your muscles are most receptive.
Other details This is your last chance to experiment with the food or drinks you may eat before and after the marathon. You can test, for example, whether a bagel eaten an hour before a long run sits well in your stomach. If you think you might take a sports drink during the race, find out which beverage will be available on the course, fill up a few water bottles with it, and plant them along the course of your long run.

DAY 13, MONDAY

Training Run or do some form of cross-training (if you have been cross-training) for 30 to 45 minutes, or take a day off to recover from your long run. Remember, rest is part of training.
Mental prep Shift gears to think countdown from here until your marathon. Rather than building up you're training, you're backing off. Visualise the race start — standing on the line feeling relaxed, confident and eager to run.
Diet Evaluate how you handled yesterday's food and fluid intake. Eat extra carbohydrates if you're hungry and drink more if your urine is still sparse or dark. It can take 24 to 48 hours after a long run to restore fluid and glycogen stores.

DAY 12, TUESDAY

Training Run for 45 to 60 minutes. After the first 20 minutes, do eight 30-second hard efforts with 30-second recoveries between each. This workout should shake your legs out but not drain you. Include pick-ups if you have been doing intervals throughout your training.

Mental prep Visualise the first five to eight miles of the race. You're holding back, letting other runners go ahead because you know you'll pass them later. You feel fresh, alert, even able to chat with those around you.

Travel If you're travelling a long distance to your marathon double check all your travel and

accommodation details are in order – especially if you are flying.

DAY 11, WEDNESDAY

Training If you usually do a midweek semi-long run, run 60 to 90 minutes today at training pace. Otherwise jog for 30 to 45 minutes.

Equipment This is a good time to make a list of race day clothing and equipment such as petroleum jelly, tape, extra shoelaces, a key holder (attaches to your shoe), plastic rubbish bags to wear at the start if it rains, containers for water and food, and clothing for before, during and after the marathon. Buy any items you need now. Don't count on being able to buy them once you arrive at the race.

DAY 10, THURSDAY

Training You should do your last hard speed

workout today. Do three- to five-minute intervals 10 to 30 seconds faster than your planned marathon pace with 30-second to two-minute recovery jogs.

Mental prep Congratulate yourself on another hard workout well done. Visualise miles five to nine of the marathon. You're settled in, running comfortably, recording even splits and making sure you take on plenty of water. You feel well trained and rested, and know you're going to have a great marathon.

Diet Plan some of your tried-and-true high-carb meals for the next 10 days. Don't try unfamiliar foods, but don't eat the same thing every day (even pasta). Choose from a variety of high-carb foods such as potatoes, vegetables, fruit, bread, rice and other grains. And don't neglect protein – add low-fat meat, poultry, fish, pulses, egg whites and low-fat dairy products to your diet as well.

DAY 9, FRIDAY

Training Take a day off or cross-train for no more than 45 minutes. Remember, nothing new now.

Equipment Go over your marathon shopping list and make sure you have everything you need.

Travel Make sure you know exactly where your air tickets are if you're flying and make sure you have all your travel documents in order.

DAY 8, SATURDAY

Training Many marathon runners do a semi-long run (no longer than two hours) or a race of 10K or less a week before their marathon. Either way, this is your last hard effort. The semi-long run keeps you in a pattern of going long without overtaxing you close to race day. You should finish feeling refreshed, not drained. Afterwards, you may want to schedule a massage to work out any kinks and help move lactic acid out of your legs.

Mental prep Visualise miles 10 to 13 of the marathon: you're still feeling great, although you're starting to work yourself a little harder. You're holding a steady pace. No one's passing you. You're looking forward to the halfway point.

Diet Are you obsessed with carbo loading? Contrary to popular belief, if you have followed a high-carb training diet, you don't need to change your pattern very much this week. You may want to increase your carbohydrate intake by roughly 10 per cent in the few days before the race by eating extra servings of bread, fruit, pasta or rice. Vary your diet, but don't add unfamiliar foods.

DAY 7, SUNDAY

Training Take an easy run or cross-train for 30 to 45 minutes.

Mental prep Listening to music or inspirational words before the start of a marathon can psych you up. If you think it may help you, prepare some tapes or CDs to bring along to the race.

Diet Continue to follow your high-carb, low-fat diet and ensure you're drinking plenty of fluids.

Equipment If you're travelling to your marathon, make a packing list and start gathering the clothes and other items you're going to need.

DAY 6, MONDAY

Training Run for 45 minutes. After the first 20 minutes, do eight to 10 pick-ups of one minute each with one-minute recoveries between. Stretch thoroughly afterwards.

Mental prep Visualise miles 14 to 17. You are working hard, running steadily, feeling calm and confident. You have taken in plenty of water, and your muscles are relaxed and loose. You're on pace for a personal best.

Travel If you're flying to your race and have to cross time zones, plan, if possible, to arrive a few days before the marathon so you have time to adjust to the new environment. The air in planes is especially dry, so drink extra fluids. And eat lightly; airline food is generally high in fat. Or, better yet, bring your own low-fat, high-carbohydrate snacks. Once you reach your destination, synchronise with the new time schedule immediately.

DAY 5, TUESDAY

Training Jog for 30 to 45 minutes.

Mental prep You may feel restless at this point and be tempted to add extra last-minute miles. Don't! Extra training now will hurt rather than help your performance by tiring you and preventing your legs from saturating with glycogen. Relax once you hit the race site, but don't spend days lying around your hotel room. Just avoid excessive walking and standing, and make sure you're sleeping well.

Diet Don't worry if you put on a few pounds between now and the race. Think of them as extra water and carbohydrates you'll need for the big day.

Equipment Check race-day forecasts and start to plan your outfit. Make a list of any items you may have overlooked and need to buy.

DAY 4, WEDNESDAY

Training Jog or cross-train for 30 minutes. If you like, do four to five pick-ups of 30 seconds each after the first 15 minutes of running.

Mental prep Visualise miles 18 to 21. This is a tough segment for many people. You have been running for two or more hours, yet you still can't smell the finish. See yourself digging down, working hard, holding your own, and starting to pass others.

Other details If friends or family have come to watch you race, make arrangements to meet them near the finish.

DAY 3, THURSDAY

Training Take the day off or jog gently for 30 minutes. Remember, the less you run now, the more stamina you'll have on race day.

Mental prep You're likely to feel keyed up and irritable in these final days. Do what feels right for you: spend time alone, hang out with a group, or visit one or two friends or family members.

Diet Your carbohydrate intake should be at least 65 per cent of total calories. But don't overdo it. You should feel comfortable after each meal, not unpleasantly stuffed.

Other details It may sound overly cautious, but you should plan to have two working alarm clocks. You never know when one will fail. Don't rely solely on a friend or a hotel wake-up call, either.

DAY 2, FRIDAY

Training Jog easily for no more than 20 minutes. Some advanced runners throw in a few light pick-ups to remind themselves they still have leg speed. This isn't necessary for most people.

Mental prep Visualise miles 22 to 26. These miles are usually the toughest, but you'll be ready because you have trained hard and raced well. Imagine yourself running strong and steady toward the finish, passing all those (fools... fools!) who started too fast. (FOOLS!)

Diet The food you eat today will help you more in the race than the food you'll eat tomorrow. Keep up your pattern of ample carbohydrates and fluids, and – especially now – don't try anything new or exotic.

Equipment Race-day weather forecasts should be detailed and accurate at this point (although surprises can happen). Plan your race-day outfit, and if you need any last-minute items, visit the marathon expo. Pick up your race package as early as possible to avoid the last-minute rush and carefully read all the instructions.

Sleep A good night's sleep matters more tonight than the night before the race. If you can't sleep, don't worry about it – lying down for your usual sleep period is still beneficial.

DAY 1, SATURDAY

Training If you run at all, jog for no more than 30 minutes. Many runners like to run the day before a marathon to iron out any kinks. Just take it easy, no matter how good you feel.

Mental prep Visualise the finish – you've made it, and you're exhausted but triumphant as you run the final few hundred yards feeling strong and steady. See yourself raising your hands as you cross the line to the cheers of thousands of spectators.

Diet Try to make one of today's meals a special event with family and friends who will relax with you and share your excitement. Contrary to popular belief, what you eat today will have little effect on your marathon as long as you stick to the usual – plenty of carbohydrates and beverages. Eat dinner early to ensure you catch a good night's sleep.

Equipment Lay out everything you plan to wear or take to the start: racing vest and shorts, tights and a short- or long-sleeved shirt if appropriate, mittens or gloves, hat, headband, bandanna, tracksuit, rainsuit, whatever you will need. Pack a separate set of warm, dry clothes for the finish. Your equipment should include your bag, running number, extra shoelaces and safety pins, bus ticket to the start, car key, beverages, containers, food for before and after, money, petroleum jelly (to prevent chafing and protect exposed areas from wind and cold), sunscreen, music, a headset and a plastic rubbish bag if it's raining or biting cold.

Sleep Marathon-related anxiety dreams such as missing the start, losing your shoes or running the wrong course are common, so don't worry if you don't sleep well. If you're generally well-rested, one night's poor sleep won't hurt you.

DAY 0, MARATHON DAY

Diet Wake up at least two hours before the start. Give yourself enough time to eat something light but high in carbohydrates. Drink water or a sports drink, stretch and arrive at the starting line with time to spare.

Mental prep Ideally you want to achieve a state of optimal arousal. That means you want to be eager and excited but not crippled by nervousness. Think back to other races to recall this feeling. If you feel too keyed up, sit or lie down, close your eyes and breathe deeply. Visualise the race or simply think peaceful, happy thoughts. On the other hand, if you're not "up" enough, walk or jog and talk to other runners, but don't tire yourself.

Equipment Keep warm and comfortable until the last possible minute before the race. Many runners wear old tracksuits to the start and discard them just before the gun. Otherwise, standing around in the cold can cramp your muscles. Make sure to apply petroleum jelly to areas likely to chafe, such as underarms, nipples and inner thighs. Mark your bag so you can find it easily at the finish. During the race, lose layers if you feel too warm, or you'll lose precious fluids through perspiration. Keep extremities covered if it's cold.

Warm-up It's not necessary to warm up extensively prior to a marathon, but do try to do some walking and a few minutes of jogging to loosen your legs and raise your body temperature otherwise you could be caught cold.

Racing Running a successful marathon is an exercise in holding back. Ideally, the hard work shouldn't begin until 20 miles. Then your training and willpower will push you to the finish. During the race, remain calm and focused. Note your splits, and take encouragement from a steady pace early on, even if others are passing you. Break the race into segments, and work through each part rather than attacking the full 26.2 miles.

Other details Don't eat or drink anything on the course that you haven't tried previously in training. If you do, you may suffer digestive woes. Take in water early and often. If you feel cramps or a stomach upset en route, walk until the problems lessen.

Finish When you come through the finish line, keep walking around and take on some fluids right away. Pat yourself on the back – you made it. Find your friends or family and go and celebrate. ■

» TOP TIPS

- Visualise marathon day. It will make it easier when the day arrives and help you deliver your best performance
- As marathon day approaches, stick to your tried and tested routines. In particular, don't change your eating patterns. Eat at least 65 per cent carbs
- Don't worry if you sleep poorly the night before the marathon. It's common and won't do you much harm as long as you have been sleeping well previously
- Lay out all you will need for marathon day the night before
- Arise at least two hours before the start

IN THE **MIND**

You're fitter than you've ever been, more active, running more races and yet...something's missing. You just don't feel that great. Perhaps the problem is in your imagination – or lack of it.

Roger Bannister's historic first sub-four minute mile, recorded on May 6, 1954, ranks as one of the greatest and most widely known moments in the history of sport. What's less well known is the fact four other runners broke through the previously impossible barrier in the next year. Knowing Bannister had run 3:59, the rest of the world's milers could no longer believe such a time was beyond them. They had little choice but to redouble their efforts to run as fast as Bannister, and faster. Which they did.

The Bannister story is perhaps the best example in running of this basic concept: negative thinking limits performance. Turn the thinking around, and suddenly the impossible becomes possible, for world record breakers and fun-runners alike.

BELIEVING YOU CAN

By 1954 more than 50 medical journals had carried articles saying it was impossible to break four minutes for the mile. Bannister didn't listen. He refused to limit his own potential. His success proved if you believe it, it can happen. With this positive attitude, you can then find out the truth about your athletic potential by living out the experience.

Far too many of us do the opposite: we decide in advance we can't. We think we're too old, too heavy, not well enough trained, not tough enough, not blessed with the right muscle fibres. The list goes on and on, developing into a litany of negative, limiting language and beliefs. And the outcome is always the same: if you think you can't, you can't.

When you believe and think "I can" you activate your motivation, commitment, confidence, concentration and excitement, all of which relate directly to achievement.

The most successful runners think like champions. The "I can" belief underlies their approach to all things in life.

The same approach will work for you. It won't necessarily turn you into an Olympic champion, but it will help you to run better and enjoy it more. The "I can" attitude will also allow you to adopt the following mind-sets, all of which are designed to help you unlock the extraordinary potential each of us possesses as a runner.

BOUNCING BACK FROM FAILURE

To succeed, every runner must learn to deal with mistakes and failures. All champions realise the path to personal excellence is cluttered with obstacles. Arriving at the top is a process that involves many setbacks. Champions accept this process, understanding that you can't stretch your limits without encountering some rough moments along the way. Losses, poor performances, injuries, training weariness, tactical misfires – all can provide important lessons.

We have all learned everything we know physically – from walking to running a marathon – by trial and error, so there's no reason to become our own worst enemies when we suffer a setback. From time to time everyone falls short of their goals. It's an illusion to believe champions succeed because they do everything perfectly. You can be certain that every archer who hits the bullseye has also missed the bullseye a thousand times while learning the skill. And will continue to miss sometimes.

When you create a mental environment that accepts mistakes, you free yourself to keep trying, to keep extending yourself, to keep taking risks. Of course, you'll have some bad days, but if you accept them as opportunities for growth, you can learn a lot from the experiences. An accepting attitude helps you perform with greater relaxation, which, as all champions know, is one of the key building blocks of success.

» THOUGHT TRAPS

Feeling stale and burned out? You could be over-training. Or does your thinking need an overhaul? If these common thought traps look familiar, it may be time for some mental renovation.

- ◆ You struggle constantly for external recognition rather than internal satisfaction
- ◆ You measure your self-worth as a runner solely on the basis of each performance
- ◆ You focus on perfection and unrealistic goals, rather than pursuing a journey of excellence
- ◆ You condemn yourself for failures, setbacks and mistakes
- ◆ You blame uncontrollable circumstances or other people when things go wrong. This leaves you feeling helpless
- ◆ You see running as something to conquer
- ◆ You have unrealistic goals that result in frustration, disappointment and distraction

A NEW DEFINITION OF WINNING

To bring out your best, you also need to adopt the champion's true attitude towards winning. There has to be more to running than taking home a medal or age-group award. Philosopher Alan Watts once said, "You don't sing to get to the end of the song." The same applies to running: you don't run to finish or to get it over with, so relax and enjoy the journey.

In his classic work *The Zen of Running,* Fred Rohd states: "There are no standards and no possible victories except the joy you are living while dancing your run... you are not running for some future reward — the real reward is now."

That's quite similar to the motto of the modern Olympic Games: "The important thing in the Games is not winning but taking part. The essential thing in life is not conquering but fighting well." If you run with this attitude, the results will take care of themselves. While running, focus on the internal battle. Concentrate on overcoming fear, self-doubt and other limiting beliefs. Forget about external issues, like your time. Such outward concerns will only deplete your energy, create tension and slow you down.

APPRECIATING YOUR OPPONENTS

Thinking like a champion also means adopting a new attitude towards your opponents. Traditionally, being a good competitor meant being a good predator. You succeeded most when you attacked and thrashed the opposition. But it doesn't have to be this way.

In the film *Running Brave*, Billy Mills slows down near the finish of one race, even as a coach stands on the sidelines screaming, "Crush your opponent! Take him for everything! Own him!" But Mills is well ahead of the other runners and understands that he will gain nothing by destroying them. That the real Mills made this choice doesn't mean he wasn't a fierce runner. In 1964, he won the Olympic 10,000 metres in Tokyo, considered by many to he one of the biggest upsets in Olympic history.

Obviously, the killer instinct isn't a requirement for optimal performance. It's much healthier and more beneficial to view opponents as partners who, because of their great efforts, afford you the opportunity to raise the level of your own performance. You depend on them to extend your limits. Think about it; how often do you run as fast in training as you do in races? Try this affirmation: "My opponents are very important to me. Because they are here, I experience greater depth as an athlete."

When we come together to try to reach our potential such as in a road race, others can only help us. With such a view, you will enter a race more relaxed, focused and energised. You can't help but perform better as a result of cooperation rather than antagonism.

SIMPLICITY IN ALL THINGS

The true champion recognises that excellence

flows most smoothly from simplicity – a fact that can become lost in these high-tech days. Some world-class runners constantly hooking themselves up to heart-rate monitors and speed-distance monitors. Sports become so complex they forget how to enjoy themselves.

Contrast this approach with that of the late Abebe Bikila, the Ethiopian who won the 1960 Olympic marathon running barefoot. Fancy clothing and digital watches were not part of his world. He simply ran. Many times in running, and in other areas of life, less is more.

Bill Rodgers won his first Boston Marathon in 2:09:55 while wearing a plain white T-shirt on which he had hand-lettered the initials of his track club. When you learn to run simply, you find you can concentrate on simply running.

Bikila and Rodgers stand as perfect examples of a philosophy Joe Henderson, RUNNER'S WORLD magazine's first editor, has expressed on many occasions: "Don't let the planning and analysing get in the way of the doing and enjoying." Because if you don't enjoy it, eventually you'll stop doing it.

BALANCE IN YOUR LIFE

Doing too much, especially in training, is one of the greatest misfortunes that can occur to a runner because it can wipe out all your hard-earned conditioning. More isn't always better. Balance is better. Unfortunately over-training is very common.

Over-trainers believe they won't excel unless they devote everything to their effort. But there are many examples of the opposite.

Nowegian runner Ingrid Kristiansen set her best marathon time two years after giving birth to her first child. Her interests in family and hobbies other than running provided balance in her life and may have enabled her to compete with less tension and anxiety.

Avoiding extremes will help you run further, more wisely and for longer in life. Adding balance to your running means decreasing injury and burnout. At the same time, you'll find yourself enjoying running more, feeling more motivated and looking forward to many years of productive, fun-filled participation.

THE ZEN-TAO APPROACH

After his superb victory at the 1990 New York City marathon, Douglas Wakiihuri, born in Kenya and trained in Japan, stated his marathon could not be separated from his search for life's truths. Wakiihuri is right. Winning at racing, as in life, is an inner journey without a destination.

In searching for both athletic and personal growth at the same time, Wakiihuri represents a new breed of champion – a sacred warrior. These runners realise they will have the most success in their external lives only if they have won the internal battle over self-doubt.

When you adopt a similar attitude, it doesn't mean you will run world records, or even personal bests. You will, however, decrease the pressure you feel when running. And this can only help you improve your performances and your appreciation of running. Focus on running as an exciting and fulfilling journey without a destination, and you will see that your running can't be anything but successful and rewarding. When you choose the right kind of thoughts, you can create the running destiny you have always wanted. ■

» TOP TIPS

- ◆ Have the courage to risk failure, knowing setbacks are lessons to learn from
- ◆ Use races to gain greater self-knowledge as well as feedback on physical improvement
- ◆ Train mental and physical processes for total performance
- ◆ Understand athletic weaknesses and train to strengthen them
- ◆ Create a life of balance, moderation and simplicity
- ◆ View competitors as partners who provide challenge and the chance to improve
- ◆ Enjoy running for the simple pleasures it provides
- ◆ Have vision. A champion dreams the seemingly impossible and says "I can"

A VOYAGE OF RECOVERY

Getting back to peak form after your marathon takes self-restraint and a little know-how. What's more, you can start before the gun even goes off

You'll recover most effectively from the marathon if you begin your recovery before the race. The reason? If your leg muscles are in optimum condition, they will be less battered by the 26.2-mile pounding they take on race day. Post-race, your muscles will need minor remodelling, rather than extensive renovations, and you'll be able to return to quality training more quickly.

Good in theory, but how do you reinforce muscles before your big day? First, reduce your training for at least three weeks before the marathon. Studies carried out in the Netherlands found that most marathon runners reach the starting line with muscles which have already been heavily battered by vigorous pre-race training. Research conducted at Harvard University determined that it takes anything up to four weeks to clear up this muscular mayhem.

In your preparation period you'll not only need to cut back your weekly mileage, but also avoid very long runs (the Dutch scientists found that efforts of more than 10 miles were the most destructive). Forget about romping through an 18-miler two weeks before race day; keep every workout nearer single figures and focus on quality rather than high-quantity training. A reasonable rule of thumb is to progressively reduce your total mileage until you've reached about 30-40 per cent of your usual total in the final pre-marathon week.

In addition to adjusting your training, you need to fine-tune your eating. That's because when muscle cells are depleted of energy, they become too fatigued to cushion your bones, tendons and

BAGGAGE RECLAIM
TIMEX
FLORA
adidas
RUNNER'S WORLD
2002

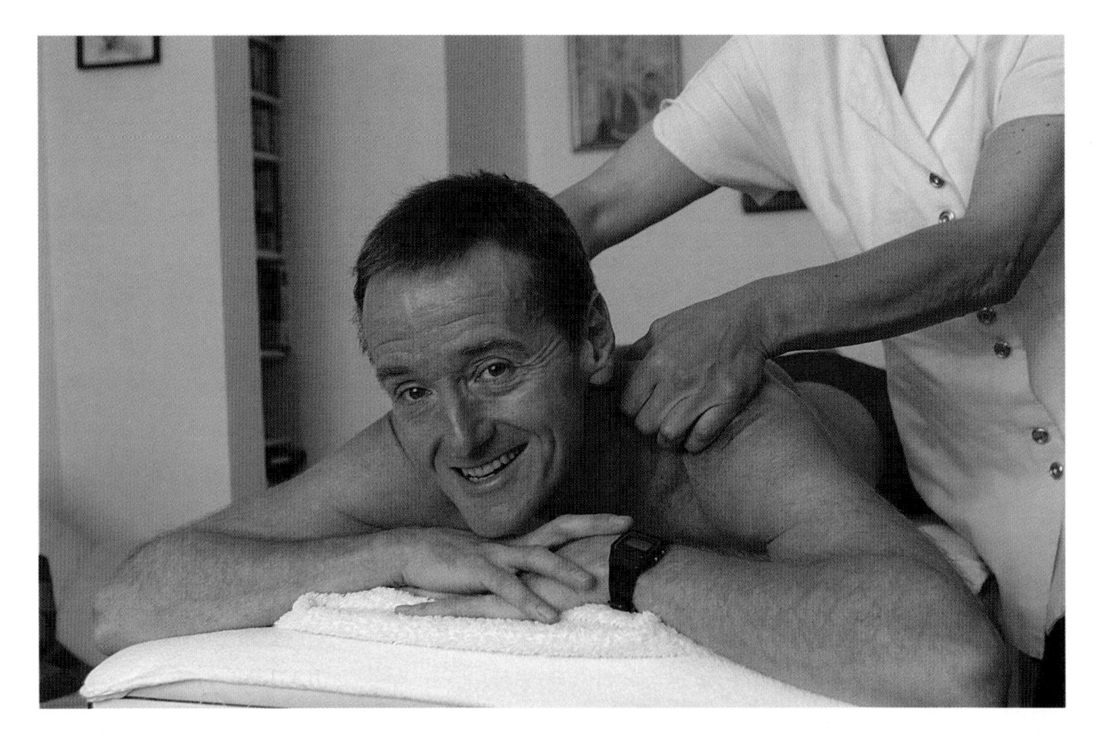

ligaments from the high-impact forces associated with running. Those impact forces are transmitted through your body about 40,000 times during a marathon (it takes that many steps to finish the race). To keep your muscles better fuelled, and thus less fatigued, it's imperative to fill them with carbohydrate before the race. You'll need four grams (16kcal) of carbohydrate per pound of body weight daily during the days before the marathon. (Actually, that's a great intake pattern throughout your pre-marathon training.) During the race itself, you'll need to keep the carbs coming with five mouthfuls of sports drink every 15 minutes or so.

These nutritional strategies will protect your legs from trauma during the race, thereby making recovery easier. However, you must also eat as soon as possible after crossing the finish line. It's no time to be a miser: the traditional post-marathon snack – a banana and some sips of sports drink – will only satisfy a couple of fibres in one of your calf muscles, leaving the remainder of your cells parched and hungry. For more complete refreshment, take two-thirds of a gram of carbohydrate for every pound of body weight immediately after the race, and the same dose within two hours. For a 10st 10lb runner, that's two separate helpings of 100g of carbohydrates, or 200g and 800kcal in all. (Two bagels and a banana add up to 100g.)

This post-race banqueting is critically important, because your leg muscles are best able to take on fuel during the two hours immediately after strenuous exertion. The sooner you can restore muscle fuel, the more quickly muscle cells will return to metabolic normality and begin to make any repairs that are needed. Don't forget to include some protein with your carbohydrate; after all, around 35-70g of protein is metabolised by your muscles for energy during the race. A couple of pots of yoghurt and a tuna sandwich will do nicely.

In the days following your race, take ibuprofen or aspirin to calm muscle inflammation and ease pain. Don't hesitate to rub anti-inflammatory creams into skin over aching joints or throbbing tendons. Research shows that salicylate ointments such as these do more than pad the bank accounts of pharmaceutical companies; they actually penetrate deep enough to limit discomfort. In addition, apply ice (wrapped in a cloth) frequently to painful parts of your legs, keeping it on for about 12 minutes at a time. Elevate your feet and legs for at least an hour after the marathon and for 30 minutes a day for the following week.

Now the big question: how do you pick up your training afterwards? For many years, exercise scientists have debated whether it is best to rest completely or jog lightly during the days that follow a marathon. The argument could go either way: light jogging should stimulate blood flow to the muscles, reduce tightness and preserve fitness. On the other hand, total rest allows the leg muscles to devote all their energies to the rebuilding process.

To gauge the relative values of rest and running, scientists in the US recently studied a large group of marathon runners. About half of the marathon runners refrained from running for a week following a marathon, while the other group jogged lightly for 30 minutes each day.

Both sets of runners were stiff and sore during the week after the race, but the resting runners recovered much more quickly. Leg-muscle endurance returned to normal after three days for the inactive runners, but was still below par after seven days for the light joggers. Muscle strength was also considerably higher in the runners who did nothing. Bottom line? Take a one-week rest from training after your marathon. You deserve the break, and your muscles will return to normal more quickly.

During this one-week respite, you can do some light walking to burn off a few calories, keep your leg muscles loose and satisfy your desire for exercise. Start with just 10 minutes on the day after the marathon, and build up gradually towards 30 minutes by the end of the post-race week. After each walk, stretch your muscles lightly. At some point during the week, let a massage therapist mould your muscles into a relaxed shape.

Once your walk week is over, you're ready to get back to your favourite sport, but prudence is the word (remember that it takes four weeks for your muscles to really return to normal). During the second, third and fourth week after the marathon, run only 30-60 per cent of your usual mileage, and avoid running over 10 miles at a time. It's OK to carry out a couple of quality efforts a week, but they should be very moderate in length. Tempo runs – about three to four miles of running at a pace that is 25 seconds per mile faster than marathon speed – seem to work especially well. Above all, you probably shouldn't throw yourself into a race again until at least four weeks have passed by. If you strength-trained before the marathon, you can resume resistance work during the second week after the race, beginning with about half your normal number of sets and reps.

One last nutritional recovery tip: scientific research indicates that many marathon runners lose around three milligrams of iron (about the amount in a serving of beef stew) per day for up to five days after the marathon, so eat foods rich in iron – including meat, spinach, beans, peaches, parsley and peas – during your post-marathon week. To promote iron absorption, drink orange juice or consume other rich sources of vitamin C with your meals.

Finally, be sure to congratulate yourself on your remarkable accomplishment. Only a tiny fraction of the population is fit enough to successfully complete a marathon – and with the right recovery, you'll be able to run many more in the future. ■

» TOP TIPS FOR RECOVERY

- ◆ Before the race, taper for three weeks, so your legs are not fatigued before the race
- ◆ Don't run at all in the week after your marathon, and don't race for a month
- ◆ Eat plenty of iron-rich food in the first week after the race
- ◆ Put your feet up – for an hour in the afternoon after the race, and for 30 minutes each day for the next week
- ◆ Make sure your post-race fuelling is sufficient, with a mix of carbohydrates and protein to aid muscle recovery

RESOURCE **GUIDE**

AAA of England
Edgbaston House
3 Duchess Place
Hagley Road
Birmingham B16 8NH
Tel: 0121 452 1500
Fax: 0121 455 9792
www.englandathletics.org

Athletic Association of Wales (AAW)
The Manor
Coldra Woods
Newport NP18 1WA
Tel: 01633 416 633
Fax: 01633 416 699
www.welshathletics.org

British Nutrition Foundation
High Holborn House
52-54 High Holborn
London WC1V 6RQ
Tel: 020 7404 6504
Fax: 020 7404 6747
www.nutrition.org.uk

British Triathlon Association
British Triathlon Association
PO Box 25
Loughborough
Leicestershire LE11 3WX
Tel: 01509 226 161
Fax: 01509 226 165
www.britishtriathlon.org

Midland Counties Athletics Association
Edgbaston House
3 Duchess Place
Hagley Road
Edgbaston
Birmingham B16 8NH
Tel: 0121 456 1896
Fax: 0121 456 4403
www.midlandathletics.org.uk

North of England Athletics Association
NoEAA Office
7a Wellington Road East
Dewsbury
West Yorkshire WF13 1HF
Tel: 0870 991 4545
Fax: 0870 991 4546
www.noeaa-athletics.org.uk

Northern Ireland Athletic Federation
Athletics House
Old Coach Road
Belfast BT9 5PR
Tel: 028 906 02707
Fax: 028 903 09939
www.niathletics.org

Scottish Athletics Federation
9a South Gyle Crescent
South Gyle
Edinburgh EH12 9EB
Tel: 0131 539 7320
Fax: 0131 539 7321
www.scottishathletics.org.uk

South of England Athletics Association
4th Floor
Marathon House
115 Southwark Street
London SE1 0JF
Tel: 020 7021 0988
Fax: 020 7620 0012
www.seaa.org.uk

UK Athletics
Athletics House
Central Boulevard
Blythe Valley Park
Solihull
West Midlands B90 8AJ
Tel: 0870 998 6800
Fax: 0870 998 6752
www.ukathletics.net

UK Athletics running club and track directory
www.runtrackdir.com

Women's Running Network
Exeter Arena
Summer Lane
Exeter EX4 3NT
Tel: 01392 683 318
www.womensrunningnetwork.co.uk

RETAILERS

BERKSHIRE

Apex Sports
171 The Broadway
Farnham Common

Slough SL2 3PQ
Tel: 01753 647 339

BRISTOL

Easy Runner
6 Horfield Rd
St Michael's Hill
Bristol BS2 8EA
Tel: 0117 929 7787

CAMBRIDGESHIRE

Advance Performance
5 Bodson Way
Fengate
Peterborough PE1 3LE
Tel: 01733 891 111
www.advanceperformance.co.uk

Reeds of Cambridge
Two Tees Boatyard
70 Water Street
Chesterton
Cambridge CB4 1PA
Tel: 01223 425 348

CHESHIRE

The Athlete's Foot
26 Bridge Street
Chester
CH1 1NQ
Tel: 01244 351 909

7 Mill St Mall
Grosvenor Center
Macclesfield
SK11 6JA
Tel: 01625 669 134
www.theathletesfoot.co.uk

Running Bear
5 London Road
Alderley Edge
Cheshire SK9 7JT
Tel: 01625 582 130
www.runningbear.co.uk

CUMBRIA

Pete Bland Sports
34a Kirkland
Kendal
Cumbria LA9 5AD
Tel: 01539 731 012

DERBYSHIRE

The Derby Runner
Unit A, B&C, Sandringham Drive
Spondon
nr Derby DE21 7QL
Tel: 01332 280 048
www.derbyrunner.com

DEVON

Frank Elford Sports
27 Mayflower St
Plymouth PL1 1QJ
Tel: 01752 265 122
www.frankelfordsports.co.uk

Ironbridge Runner
10 Lower North St
Exeter
Tel: 01392 436 383
www.ironbridgerunner.co.uk

Running Forever
2 Station Road
Taunton TA1 1NH
Tel: 01823 331 669
www.runningforever.com

DORSET

Blandford Sports
4 West Street
Blandford Forum
Dorset DT11 7AJ
Tel: 01258 452 320

Running Free
22a Bournemouth Road
Poole
Dorset BH14 0ED
Tel: 01202 741 900
www.runningfree.net

Top Trainers
11 Burlington Arcade
Bournemouth
Dorset BH1 2HZ
Tel: 01202 556 237
www.top-trainers.co.uk

ESSEX

53-12
Unit A25 Cowdray Centre
Cowdray Avenue
Colchester
Essex CO1 1BH
Tel: 01206 505 011
www.53-12.com

Run-In
72 Borders Lane
Loughton
Essex IG10 3QX
Tel: 020 8502 1481
run-in@loughton72.fsnet.co.uk

Runnersworld East
2 Chadwell Heath Lane
Chadwell Heath
Essex RM6 4LZ
Tel: 020 8590 0318
www.runnersworld.ltd.uk

HAMPSHIRE

Alexandra Sports
140 Gladys Avenue
Portsmouth
Hants PO2 9BL
Tel: 02392 698 285
www.alexandrasports.com

Alton Sports
110 High Street
Alton
Hants GU34 1EN
01420 84 101
www.altonsports.co.uk

HERTFORDSHIRE

Letchworth Tri Sports
11-12 The Wynd
Letchworth
Herts SG6 3EL
Tel: 01462 683 615

Ontherun
10 How Wood
Park Street
St Albans
Herts AL2 2RA
Tel:01727 875 354
www.ontherun.co.uk

KENT

The Runners Shop
106 Beckenham Road
Beckenham
Kent BR3 4RH
Tel: 020 8663 0630
www.runnersshop.co.uk

LANCASHIRE

Complete Runner
Leeds Road
Nelson
Lancs BB9 8EA
Tel: 01282 690 111

Ontherun
39 Harpers Lane
Chorley
Lancs PR6 7AB
Tel: 01257 269 137
www.ontherun.co.uk

LEICESTERSHIRE

Running Fox
70 Ashby Road
Loughborough
Tel: 01509 231 750

LINCOLNSHIRE

The Lincolnshire Runner
455 High St (South End)
Lincoln LN5 8JA
Tel: 01522 512 733
sales.lincolnshirerunner@ntlworld.com

GREATER LONDON

London City Runner
10 Ludgate Broadway
London EC4V 6DU
Tel: 020 7329 1955

London Marathon Store
63 Long Acre
Covent Garden
London WC2E 9JN

Run and Become
42 Palmer Street
Victoria
London SW1
Tel: 020 7222 1314

Runner's Need
34 Parkway
Camden Town
London NW1 7AH
Tel: 020 7267 7525

Brody House
Strype Street
nr Liverpool Street Station
Tel: 020 7247 3500
www.runnersneed.co.uk

GREATER MANCHESTER

Foot Traffic
463 Blackburn Road
Bolton BL1 8NN
Tel: 01204 301 230
www.foot-traffic.co.uk

Sporting Supplies
60 Preston Road
Standish
nr Wigan WN6 0HS
Tel: 01257 422 647

Tobutt Sports
508 Blackburn Road
Astley Bridge
Bolton BL1 8NW
Tel: 01204 308 506

MIDDLESEX

Runnersworld
333 Rayners Lane
Pinner
Middlesex HA5 5EN
Tel: 020 8868 6997
www.runnersworld.ltd.uk

NORFOLK

The Runners Centre
145/147 Nelson Street
Norwich NR2 4DS
Tel: 01603 665 398
www.runnerscentre.co.uk

Sportlink
Unit 6 Drayton Industrial Park
Taverham Road
Norwich NR8 6RL
Tel: 01603 868 606
www.sportlink.co.uk

NORTH YORKSHIRE

Bedale Sports & Outdoors
19 North End
Bedale
North Yorkshire DL8 1AF
Tel: 01677 423 746
www.dale-sport.co.uk

NORTHAMPTONSHIRE

The Running Shop
11 St Leonards Road
Northampton NN4 8DL
Tel: 01604 701 961

STAFFORDSHIRE

Bourne Sports
36-42 Church Street
Stoke-on-Trent
ST4 1DJ
Tel: 01782 410 411
www.bournesports.com

OXFORDSHIRE

Fit 2 Run
Dunmore Court
Wootton Road
Abingdon
OX13 6BH
Tel: 01235 531 050
www.fit-2run.co.uk

SURREY

Top Runner
17 Church Street
Leatherhead
Surrey KT22 8DG
Tel: 01372 384 160
www.toprunner.co.uk

Tortoise & The Hare
Unit 6 Smith Brook Kilns
Horsham Road
Cranleigh
Surrey GU6 8JJ
Tel: 01483 273 372

SUSSEX

The Jog Shop
39 George Street
Brighton BN2 1RJ
Tel: 01273 675 717

Run Shop
46 Blatchington Road
Hove BN3 3YH
Tel: 01273 770 972
www.run-shop.co.uk

The Tri Store
49 Grove Road
Eastbourne
East Sussex BN21 4TX
Tel: 01323 417 071
www.thetristore.com

TYNE & WEAR

Northern Runner
52 Low Friar Street
Newcastle-Upon-Tyne NE1 5UE
Tel: 0191 241 1111
www.northernrunner.com

WEST MIDLANDS

Birmingham Runners' Shop
1506 Stratford Road
Robin Hood Island
Hall Green
Birmingham B28 9ET
Tel: 0121 745 6007
www.birmingham
runner.com

Lorraine Baker Runner
223 Burnaby Road
Radford
Coventry CV6 4AX
Tel: 024 7666 8498
www.lorrainebaker
runner.co.uk

WILTSHIRE

Sole Obsession
29 Harnham Road
Salisbury SP2 8JG
Tel: 01722 421 000
www.soleobsession.co.uk

WORCESTERSHIRE

Runaround Sports and Health
45 Foregate Street
Worcester WR1 1EE
Tel: 01905 330 555
www.runaroundsports.
co.uk

YORKSHIRE

Complete Runner
Leeds Road
Ilkley
West Yorkshire LS29 8EQ
Tel: 01943 601 581

Keep On Running
710 Attercliffe Road
Sheffield S9 3RP
Tel:0114 244 5335

Simply Running
4 Albion House
Albion Street
Hull HU1 3TD
Tel: 01482 222 169
www.simplyrunning.biz

Triangle
85 New Road Side
Horsforth
Leeds
West Yorkshire LS18 4QD
Tel: 0113 259 0477

SCOTLAND

Achilles Heel
593 Great Western Road
Glasgow
Tel: 0141 342 5722

The Dundee Runner
116-118 Logie Street
Dundee DD2 2PY
Tel: 01382 665 915

Run and Become
66 Dalry Road
Edinburgh EH11 2AY
Tel: 0131 313 5300

Run 4 It
Tiso Glasgow Outdoor
Experience
50 Couper Street

Townhead
Glasgow G4 0DL
Tel: 0141 559 5450

21 Holborn Street
Aberdeen AB10 6BS
Tel: 01224 594 400
www.run-4-it.com

WALES

The Athlete's Foot
26 Mostyn Street
Llandudno LL30 2RP
Tel: 01492 872 232
www.theathletesfoot.co.uk

Run and Become
12 Wood Street
Cardiff CF10 1ER
Tel: 029 2023 2346

ONLINE RETAILERS

Girls Run Too
Tel: 01568 617 517
www.girlsruntoo.co.uk

Kit 4 Fit
Tel: 0845 0900 192
www.kit4fit.co.uk

Leisureways
Tel: 01709 376 773
www.leisureways.co.uk

Less Bounce
Tel: 08000 363 840
www.lessbounce.com

Look4Leisure
Tel: 01279 814 661
www.look4leisure.com

M&M Sports
Tel: 01568 616 161
www.mandmsports.com

Natterjack Running Centre
Tel: 01704 534 040
www.natterjack.co.uk

Newline Sport
Tel: 01732 846 616
www.newline.dk

Red Lion Sports
Tel: 01926 642 303
www.redlionsports.co.uk

Sports Shoes Unlimited
Tel: 08700 434 555
www.sportsshoes.com

Start Fitness
Tel: 0870 759 8803
www.startfitness.co.uk

Sweat Shop
Branches in:
Birmingham 01384 344 062
Bristol 0117 950 7788
Cambridge 01223 415 345
Chorley 01257 269 814
Dartford 01322 311 119
Dundee 01382 537 517
Edinburgh 0131 467 8740
Glasgow 0141 586 9126
Ipswich 01473 726 652
London (The City) 020 7626 4324
London (Covent Garden) 020 7497 0820
London (Harrods) 020 7730 1234 x2102
London (Fulham) 020 7351 4421
London (North Finchley) 020 8445 3334
Maidstone 01622 735 520
Milton Keynes 01908 662 202
Nottingham 0115 950 2036
Reading 0118 957 3826
Teddington 020 8943 0239
Woking 01483 729 221
Wrea Green 01772 683 822
York 01904 426 402
www.sweatshop.co.uk

Up & Running
Tel: 01423 562 162
www.runningshoes.co.uk

Wiggle
www.wiggle.co.uk

INJURY CLINICS

BEDFORDSHIRE

Osteopathy and Sports Injury Clinic
Wendy Russell-Rayner
10 Greenacres
Putnoe
Bedford MK41 9AJ
Tel: 01234 294 954
wendy@russell-rayner.co.uk

BERKSHIRE

SportsFeet UK – Maidenhead Office
52B Queen Street
Maidenhead
Berkshire SL6 1HY
Tel : 01628 778 512
Fax : 01628 778 512
alex@sportsfeetuk.co.uk

BUCKINGHAMSHIRE

David Wells Osteopath
Little Chalfont Clinic
Buckinghamshire
Tel: 07766 758 066

Orthosport
14 Redgrave Place
Marlow
Bucks SL7 1JZ
Tel: 01628 477 377
www.orthosport.co.uk

CAMBRIDGESHIRE

Cambridge Chiropody and Podiatry
79 Histon Road
Cambridge CB4 3JD
Tel: 01223 322 636
www.cambridgepodiatry.co.uk

CHESHIRE

Paul Stockton Sports Therapy
53 Park Road
Hale
Altrincham
Cheshire WA15 9LS
Tel: 0161 980 3259
sportsinjuries@tiscali.co.uk

Sport Med
Norbury Chambers
2-6 Norbury Street
Stockport SK1 3SH
Tel: 0161 474 7469
www.sport-med.co.uk

SportsFeet UK - Chester Office
80-82 Brook Street
Chester
Cheshire CH1 3DN
Tel : 01244 341 839
kris@sportsfeetuk.co.uk

DORSET

Hunsson Chiropractic Clinic
16 Granby Court
Surrey Close
Weymouth DT4 9XB
Tel: 01305 814 428

Open You Gait
Littledown Sports Centre
Bournemouth
Tel: 01202 417 600

ESSEX

Graeme Stroud Sports Injury Clinic
Basildon – 01268 287 733

HERTFORDSHIRE

Foot Clinic
Clinics in Harlow, Hitchin,
Welwyn Garden City,
Rickmansworth and Watford.
Tel: 0870 873 5511
info@foot-clinic.co.uk

Osteopathy and Sports Medicine Practice
22 Lancaster Road
St Albans.
Tel: 01727 856 852

KENT

The Foot Clinic
191 Old Road West
Gravesend
Kent DA11 0LU
Tel: 01474 535 373
info@thefootclinic.co.uk

GREATER LONDON

Balance Performance Technology in Motion
132-134 Arthur Road
London SW19 8AA
Tel: 020 8944 9919
www.precisionfeet.co.uk

East Finchley Clinic
3 Bedford Mews
Bedford Road
East Finchley
London N2 9DF
Tel: 020 8883 5888

Foot Factor
3 Gower Street
London WC1E 6HA
Tel: 020 7436 9032 (enquiries);
020 7436 8960 (appointments)
www.portlandphysio.co.uk

Milligan & Hill Ltd
16 St Helen's Place
London EC3A 6DF
Tel: 020 7628 3575
www.milligan-and-hill.co.uk

Physio in the City
(Based inside health clubs)
City **Tel:** 020 7283 0108
West End **Tel:** 020 7724 8008
Bloomsbury **Tel:** 020 7813 0555
Wimbledon **Tel:** 020 8947 9627
Twickenham **Tel:** 020 8892 2251
www.physiointhecity.co.uk

MIDDLESEX

Middlesex Physiotherapy Clinic
The Burroughs Sports Club
Middlesex University
Hendon NW4 4JF
Tel: 020 8411 4736
www.middlesex-physiotherapy.co.uk

MIDLANDS

Dean Walsh Chiropody - Podiatry
329a Chester Rd
Castle Bromwich
Birmingham B36 0JG
Tel: 0121 749 6313
www.walshchiropody.com

NORTH YORKSHIRE

Rebound Lower Limb Injuries Clinic
The Sidlings

Settle
North Yorkshire BD24 9RP
Tel: 01729 825 900
www.reboundclinic.co.uk

NORTHAMPTONSHIRE

The Northampton Sports Injury Clinic
322 Wellingborough Road
Northampton NN1 4EP
Tel: 01604 629 339
www.northamptonsportsi njuryclinic.com

NOTTINGHAMSHIRE

The Nottingham Sports Injury Clinic
736 Mansfield Road
Nottingham NG5 3FW
Tel: 0115 960 9553
www.nottingham sportsinjury.co.uk

SOUTH YORKSHIRE

The Barn Podiatry Clinic
Sharrow Lane
(Adjoining 286)
Sheffield S11 8AS
Tel: 0114 221 4780
www.inyourstride.net

SURREY

Foot Mechanix
22a Station Approach
West Byfleet
Tel: 01932 353 568
www.footmechanix.co.uk

Kate White Sports Injury Clinic
Tel: 07799 418 208
enquiries@sportstherapy online.co.uk

Kingston Physio & Sports Injuries Clinic
Arena Health Club
Kingston Hall Road
Kingston KT1 2AQ
Tel: 020 8541 5556

8 Dukes Avenue
Kingston KT2 5QY
www.kingston physiotherapy.com

John Sullivan Sports Injury Clinic
11 Tudor Road
Kingston-upon-Thames
Surrey KT2 6AS
Tel: 020 8546 6460

STAFFORDSHIRE

Sub-4
First Floor, 342 Waterloo Road
Cobridge near Hanley
Stoke-on-Trent ST1 5EH
Tel: 01782 261 644
www.sub-4.co.uk

WORCESTERSHIRE

Runaround Sports & Health Physio Clinic
45 Foregate Street
Worcester
Tel: 01905 330 555

SCOTLAND

Footworks Orthotic Centre
14/15 Bruntsfield Place
Edinburgh EH10 4HN
Tel: 0131 229 2402
www.footworks-uk.com

WALES

Cardiff Foot Clinic
6 Minster Rd
Roath
Cardiff
Tel: 029 2045 5352

MAJOR EVENTS

Flora London Marathon
Tel: 020 7902 0200
www.london-marathon. co.uk

Bupa Great North Run
Newcastle House
Albany Court
Monarch Road
Newcastle-upon-Tyne
NE4 7YB
Tel: 0191 272 7033
www.greatrun.org

Race For Life
Cancer Reseach
P.O. Box 123
Lincoln's Inn Fields
London WC2A 3PX
Tel: 020 7009 8820
www.raceforlife.org